W9-AFR-752

EXPRESSION OF THE EMOTIONS IN MAN

EXPRESSION OF THE EMOTIONS IN MAN

Edited by

PETER H. KNAPP, M.D.

INTERNATIONAL UNIVERSITIES PRESS, INC.
New York

Library of Congress Catalog Card Number: 63-22481

The Symposium on Expression of the Emotions in Man was held at the meeting of the American Association for the Advancement of Science in New York on December 29-30, 1960.

Manufactured in the United States of America

Table of Contents

Part I

ORIGINS

PART II

LEVELS: AN ANALYSIS

PART III
TOWARD A SYNTHESIS

Participants

KNAPP, PETER H., M.D., *Chairman*
Research Professor in Psychiatry, Boston University School of Medicine, Boston, Massachusetts.

AX, ALBERT F., PH.D.
Head, Psychophysiology Laboratory, Lafayette Clinic, Detroit, Michigan.

BATESON, GREGORY, M.A.
Ethnology Section, V. A. Hospital, Palo Alto, California.

BIRDWHISTELL, RAY L., PH.D.
Professor of Research in Anthropology, Temple Medical Center at Eastern Pennsylvania Psychiatric Institute, Philadelphia, Pennsylvania.

BROSIN, HENRY W., M.D.
Chairman, Department of Psychiatry and Director, Western Psychiatric Institute and Clinic, University of Pittsburgh School of Medicine, Pittsburgh, Pennsylvania.

COLBY, KENNETH MARK, M.D.
Department of Psychology, Stanford University, Stanford, California.

DEUTSCH, FELIX, M.D.
Honorary Professor of Psychiatry, Boston University School of Medicine, Boston, Massachusetts.

DITTMANN, ALLEN T., PH.D.
Laboratory of Psychology, National Institute of Mental Health, Bethesda, Maryland.

ENGEL, GEORGE L., M.D.
Professor of Psychiatry and Associate Professor of Medicine, University of Rochester School of Medicine and Dentistry, Rochester, New York.

ESCALONA, SIBYLLE K., PH.D.
Professor of Psychology, Albert Einstein College of Medicine, Yeshiva University, New York, New York.

GREENBLATT, MILTON, M.D.
Assistant Superintendent and Director of Research and Laboratories, Massachusetts Mental Health Center; Associate Clinical Professor of Psychiatry, Harvard Medical School, Boston, Massachusetts.

HAMBURG, DAVID A., M.D.
Professor and Executive Head, Department of Psychiatry, Stanford University School of Medicine, Palo Alto, California.

HARLOW, HARRY F., PH.D.
Primate Laboratory, Department of Psychology, University of Wisconsin, Madison, Wisconsin.

KAGAN, JEROME, PH.D.
Chairman, Department of Psychology, Fels Research Institute, Yellow Springs, Ohio.

KENNARD, EDWARD A., PH.D.
Chairman, Department of Anthropology, University of Pittsburgh, Pittsburgh, Pennsylvania.

KEPECS, JOSEPH G., M.D.
Institute for Psychosomatic and Psychiatric Research and Training, Michael Reese Hospital, Chicago, Illinois.

LACEY, BEATRICE C., M.A.
Research Associate, Department of Psychophysiology-Neurophysiology, Fels Research Institute, Yellow Springs, Ohio.

LACEY, JOHN I., PH.D.
Chairman, Department of Psychophysiology-Neurophysiology, The Fels Research Institute, Yellow Springs, Ohio.

MACLEAN, PAUL D., M.D.
Chief, Section on Limbic Integration and Behavior, Laboratory of Neurophysiology, National Institute of Mental Health, Bethesda, Maryland.

MAHL, GEORGE F., PH.D.
Associate Professor, Department of Psychiatry, Yale University, New Haven, Connecticut.

MEAD, MARGARET, PH.D.
Associate Curator of Ethnology, Department of Anthropology, American Museum of Natural History, New York, New York.

MOSS, HOWARD A., PH.D.
Research Associate, Department of Psychology, Fels Research Institute, Yellow Springs, Ohio.

NOVEY, SAMUEL, M.D.
Assistant Professor of Psychiatry, Johns Hopkins University, Baltimore, Maryland.

OSTOW, MORTIMER, M.D.
New York, New York.

PRIBRAM, KARL H., M.D.
USPHS Professor, Departments of Psychiatry and Psychology, Stanford University School of Medicine, Palo Alto, California.

REISER, MORTON F., M.D.
Professor and Director of Research, Department of Psychiatry, Albert Einstein College of Medicine, Yeshiva University, New York, New York.

RENNEKER, RICHARD E., M.D.
Department of Psychiatry, University of California Medical Center, Los Angeles, California.

ROBBINS, LEWIS L., M.D.
Medical Director, Hillside Hospital, Glen Oaks, New York.

SCHAFER, ROY, PH.D.
Division of Student Mental Hygiene, Yale University, New Haven, Connecticut.

SCOTT, JOHN PAUL, PH.D.
Senior Staff Scientist, Roscoe B. Jackson Memorial Laboratory, Bar Harbor, Maine.

SPITZ, RENÉ A., M.D.
Visiting Professor, Department of Psychiatry, University of Colorado Medical Center, Denver, Colorado.

WOLF, STEWART, M.D.
Professor and Head of the Department of Medicine, University of Oklahoma Medical Center, Oklahoma City, Oklahoma.

EXPRESSION OF THE EMOTIONS IN MAN

Part I

ORIGINS

CHAPTER 1

Introduction: Emotional Expression—Past and Present

PETER H. KNAPP, M.D.

A symposium may properly begin with Plato. His celebrated metaphor in *Phaedrus* depicts the soul as "a charioteer and a pair of winged horses . . . one of them is noble and of noble breed; the other is ignoble and of ignoble breed; and the driving of them of necessity gives a great deal of trouble to him." Shortly thereafter he refers to the soul as "enshrined in that living tomb which we carry about, now that we are imprisoned in the body like an oyster in his shell." His *Dialogue* presents sharply the dualistic aspects of platonic thought: right opposed to wrong, psyche to soma, and will to emotion.

In his psychoanalytic study of history, Norman Brown describes Western European culture as "2000 years of higher education based on the notion that man is essentially a soul for mysterious accidental reasons imprisoned in a body" (1959, p. 31). The medieval era preserved certain rudimentary physiologic facts about emotion, taken largely from Aristotle. But the intellectual climate which opposed mind to matter tended to lump emotional phenomena with the latter, as part of man's animal inheritance, alien to his "self." "The heart has its reasons which reason knows not," said Pascal. By and large, these were left to the mystic—to "the poet, lunatic and lover." They were not the object of great concern for the philosopher or his descendent, the scientist.

As another author put it, "Most writers on the emotions and human conduct seem to be treating rather of matters outside nature than of natural phenomena following nature's general laws. They appear to conceive man to be situated in nature as a kingdom within a kingdom: for they believe that he disturbs rather than follows nature's order, that he has absolute control over his actions. . . ." The words are those of Spinoza (p. 128), an exception to the dualistic tradition. He viewed all of natural phenomena, including body and mind, as interrelated parts of a single universe. It was perhaps no accident that he was one of the first philosophers to deal systematically with emotional processes and to recognize their enormous power in determining human behavior. He was thus clearly a spiritual ancestor of Darwin and Freud.

The title of this symposium pays tribute to Darwin as pioneer on the road toward the more unified modern view. Darwin's specific contributions to the study of the emotions were limited by available facts. He attempted to explain expressive behavior by three principles. Of these the first, that of associated habits—bared teeth in the dog, the better with which to bite—and the second, that of antithesis—fawning in the dog as a pattern opposite to his aggressive stance—were perceptive and productive hypotheses, supported by further evidence. His third principle: that certain expressive manifestations resulted from "direct action of the excited nervous system"—for example, writhing, in the dog, simply due to pain—in large part confessed ignorance, though honestly as Hilgard (1960) remarks. Yet even this principle foreshadowed current notions about states of central arousal, themselves serving highly adaptive ends. Darwin's particular principles thus proved useful. Far more important was his general viewpoint that emotional phenomena were among the evolving attributes of man which had developed like man himself from antecedents in his animal forebears.

The prophet did not bring the millennium. After Darwin, dualistic modes of thought persisted. Indeed, perhaps one of the tasks of the student of emotion is to trace and to explain what might be called the emotional roots of dualism. To do so would go beyond this essay. In historical fact, a few general syntheses were attempted, such as the tridimensional theory of Wundt (cf. Boring) or the treatise of Shand; but most of the study of emotional processes tended to divide itself between two streams, one physiological, one psychological.

The rise of modern physiology led James and Lange independently to seize upon physiologic reaction as the essential ingredient in emotional experience. More crucial than the relatively sterile debate which followed were the advances in physiology itself. The work of Cannon, and later the hypothesis of Selye, about adaptive responses to stress, led to the accumulation of abundant evidence as to how the organism accomplished such adaption. The classical Pavlovian approach, and the later development of operant conditioning, offered a systematic method for study of many automatic anticipatory processes important in learning. These applied not only to voluntary or new brain mechanisms but to visceral processes as well (cf. Bykov) and had profound bearing on "emotion." The so-called psychosomatic movement lent further impetus. Correlations between psychological and physiologic observations led to increased understanding of cardiovascular reactions (Alexander, Greenblatt, Reiser), gastrointestinal behavior (Engel, Mirsky, Margolin), dermatologic conditions (Deutsch, Kepecs), and endocrine function (Hamburg, Grinker et al., Wittkower) to name only some areas within this expanding field. Especially important was the developing interaction between conditioning studies and the newer techniques of neurophysiology. The rapid expansion of neurophysiologic knowledge increased our understanding of the central organization of emotional behavior. It illuminated in particular the key role of the archipallium and its connections with the autonomic and endocrine systems (Papez and McLean); the importance of nonspecific arousal systems (Magoun); and the existence of specific areas which have powerful self-rewarding or self-punishing function (Olds, Lilly).

Closely related studies of animal behavior, particularly by the ethologists such as Lorenz and Tinbergen, have led to clarification of the concept of instinctive behavior, which is seen as a group of patterns of neural and behavioral organization, unfolding at or after birth in constant interaction with experience. Similar patterns, detected in children, play an important role in the "emotional" reactions of the developing human, as Bowlby has stressed and as will be emphasized by Spitz in Chapter 3.

Finally, anthropology since Darwin has stressed not only lines connecting man to the rest of the animal kingdom but the precise paths of divergence, those evolutionary elements which favored his acquisition of technical skills, social communications, "self-domestication," to use the phrase of Washburn (1960) by "suppression of rage and of the uncontrolled drive to first place in the hierarchy of dominance." This thesis will be developed by Hamburg in Chapter 11.

Psychosomatic studies, brain investigation, animal observation, and the anthropological method all offer bridges to more purely psychological investigations of "emotion." In general, the latter followed a different course, stressing the importance of subjective experience as a source of information about emotional life. Purely introspective studies, however, encountered difficulties. As Farber and West (1960) point out, these tended to become "progressively more impoverished." In part the fault appears to lie with their attempt to snare complex happenings in an oversimple cognitive net and reduce emotions to neat sensory analogies. In part, the difficulties, I think, go deeper. The phenomenological and later the existentialist approaches were more subtle, insisting upon the intricate nature of personal emotional experience; but as conceptual systems they suffer from the tendency to perpetuate the notion of ineffable human essence, transcending natural phenomena. Furthermore, as methods, they place unwarranted reliance upon consciousness. Conscious awareness and report, even if only to oneself, is by no means a clear-cut entity, but much more a creative act, created specially for varying circumstances. Though it may provide crucial data about emotional events, it alone cannot be the absolute indicator of them. In any individual there is a multitude of expressive manifestations which an outside observer will have no hesitation in labeling "emotional," though at any given moment an introspective report may indicate complete unawareness of them. Also there is a host of dim or fleeting ideational manifestations which an observer infers are serving as "emotional signals" and which also may operate far beyond a subject's conscious awareness. (The need to consider unconscious aspects of emotional processes is discussed elsewhere [Knapp, 1958] and is amplified later in Chapter 10 by Engel.)

A lineal descendent in the psychologic sphere of the unitary view espoused by Spinoza and Darwin was Freudian psychoanalysis. What was the contribution of its biologically broader and methodologically "deeper" view? The discipline which had exposed the power of man's instinctual impulses, and which dealt daily with the conflicts and perversities of his erotic life, with his hate, fear, and guilt, his mourning and melancholia, would be expected to have much to say about "emotion." An apparent paradox arises from the fact that actually little was systematically written about the theory of the emotions. Rapaport in 1953 spoke of having to "piece together the existing fragments of this theory."

The paradox is in part resolved when we see that psychoanalysis did have much, almost too much, to say about the whole area heretofore called that of the emotions, so that it endeavored to break down its complexity. It saw "emotional" life as a hierarchy of motivational processes, conceptualized as derivatives of basic instinctual drives. It should be noted that Freud used the term "instinct" as a "borderland concept," "a demand upon the mental apparatus by virtue of its connection with the body" (1915a). In so doing he betrayed lingering difficulties with the dilemma of dualistic thinking, reflected in his determination to work with a purely "mental" model. The latter was, of course, an important heuristic step. It facilitated elucidation of the complex interaction between powerful motivations and countermotivations, their relationship to significant humans, their role in initiating and maintaining repression and other defensive maneuvers.

The terms "emotion" or "affect" were by and large reserved for overt and manifest expressive manifestations. In the most thorough single synthesis of the psychoanalytic viewpoint, Rapaport (1953) described affects as determined by three components: (a) inborn "affect discharge channels"; (b) the use of these, modified during development, for the formation of "affect charges," which were conceived as representations of underlying drives, following a parallel course to that of "ideas," as the latter emerged during development; and (c) the progressive "taming" of emotional processes until they became "affect signals."

This somewhat abstract terminology requires certain elaborations and qualifications, stressed by other workers. First, as already stated, and as Novey (1959) and Engel (Chapter 15) and others (Knapp, 1958; Reid, 1950) point out, emotional processes cannot be equated only with conscious states.

Second, emotions cannot in any fundamental sense be entirely reduced to conflict. As Jacobson (1953), in particular, has pointed out, certain affective experiences, especially pleasurable ones, can occur under conditions of apparent nearly pure release of tension or drive; the paradigm of such experience is sexual orgasm. The notion that emotional reactions may result from direct excitation not dependent upon conflict is supported by neurophysiologic self-stimulation studies with reward and punishment centers.

Third, the progressive development in the human of the signal function of his emotions as well as its breakdown—"resomatization" as well as "desomatization," to quote Schur (1953)—implies mechanisms of inhibitory restraint. These need more study. They have a complex epigenesis, related to the growth of self-regulation and of intellectual and social abilities.

It follows, fourth, that there is an intimate relationship between emotional and cognitive, especially symbolic functions (Knapp, 1958). As Whitehead says (1929), the word emotion is a "high abstraction." In actual context it is part of experience inevitably amalgamated with other components. It seems as though some of these, particularly the cognitive flash which grasps the import of an arousal scarcely started, allow emotional phenomena to serve as mobile and rapid signals.

Fifth, emotional processes have not only a relationship to quasi-cognitive processes but to important objects in the environment. In the human infant they become oriented around the child's own body and his interaction with the key human around him, mother or surrogate. These central objects of intense emotional reactivity later persist in characteristic clusters of fantasy. Schmale (1958), Engel (Chapter 15), and especially Jacobson (1953, 1954) have stressed the intimate interweaving in emotional life of fantasies about self and object—what I have elsewhere spoken of as "two-person universe" (1958).

Sixth, the concept of emotion and the concept of drive embrace a continuum, an observation which Novey (1959) has also made. The notion of "psychic energy," stemming from instincts so remote as to be almost mystical, is being replaced in the minds of many by the ethological conception of instinctual drives as inherent, neurologically organized patterns of behavior. Even so, the scope of the term "drive" is wide. It may refer to processes of long-term mobilization or readiness for action. One thus speaks of a person as having strong sexual or aggressive drives. The concept can also connote emergent manifestations, the immediate accumulation of "tension" preceding overt expression. It becomes a matter of precise language for a speaker to indicate what phenomenon of drive or affect he means, whether something in the hierarchy of broad motivational tendencies, or some actual process of arousal, with or without conflict, or some progressively more rarified cognitive impression of one of the preceding. Such a view would fit emotional responses along a scale running from the more to the less differentiated, not necessarily paralleling a similar, continuum of "ideas."

Finally, the adaptive point of view, which was only beginning to make itself felt in psychoanalysis at the time of Rapaport's paper, is enormously important for emotions. "Discharge mechanisms" or, to use a less easily concretized metaphor, intrinsic patterns of arousal, inhibition, and expression have been known since Cannon to have important functions in mobilizing the individual for emergency activity. Recently Hamburg (1959) has commented on the equal importance of mechanisms for demobilization and restraint. In addition, the subjectively felt affect state, as Rapaport (1953) mentions, serves important functions in reality testing from moment to moment. Also, it plays an obviously vital role in adjustment to long-term roles and tasks. Possibly still more important is the communicative value to man, both of his actual involuntary emotional processes and of his subjective report about them. Feeling binds man to his fellow man.

Thus the psychoanalytic view sees emotional phenomena originating from innate patterns of expressive reaction, closely related to those subsumed under the concept of instinctual drive. Their original massive and undifferentiated nature becomes modified under the impact of maturation and learning, until they become refined to important signals, with a quasi-cognitive character. They have a variable relationship to consciousness and to conflict; they are closely related in reality and fantasy to key humans; they have enormous adaptive importance. Many unanswered questions remain, to some of which we will return; but this view provides the skeleton of a theory of emotional processes.

It should be noted that from a viewpoint of *definition*, there are three groups of phenomena which, as Reid pointed out (1950), have been generally included under the term "emotion." With full awareness of the complexities already mentioned, it seems worth while to paraphrase Reid's definition for this Symposium as a pragmatic starting point. Slightly altered, it states that the term "emotion" (or, synonymously, affect) is an organizing concept referring to the following interrelated kinds of data:

(a) observations about *processes of physiologic arousal and restraint,* relating to the individual's involuntary adaptive interaction with the environment, prominently though not exclusively associated with his autonomic nervous and endocrine systems and their connections

(b) observations about *states of experiences, felt as private,* which tend to occur simultaneously with the above, as these are perceived introspectively or reported to an outside observer

(c) observable *expressive manifestation* over vocal, motor, or autonomic nervous pathways, which tend to be associated with the above processes and states, and which allow communication about them to the environment.

A certain overlap is inevitable among these categories. Their inclusion is not intended to settle all the associated logical or semantic issues, for example, those surrounding the term "private states." Rather, the intent is to indicate the variety of phenomena which are called "emotional." Our further purpose in this Symposium is to focus on only one category, namely, the third, or *expressive* manifestations.

Even "expression" connotes such a wide range of manifestations that we have had to exclude several areas recommended by Darwin as deserving further study—such as expression *by* man in the wide range of the visual creative arts.

Somewhat arbitrarily, the papers which follow fall in three main groups.

First, in the Darwinian tradition, we will be concerned with origins. Before we reach our primary objective, namely, the human and the adult, two introductory chapters after this one, the papers by MacLean and Spitz, will touch on phylogenesis and ontogenesis, that is, on certain emotional manifestations in animals and in human infants.

The second group of papers takes as its starting point the clinical situation, and concerns itself with the various levels at which emotional phenomena can be specified.

One hope behind this volume is to promote contact between the clinician, who is in daily intimate touch with intense emotional experience, and the experimentalist, who is acquiring an expanding mass of information about emotional mechanisms. A brief digression is appropriate about the clinician and what he knows about emotional expression. The answer is: much and little. He knows much because he is intuitively tuned to the affect of his patient, constantly reacting to it, much of the time using his own empathic response as his most reliable guide (Schafer, 1959). He knows little, being still drastically limited in his ability to understand and overcome the defensive forces which prevent emergence of his patient's deepest and strongest feelings. Indeed, we are still comparatively ignorant of what happens when such feelings do emerge. We now know, I think, that they are a necessary though not sufficient condition for therapeutic progress, but much else in the experience we call "catharsis" remains mysterious.

The clinician, furthermore, has done little to make explicit his intuitive empathic knowledge about expressive phenomena. Among psychoanalysts, Wilhelm Reich (1933) stressed their importance in what he called "character armor"; a few other authors have discussed particular bits of expressive behavior (e.g., Searl, 1933; Rangell, 1954; Kris, 1939); still fewer have dealt systematically with the observations about emotional manifestations which are possible in the clinical situation. Braatoy (1954) has discussed them at length; and Felix Deutsch (1952, 1959), in a series of papers on postural observations, has indicated the wealth of information available even in the comparative restriction of the psychoanalytic situation.

Indeed, one is forced to wonder whether that restriction is not, to an extent, constriction, whether the analyst has not deliberately blinded himself to some of what he can see. One can preserve the couch and the purposes it serves, yet still be physically able to observe from a position at a 45-degree angle behind and to one side of the patient (Braatoy, 1954). Could it be that there has been in some therapists a reluctance to admit the influx of emotional data, along with its inevitable emotional impact? In a more barbed phrase, Braatoy asks whether some analysts "feel the deep chair behind the patient's couch not as a prison but as a position where he at last can whisper to his deceased mother the famous epitaph: 'Now you have peace—and so have I.' "

However alert the clinician, and however intensely in contact with his patient, his insights can be richly supplemented by more precise methods of recording expressive and communicative behavior. These have made great strides in the past fifteen years, contributed to by many who are participating in this Symposium, Mahl, Birdwhistell, Dittmann, Renneker, Mead, and others. Investigators in this area have pointed out that information about emotion comes over multiple channels: by lexical cues, by acoustic-linguistic indicators, by gestures and bodily movement, and finally by visceral changes.

Although these levels are abundantly interconnected, demands of clarity have dictated discussion of each separately. Each requires separate methods and poses separate questions. At the lexical level we must ask to what extent words alone can still yield further information in the study of emotional processes. Language, inspired by passion, undergoes a wide variety of formal changes, a breakdown of grammatical structure, shift of tense to the present, the use of imitative sound, sensory detail, repetition of words, introduction of rhetorical questions or imperative or exclamatory mood, confusions of subject and object—devices used by the orator and poet. In the related area of analysis of content, how can we go further toward identifying characteristic categories which bear on significant emotion; especially how can we best meet with the competing demands for reliability and for significance? Mahl's application of his careful methods to the clinical sample taken as a starting point will indicate how far we have come toward answering some of these questions.

In terms of acoustic and motor phenomena, to what extent is detailed awareness of the enormous amount of information which ordinarily goes unnoticed necessary for understanding significant emotion? Is there at the time the danger of confusing the objectifiable with the relevant? Other questions arise. How far can we extend inferences from linguistic and kinesic phenomena alone; how much do they still need to be correlated with more global, clinical, and systematic analysis of content and context in order to yield full meaning? How much do the new media, facilitating observation, distort what they observe?

In terms of visceral phenomena, both of the latter questions apply still more strongly. My own opinion is that one can make valid observations and conduct valid psychotherapy in the face of extraordinary encroachments by simultaneous physiologic observations, but not everyone would agree with this position. Certainly in the visceral sphere, the problems of referent of the message, to what extent and in what way it may be translated into verbal language, remain major ones.

Finally, in our third section, still broader questions will be asked. A symposium, like Plato's, may end in somnolence, but at the start there is no limit to its ambition. In an exchange of viewpoints the experimentalist lion will lie down briefly with the psychoanalyst lamb. From the former we may get hints as to how sophisticated method may inform our efforts to study that recalcitrant and reluctant experimental animal, man. With the latter we may ponder how his cumbersome instrument, full of idiosyncrasy and redundancy, difficult if not impossible to study in totality, can best be used in investigation of emotional processes. It still may provide unique information not obtainable in other ways, and it may be possible to simplify the clinical situation without destroying its richness, as has been done, for example, in certain efforts to use the tool of prediction (Benjamin, 1959; Escalona and Heider, 1959; Knapp, 1960).

In our closing papers we hope to make some attack on the formidable problems of classifying emotional phenomena and setting them in a wider biological framework. What may emerge are some areas of agreement that will allow us to grope toward our neurophysiologic colleagues not only with better methods but with more sophisticated models of emotional processes. In this regard, Pribram's indication of the sophistication in Freud's original "Project" picks up again the historical thread of this introduction.

The opinions in this volume seem to agree on one theme, that the psychosomatic phenomena of emotion can be encompassed within a unified, adaptively oriented, theoretical framework. Theories about emotion must also comprehend the polyphonic richness of emotional experience. They need to account for other elements, some of which will become apparent in the pages that follow. It is obvious that such theories will be more complex than the old tripartite model, as Colby has called it, of id, superego, and ego. Indeed, one might speculate that this model itself may have originated from within our emotional selves, ultimately from our central nervous organization, subdivided into basic parts, as MacLean shows it to be. Most pertinent to our schematizations of psychic "structure" are: the old mammalian brain itself divided between (a) arousal systems and (b) opposing inhibitory mechanisms, and finally (c) the phylogenetically more recent neural areas which allow rapid, skilled activity, abstraction, memory, and foresight—a present-day charioteer.

CHAPTER 2

Phylogenesis

PAUL D. MACLEAN, M.D.

Man finds himself in the predicament that Nature has endowed him, essentially, with three brains which despite great differences in structure must function together and communicate with one another. The oldest of these brains is basically reptilian. The second has been inherited from lower mammals, and the third is a late mammalian development which in its culmination in primates has made man peculiarly man.

Three brains within a brain! Speaking allegorically, we may imagine that when the psychiatrist bids the patient to lie on the couch, he is asking him to stretch out alongside a horse and a crocodile. The crocodile may be willing and ready to shed a tear and the horse to neigh and whinny, but when they are encouraged to express their troubles in words, it soon becomes evident that their incapability is beyond the

---

Part of this material was contained in a lecture on Cerebral Substrates of Sexual Function, given in connection with the Interdisciplinary Training Program of Sciences Related to Mental Health, University of California Medical School, San Francisco, California, November 15, 1960. An expanded version has appeared in *J. Nerv. Ment. Dis., 135:*289-301, 1962.

help of language training. Little wonder that the patient who has personal responsibility for these animals and who must try to serve as their mouthpiece is sometimes accused of being full of resistances and reluctant to talk; or that the psychiatrist's interpretations and diagnosis suggest a certain lack of training in veterinary neuropsychiatry!

In this presentation I shall focus attention on some new findings pertaining to the representation of sexual functions in the lower mammalian brain. Later, in discussing these findings, I shall try to show how they have particular relevance to neuropsychiatry. (1) I shall show how, combined with previous knowledge of oral representation, they attest to the close organization of oral and sexual functions in the brain. (2) I shall indicate how they give insight into the close ties between oral and sexual manifestations on the one hand, and fear and aggression on the other. (3) Finally I shall point out how the discoveries pertaining to sexual representation possibly shed light on the evolutionary social structure of animals and acculturation in man. Curiously enough, in view of the complexities of sociosexual behavior involved in the preservation of the species there has existed heretofore little evidence of representation of sexual functions above the primitive level of the hypothalamus.

Background

As background for what is to follow, it will be helpful to make a few general remarks about the functions and the anatomy of the lower mammalian brain. On the basis of investigations of the last twenty years it may be inferred that this lower mammalian brain which we share with all mammals derives and acts upon information in terms of feelings, particularly emotional feelings that guide our behavior with respect to the two basic life principles of *self-preservation* and the *preservation of the species* (MacLean, 1958a, 1959).

The lower mammalian brain comprises the phylogenetically old cortex and its related nuclei. This entire constellation of structures is now commonly referred to as *the limbic system.* This is because most of the old cortex is found in a large cerebral convolution called the limbic lobe. The term limbic, introduced by Broca in 1878, is descriptive of the fact that this convolution surrounds the brain stem. Limbic means literally "to form a border around."

Figure I, in which the brains of the rabbit, cat, and monkey are drawn roughly to scale, illustrates that the limbic lobe is found as a common denominator in the brains of all mammals. The cortex of this old mammalian brain, surrounding the brain stem like a doughnut, is shown in black. The cortex of the new mammalian brain is represented in white.

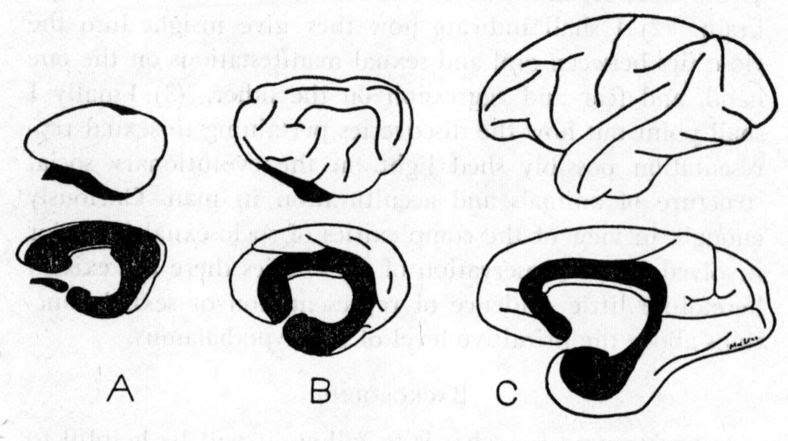

FIGURE I

Most of the cortex of "the lower mammalian brain" is found in the limbic lobe. As the above drawing illustrates, this lobe (represented in black) is found as a common denominator in the brains of all mammals. A, B, and C show lateral (above) and medial (below) surfaces of brains of rabbit, cat, and monkey, respectively, drawn roughly to scale. (From MacLean, 1954.)

It should be emphasized that the limbic cortex is relatively crude and simple compared with the new cortex, and one might infer from this alone that it functions at an animalistic level in both animal and man. It should also be emphasized that in contrast to the new cortex, the limbic cortex has strong connections with the hypothalamus which is so important in integrating the performance of mechanisms involved in self-preservation and procreation.

The rest of the anatomy that we need to consider may be simplified if, as in Figure II, we look at the limbic system in a two-dimensional scheme. The doughnut-shaped structure in

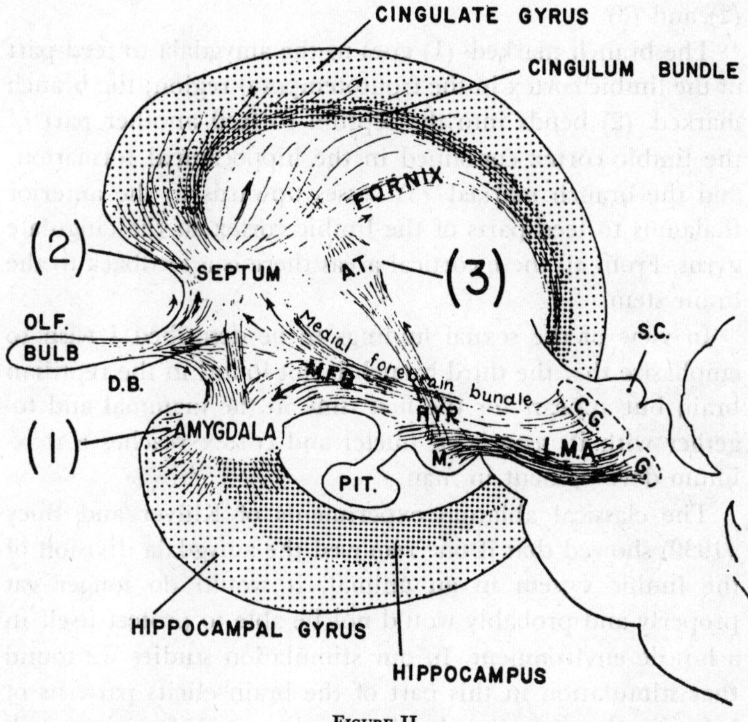

FIGURE II

This diagram emphasizes that the medial forebrain bundle (MFB) is a major line of communication between the limbic lobe (in stipple) and the hypothalamus, midbrain, and other structures of the brain stem. Only ascending pathways of this neural trunk are indicated. Major branchings to the amygdala, septum, and anterior thalamus are, respectively, designated by the numerals (1), (2), and (3), and their significance is discussed in the text. They supply the limbic cortex of the frontotemporal region, hippocampus, and cingulate gyrus. The limbic cortex in turn feeds back to the brain stem. Abbreviations: A.T., anterior thalamic nuclei; C.G., central gray of midbrain; D.B., diagonal band of Broca; G., ventral and dorsal tegmental nuclei of Gudden; HYP., hypothalamus; L.M.A., limbic midbrain area of Nauta; M., mammillary body; PIT., pituitary; S.C., superior colliculus.

stipple represents the limbic lobe itself. The drawing emphasizes that the medial forebrain bundle is a major line of communication between the limbic lobe and the hypothalamus, midbrain, and other structures of the brain stem. One might imagine that this bundle is like the trunk of a tree with three main branches carrying the neural sap up and down. The branches are indicated by the numerals (1), (2), and (3).

The branch marked (1) goes to the amygdala to feed part of the limbic cortex in the frontotemporal region; the branch marked (2) bends into the septum to feed another part of the limbic cortex contained in the hippocampal formation; and the branch marked (3) passes upwards to the anterior thalamus to feed parts of the limbic cortex in the cingulate gyrus. From all these cortical areas there is a feedback to the brain stem.

In view of the sexual findings to be described I wish to emphasize that the third branch is not found in the reptilian brain but appears for the first time in the mammal and together with its associated nuclei and cortex reaches a maximum development in man.

The classical ablation experiments of Klüver and Bucy (1939) showed that if one removed the amygdala division of the limbic system in an animal, it would no longer eat properly and probably would not be able to protect itself in a hostile environment. In our stimulation studies we found that stimulation in this part of the brain elicits patterns of behavior that are related either to alimentary functions such as eating, swallowing, and the like, or to searching, fighting, and self-defense (MacLean, 1952; MacLean and Delgado, 1953). The clinical study of psychomotor epilepsy reveals that epileptogenic foci in this part of the brain may trigger many of the same forms of behavior, as well as the feelings associated with threats to self-preservation. From these observations it may be inferred that this amygdala circuit is largely concerned with self-preservation as it pertains to feeding and to the behavior involved in the struggle to obtain food.

One of the most striking features of the Klüver-Bucy syndrome is the bizarre hypersexuality that develops. It would appear that removal of the amygdala and related structures gives release, in the Jacksonian sense, to other parts of the brain concerned with sexual behavior.

Exploration in cats of the septal circuit of the limbic system revealed the striking finding that stimulation of the hippocampus, and the anatomically related septum, was frequently followed by enhanced pleasure and grooming reactions and sometimes penile erection (MacLean, 1955, 1957). The general behavior was reminiscent of courtship behavior of male cats. These findings together with complementary observations in the rat led me to the inference that this part of the limbic system was concerned with expressive and feeling states that are conducive to sociability and other preliminaries of copulation and reproduction. In other words, next door to the amygdala was a system of structures that seemed to be involved *in sustaining the species rather than the self.*

New Findings

Although the brain has been extensively explored by electrical stimulation during the past eighty years, there has been a surprising lack of information about the localization of structures involved in penile erection. In a continuation of stimulation studies on the cerebral representation of sexual functions, we have used the response of penile erection as one indicator that a structure is implicated in sexual behavior (MacLean and Ploog, 1961). For this work it was desirable to use an animal more akin to man than the carnivore. We chose the squirrel monkey *(Saimiri sciureus)* because this little New World primate which weighs as little as the guinea pig has a brain comparable to the cat's in size, and, therefore, of desirable dimensions for neuroanatomical and neurophysiological studies.

A special platform is fixed to the animal's head which allows one to explore the brain millimeter by millimeter while the animal sits peaceably in a restraining chair. During an experimental day we lower two electrodes millimeter by millimeter, alternately stimulating through one and then the other, using a variety of stimulus parameters. Electrodes are returned to positive points and fixed in place so that we can repeat stimulation and recording on subsequent days. Because of previous findings in the cat, we routinely monitor the bioelectrical activity of the hippocampus.

Figure III shows on brain diagrams the positive loci for erection found in the first study. The positive points are represented by diamonds and squares. The squares give the added information that penile erection was associated with hippocampal afterdischarges. The vertical dashes are points explored and found to be negative. It is to be emphasized that all points are checked histologically in stained serial sections of the brain.

In summary, the positive loci for erection in the forebrain and diencephalon are found distributed along parts of three corticosubcortical subdivisions of the limbic system. First, there is evidence that they coincide with the distribution of known hippocampal projections to parts of the septum, anterior thalamus, and hypothalamus. Second, they have been located in parts of the so-called Papez circuit, comprising the mammillary bodies, the mammillothalamic tract, the anterior thalamic nuclei, and anterior cingulate gyrus. Finally, they have been found in parts of the medial orbital gyrus, the medial part of the medial dorsal nucleus of the thalamus, and regions of their known connections.

In regard to this last finding it is pertinent to recall that frontal lobotomy, which severs the connections between the medial dorsal nucleus and the orbitofrontal and prefrontal cortex, sometimes results in bizarre, uninhibited sexual behavior.

The medial part of the medial dorsal nucleus and the medial septopreoptic region appear to be nodal points for erection. The medial forebrain bundle appears to be the

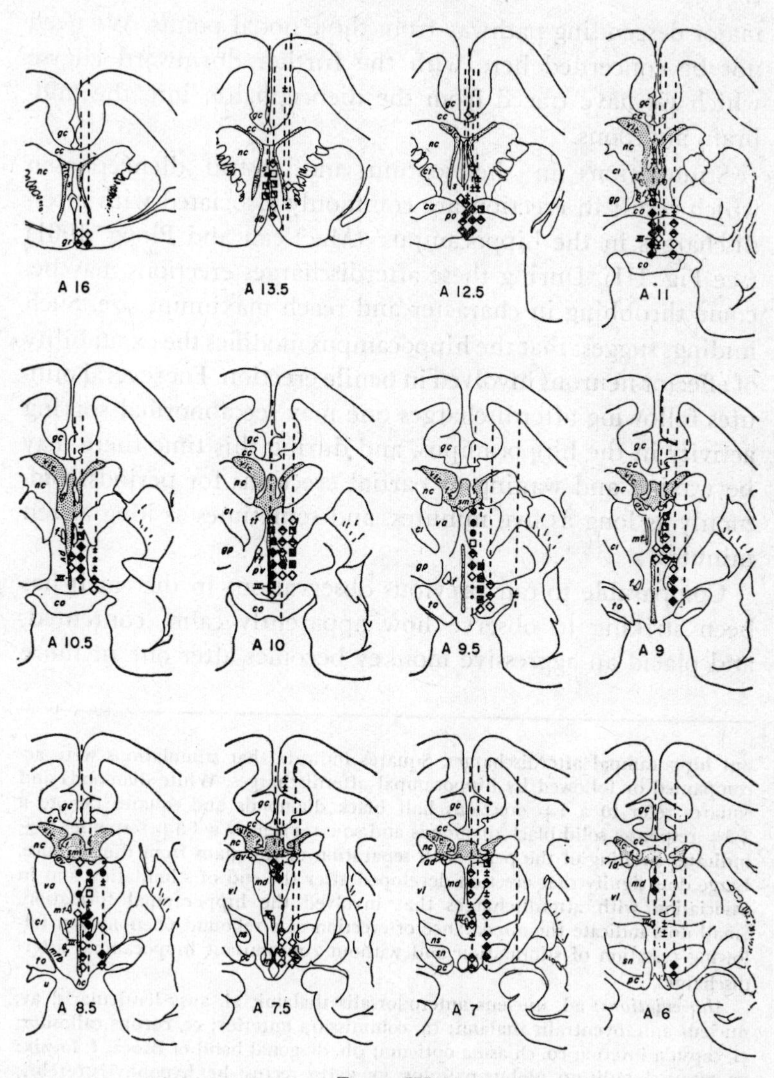

FIGURE III

In the first of a series of investigations on the cerebral representation of sexual functions, it was found that positive loci for penile erection are located within parts of three major cortical subcortical subdivisions of the limbic system (MacLean and Ploog, 1961). This conclusion was based on findings summarized in the above diagrams on which are plotted positive and negative points with respect to penile erection.

Vertical dashes represent points explored and found to be negative. Diamonds and squares symbolize positive loci. Diamonds refer to erection elicited with-

major descending pathway from these nodal points. We need not be concerned here with the further downward course which we have traced from the diencephalon into the midbrain and pons.

Stimulations in the septum and rostral diencephalon which result in erection are commonly associated with afterdischarges in the hippocampus (MacLean and Ploog, 1961) (see Fig. III). During these afterdischarges erections may become throbbing in character and reach maximum size. Such findings suggest that the hippocampus modifies the excitability of effector neurons involved in penile erection. For several minutes following afterdischarges one may see abnormal spiking activity in the hippocampus, and during this time there may be waxing and waning of partial erections for periods commonly as long as five minutes, and sometimes as long as ten minutes.

Comparable to our previous observations in the cat it has been striking to observe how apparently calm, contented, and placid an aggressive monkey becomes after one or more

---

out hippocampal afterdischarges. Squares indicate that stimulations were accompanied or followed by hippocampal afterdischarges. White diamonds and squares refer to a 1+ erection; half black diamonds and squares denote a 2-3+ response; solid black diamonds and squares signify a 4-5+ response; a ± indicates swelling of the penis with separation of the glans from the prepuce. Large dots signify that erection developed after the end of stimulation and in association with afterdischarges that involved the hippocampal formation. Small dots indicate the appearance of erection as a rebound phenomenon following cessation of stimulation and without concomitant hippocampal afterdischarges.

Abbreviations: ad, nucleus anterodorsalis thalami; al, ansa lenticularis; av, nucleus anteroventralis thalami; ca, commissura anterior; cc, corpus callosum; ci, capsula interna; co, chiasma opticum; db, diagonal band of Broca; f, fornix; gc, gyrus cinguli; gp, globus pallidus; gr, gyrus rectus; hc, hypophysis cerebri; ld, nucleus lateralis dorsalis thalami; m, corpus mammillare; md, nucleus medialis dorsalis thalami; mfb, medial forebrain bundle; mt, fasciculus mammillothalamicus; nc, nucleus caudatus; ns, nucleus subthalamicus; nst, nucleus stria terminalis; p, putamen; pc, pedunculus cerebri; po, area preoptica; pv, nucleus paraventricularis hypothalami; s, septum pellucidum; sm, stria medullaris; sn, substantia nigra; st. stria terminalis; to, tractus opticus; t, tuberculum thalami; u, uncus gyri hippocampi; va, nucleus ventralis anterior thalami; vl, nucleus ventralis lateralis thalami; vlc, ventriculus lateralis cerebri; III, ventriculus tertius. (From MacLean and Ploog, 1961.)

hippocampal afterdischarges have been elicited. These apparent changes in mood may last for several hours.

Discussion

Figure II emphasizes the proximity of the amygdala and septum, which, as the stimulation experiments have shown, are involved, respectively, in oral and sexual behavior. The amygdala has strong connections with the septum and, as Nauta (1960) has shown, with the medial dorsal nucleus as well. It has been curious to find that with stimulation in the amygdala one may obtain chewing and salivation, with partial erection occurring as a recruited response after many seconds of stimulation or as a rebound phenomenon after stimulation is terminated (Reis, et al., 1963). In other words, excitation in a region involved in oral mechanisms readily spills over into others concerned with genital function.

In the light of this close relationship it appears less surprising that there is often an intimate blending of behavior in the oral and sexual spheres, of which love-making is a happy illustration. At the same time there commonly seems to be a bizarre mix-up of these behaviors. Such a mix-up is readily taken for granted in animals, but one has only to look at the last fifty years of Freudian psychology to realize the trouble that it may lead to in human affairs.

If there is any neural agency responsible for this mix-up, which society regards as a perversity, then the olfactory sense, perhaps more than any other, must be considered the culprit (MacLean, 1959). When the animal is looked at in the ordinary elongated position the oral and anogenital regions appear to be at opposite poles. A corresponding relationship is maintained in the topographical representation of the body in the postcentral gyrus of the neocortex. When it came to the cerebral organization of the limbic lobe, however, Nature apparently had to do a deep knee-bend in order to permit the olfactory sense an intimate participation in both oral and anogenital functions.

This oral-genital affinity is germane to the close connection between sexuality and fear and aggression. As is well recognized, fighting is frequently a preliminary to both feeding and mating. One sees combative behavior even in the babe who will angrily fight the breast if no milk is forthcoming. At the same time he may develop penile erection. From the level of the anterior commissure caudally, one can follow neural structures involved in anger and fear and combative behavior lying next to those concerned with feeding and sexual responses. Within the space of a millimeter, one may pass from a point at which stimulation results in erection and an apparent state of placidity to one at which the electrical current elicits erection in conjunction with an angry or fearful type of vocalization and showing of fangs. As one lowers the electrode a little deeper one may obtain only fearful or angry-like manifestations during stimulation, but see erection appear as a rebound phenomenon after stimulation is terminated.

One is reminded of Freud's observation in his *Three Contributions to the Theory of Sex* (1905) that "the sexually-exciting influence of some painful affects, such as fear, shuddering and horror is felt by a great many people throughout life and readily explains why so many people seek opportunities to experience such sensations" (p. 62).[1]

A few additional quotations from this same monograph will serve to introduce some naturalistic observations on the squirrel monkey that are relevant to the close relationship of sexual and aggressive behavior. In discussing the origins of the sexual impulse, Freud mentions the looking impulse and the cruelty impulse.

In regard to the looking impulse he says, "The little child is above all shameless, and during its early years it evinces definite pleasure in displaying its body and especially its sexual organs. A counterpart to this desire . . . is . . . the curiosity to see other persons' genitals. . . . I must conclude that the im-

[1] This quotation as well as the subsequent ones from Freud's *Three Contributions to the Theory of Sex* (1905) are from A. A. Brill's translation (New York: Nervous and Mental Disease Monographs, 1948).

pulse for looking can appear in the child as a spontaneous sexual manifestation" (p. 52).

In discussing the cruelty component of the sexual impulse Freud states, "Children who are distinguished for evincing especial cruelty to animals and playmates may be justly suspected of intensive and premature sexual activity in their erogenous zones" (p. 53). A few pages later he remarks: "A number of persons report that they experienced the first signs of excitement in their genitals during fighting or wrestling with playmates. . . . The infantile connection between fighting and sexual excitement in many persons acts as a determinant for the future preferred course of their sexual impulse" (p. 62).

These comments on the looking and cruelty impulse have comparative interest relevant to a study of the social behavior of the squirrel monkey that we have conducted in parallel with our stimulation experiments. Figure IV shows a group of six monkeys which with Dr. Detlev Ploog and others we observed for over a year in an attempt to evaluate and quantify certain aspects of their behavior. As shown, they lived in a glass house with a plastic glass tree in the middle. This group contained four males and two females.

Among the most interesting things brought to light by this study was the finding that the squirrel monkey displays penile erection under a variety of conditions (Ploog and MacLean, 1963). It may be performed at a distance between two strange animals, presumably as a kind of greeting. One of the most impressive ways of eliciting this response is to hold a mirror up to one of these monkeys. In the communal situation the male may display penile erection to the female in the act of courtship, or it may display to another male as a means of exerting and establishing dominance. As illustrated in Figure V, in both the courtship and dominance situation the display is performed with the thighs spread and the erect penis thrust up almost into the face of the other animal. In the case of two males, if the animal receiving the display does not remain quiet and submissive during the display, it may be viciously assaulted by the dominant male.

FIGURE IV

Group of six squirrel monkeys (four males and two females) that was used in the behavioral study described in text. Throughout the year of observation they lived in the glass viewing cage shown here. The dominant male, Caspar, is on floor at the right next to the food dish; Edgar, lowest in rank of the males, is in left hand corner. (From Ploog and MacLean, 1963.)

Caspar, the animal which proved to be the dominant male in the colony, displayed to all the other males but none in turn displayed to him. In contrast, the male lowest in rank,

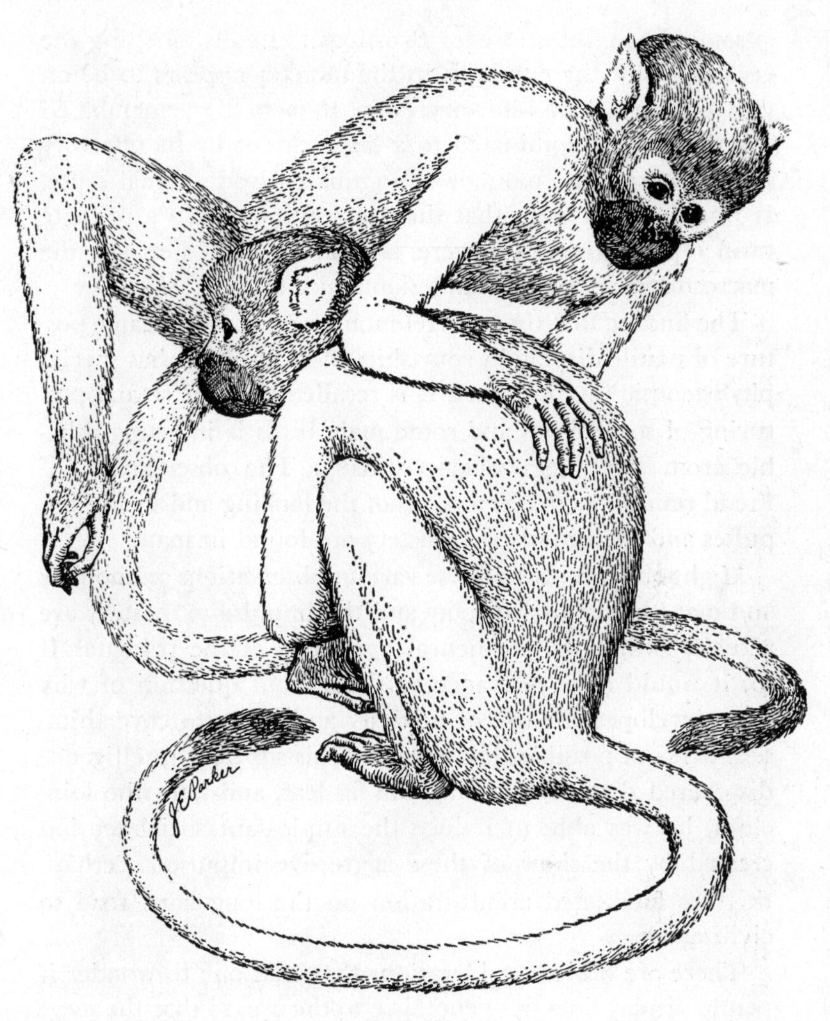

FIGURE V

In the communal situation, the male squirrel monkey may display penile erection in the act of courtship, or, as illustrated above, it may display to another male as a means of exerting and establishing dominance. In each case the display is performed with the thighs spread and the erect penis thrust almost into the face of the other animal. (From Ploog and MacLean, 1963.)

Edgar, displayed to none of the other males, but all displayed to him. Edgar displayed only to humans!

The position that two monkeys assume during the display

is somewhat reminiscent of two dogs mutually smelling the genitalia. But the emphasis in the monkey appears to be on visual rather than olfactory cues. It is to be remembered that the dog is dominated to a large extent by its olfactory sense, whereas the monkey is dominated by its visual sense. It would almost seem that the squirrel monkey is a primate form representing, as it were, a "missing link" between the macrosmatic and the visually dominant animal.

The finding that the squirrel monkey assumes the same posture of penile display in courtship and aggression has special phylogenetic interest when it is recalled that the sexual posturing of some fishes and some male birds is indistinguishable from their aggressive posturing. The observations of Freud remind us that remnants of the looking and seeing impulses and the impulse to mastery are found in man.

Might one infer from these various observations on monkey and man that genital display and the impulse to mastery are actually built into the neural apparatus of the primate? If so, it would have relevance to the age-old question of why man developed a sense of modesty and chose to cover himself. Is it not possible that man with his superior intelligence discovered that by assuming the fig leaf, and later the loincloth, he was able to reduce the unpleasant social tension created by the show of these aggressive impulses? Perhaps this has facilitated acculturation on the long hard road to civilization.

There are other considerations that lead one to wonder if penile display does not generalize to the eye, so that the mere act of one animal's looking into the eyes of another becomes in itself an aggressive act. Some monkeys such as the macaque seem in general to try to avoid looking each other in the eye, or indeed people in the eye. If one looks the macaque in the eye, it will charge. In this connection it is interesting to recall that looking in the eye spells panic to some patients and particularly some schizophrenic patients. They find it impossible to follow the half-polite, half-aggressive social dictum that is inculcated from an early age of looking people straight in the eye.

Thus far I have considered neural and behavioral findings which would appear to shed some light on psychiatric observations that the acts of mastering, devouring, and procreating seem to be inextricably tied to one another.

In concluding, I have yet to consider a subject that goes to the roots of man's idealism and altruism—namely, the close connection of feeding, sustaining, and sexuality. A concern for the welfare and preservation of the species is based on sexuality. The mother when feeding her baby at the breast experiences well-being and may have sensations associated with tumescence in the genital region. Subjective analyses have shown that there may be a comparable reaction in the feelings of those who find joy in helping and sustaining others.

In giving the results of the stimulation studies I pointed out that penile erection was obtained by stimulating structures along the course of the mammillothalamic tract and in parts of the anterior and medial thalamic nuclei. Heretofore these structures have been looked upon as silent areas of the brain. The mammillothalamic pathway, the pathway numbered (3) in the original diagram (Fig. II), is, as Le Gros Clark emphasized, not found in the reptilian brain but appears for the first time in the mammal. It is possibly pertinent to the increasingly complicated sociosexual behavior that one finds in ascending the phylogenetic scale of the mammal that this pathway and its related nuclei attain their greatest size in man. Thus there are indications that Nature did not stop at the primitive level of the hypothalamus, but endowed us with considerable brain stem and cortex with which to promote the preservation of the species.

It may be particularly significant that the medial dorsal nucleus which projects to the orbital and prefrontal cortex develops in association with the anterior group of nuclei and literally embraces them. As pointed out, the ancient midline portion of the medial dorsal nucleus is implicated in penile erection. Indeed, it is such a potent point that stimulation here may elicit close to full erection even under deep anesthesia.

The prefrontal cortex which is connected to the medial dorsal nucleus is a relatively new addition to the new mammalian brain. From our limited knowledge of its functions, it might be inferred that it is largely concerned with anticipation and planning as it pertains to both self-preservation and the preservation of the species. From the latter standpoint, it might be commented that it takes not only a good deal of planning, but also a long deferment of gratification (in neural terms, a great deal of inhibition) to keep planning and working as Jacob did fourteen years for Rachel and the anticipated progeny of that union. It requires a far higher order of extrapolation and a far deeper concern for the species to work as those in the medical sciences are working, not only for patients currently under treatment, but also through research for the progeny that we wish to prevent from suffering and dying in years to come.

In the complex organization of the old and new structures under consideration, we presumably have a neural ladder—a visionary ladder—for ascending from the most primitive sexual feeling to the highest level of altruistic sentiments.

Discussion

Stewart Wolf, M.D.

It appears that a major purpose of this Symposium is to take steps toward the development of better communication among neurophysiologists, social scientists, and psychiatric clinicians. English-speaking neurophysiologists do not formulate their findings in psychological terms, although they are dealing with the stuff, if you will, of emotional expression. Dr. MacLean is an important exception. As a rule the languages of the neurophysiologist, the clinician, and the social scientist are so disparate as to make communication very difficult. Not only do the languages differ, but so do the methods of study of each of these groups and of groups among the groups. For example, among social scientists there is a tremendous difference with respect to the need for hypothesis. To the psychologist it is indispensable; and to the anthropologist it is almost superfluous. Finally, what various groups of scientists accept as evidence differs to such a degree as to make communication among them all the more difficult.

Broadly speaking, all gestures in behavior are expressions of emotion. The movements of a person with Huntington's chorea bear a close resemblance to those of an individual with hyperthyroidism, or indeed to those of a very anxious person with neither hyperthyroidism nor Huntington's chorea. I hope that this observation will suggest that there is not a fundamental difference between the effector neural pattern for structural as opposed to functional disorders—in fact, contrasting "structural" to "functional" is not really very profitable anyway.

A good many workers have suggested that the movements one sees in seizures or associated with lesions of the brain are purposeful. They certainly are in the sense that the same movements often might occur in the intact individual in the course of self-expression. The similarity is most vividly illustrated in the temporal lobe seizure. C. G. Gunn told me of a mild-mannered young man with an ingratiating posture, a sort of Uriah Heep, who had done very well by himself. He had married the boss's daughter and later had taken over the business. One day in church, while he was walking with his wife and children to the altar for communion, he had a temporal lobe seizure. He immediately started pushing his family ahead, and pushing others out of the way, elbowing, and saying loudly, "Push them out of the way, push them out of the way. That's the only way you can get ahead."

Dr. MacLean has emphasized the purposeful nature of the expression of emotions in the sense of their being adaptive, serving the goals of the species and individual. The coupling of eating, hostility, and sexual function in terms of their emotional expression apparently requires that the language of emotions be widely generalized among animals on the one hand, and yet highly specific for certain groupings. The mating practices of eastern and western birds in the United States provides a good example. George Sutton, the distinguished ornithologist, likes to live in Oklahoma because the eastern and the western birds meet there and may even share the same tree. The extraordinary thing is that they retain their distinctive eastern or western characteristics. They are quite capable of intermating; they can fertilize one another, but they do not cross-breed because the courting behavior of the eastern birds is not intelligible to the western and vice versa. Therefore they sit on the same tree without ever producing the cross-breed that one would expect.

In man there are many examples of generally recognized emotional expressions and many that have a special meaning for certain groups. The outstretched arm with palm up means to anyone a "handout," with the elbow bent and the palm forward you have the universal gesture of peace. On the other hand, the making of horns, with the index and fifth fingers extended from the fist has a very different meaning on either side of the Atlantic, and in the Orient again a different one. In fact, this gesture has at least five entirely distinct meanings that would get you either a smile, a pat on the back, or a punch in the nose.

Dr. MacLean made another point which deserves comment. He indicated that solicitude of one individual for another is indispensable not only to the health of social groups and larger societies but to the individuals themselves. René DuBos (1959), in his *Mirage of Health,* has emphasized that man has evolved not only through competition but also through a great variety of manifestations of symbiosis and mutual support.

According to some, one of the fundamental steps in the development of society was to bring about a circumstance where males could live together without killing one another to assert sexual dominance. Perhaps, as Dr. MacLean suggested, the loincloth was adopted to serve this purpose by playing down, as it were, the emphasis on sex. Certainly waving or clasping hands with the hand that normally holds the sword is another gesture with similar significance. If achieving a state where males can live together amicably was a fundamental step in the evolution of man and his society, certainly the achieving of a state where differences can be tolerated is fundamental to the survival of society in this shrinking world. Introducing a white leghorn chicken into a coop with Rhode Island reds will inevitably arouse destructive emotions. Man's attitudes may be more advanced, but it is nevertheless his inability to tolerate differences in religion, ideology, social and economic patterns that is perhaps our greatest problem today.

This Symposium has contained a good deal of emphasis on primitive emotions, largely hostile and acquisitive ones. Doubtless the development of emotions has something to do with the development of the brain. If the issue for survival in the next era, as Dr. MacLean has already suggested, is whether or not the differences in people and their points of view can be reconciled adaptively, man needs a new emphasis in his emotional behavior. Hostility and acquisitiveness must be more richly admixed with the expression of such emotions as love, admiration, human concern, and generosity. I hope that our brains have developed sufficiently to make that possible.

CHAPTER 3

Ontogenesis: The Proleptic Function of Emotion

RENÉ A. SPITZ, M.D.

When in 1872 Charles Darwin reviewed the spectrum of the expression of emotions in man and animal, he found it necessary to write a book of more than 360 pages. He found that he had to consider the development of emotions both phylogenetically and ontogenetically. In the space at my disposal I will have to omit emotions in animals and consequently phylogenesis. I will limit myself to the ontogenesis of emotion in man. Even then I will not be able to do more than to examine its earliest phase, beginning with birth, to what we can observe in the first few months and to what we can conclude from these observations.

The numerous and mostly unclear definitions of emotion that have been attempted since Darwin's times are not relevant to this study, for which I will choose as my point of departure the following two statements by Freud: "It is surely the essence of an emotion that we should be aware of it, i.e. that it should become known to consciousness" (1915b, p. 177).

In other terms, Freud considers emotion to be something which has a *conscious* component. The second statement of Freud's reads: "Affects[1] and emotions correspond with processes of discharge, the final expression of which is expressed as feeling" (1915b, p. 178).

Freud consistently refuses to assume the existence at birth of a division of the psychic apparatus into conscious and unconscious; neither does he assume the presence of an ego, of memory, in one word, of psychic functioning *as such*, or of emotion, in the neonate. From personal observations conducted on a large number of neonates and from experiments performed on them, I can fully confirm Freud's thesis. I believe that one cannot speak of emotions in the neonate in the sense in which we speak of them in the adult. At birth one can only speak of excitation.

In the neonate this excitation appears to be preponderantly of a negative nature. For the sake of brevity, I will speak of this as unpleasure. I will not use this term in its popular meaning, but to connote an increase of tension, according to Freud's usage. Its counterpart, pleasure, will be used to connote decrease of tension. Neither of the two terms, as used here, will assert or deny any of the feeling connotations implied in the everyday usage of these words.

If in the neonate the negative manifestations seem preponderant, this is perhaps because their counterpart, the positive manifestations, are so inconspicuous and because they do not conform to the popular use of the term "pleasure." The positive side in the newborn's behavior is manifested primarily as quiescence, that is, as inactivity. The only active counterpart to unpleasure manifestations in the neonate is the "turning-toward" in response to certain key stimuli.

We would probably be well advised to speak of negative excitation and of its counterpart, of quiescence, as prototypes or precursors of emotions in the neonate. At this early stage,

[1] In this paper the term "affect" will be used interchangeably with the terms "emotion" and "feeling." The literature does not distinguish clearly between them.

they are mainly manifested in the infant's facial expressions, in his random movements, and in his vocalization.

The concept of psychological prototypes was present in Freud's thinking already at a very early stage of his work and found its definitive formulation in his book *Inhibitions, Symptoms and Anxiety* (1926). He suggests that the physiological changes in the infant during delivery (i.e., in the birth situation), the excessive degree of excitation, the physiological consequences of the break-through of the stimulus barrier (i.e., the protective shield against stimuli in the neonate), are the somatic prototypes for the expression of the affect of anxiety. Thus the manifest part of the affective state of anxiety is modeled after an archaic mnemic image, which is the precipitate of neonatal traumatic experience. Freud furthermore advanced the proposition that the ontogenesis of affects generally tends to follow this pattern. This statement of Freud's will form one of the main arguments of my presentation.

In previous publications I have spoken both of prototypes and of precursors.[2] In the following, when I use the term precursor, the accent will be on maturation; and in my usage of the term prototype, the emphasis will be on development. The concepts of maturation and development, generally used in psychology, were introduced into psychoanalytic literature by Hartmann, Kris, and Loewenstein (1946).

Maturation refers to those processes of progressive change and of growth which are due to factors transmitted by genes and chromosomes. This growth and these changes take place both in the somatic and in the psychological sector of the personality. Besides those contributing specifically to matu-

[2] It is debatable whether, besides prototypes, one should also speak of precursors of psychological phenomena, and differentiate the two. It might be argued that physiological precursors of later psychological phenomena develop in a straight genetic line and their unfolding is due to maturation. It remains somewhat questionable whether any such phenomena are demonstrable. Prototypes, on the other hand, serve as the physiological *models* for the later establishment of psychological functions and phenomena. In this process, development plays the major part.

ration there are other innate factors operating from birth. The totality of innate factors is the infant's congenital equipment. The term *development* designates the modifications effected by the surround on the inborn congenital equipment. Accordingly, congenital equipment will be modified in the course of development by the organism's adaptation to environmental circumstances. On the other hand, congenital equipment is also modified by two kinds of stresses: (1) by those arising from maturational factors, (2) by those accompanying biological growth and function.

Before going into the substance of my argument, I feel it necessary to explain certain concepts used by me which to the psychoanalytic reader might appear self-evident. I am referring to the fact that in my explanations I am consistently speaking of phenomena connected primarily with orality and oral need gratification. I am using this approach for the purpose of simplifying my text. It should be evident from my previous publications (Spitz, 1955, 1957) that I do not believe that the oral stage is exclusively concerned with the mouth and the perioral zone. The needs of the infant involve many other modalities besides the oral intake, some of them of equal importance. In those publications I have spoken of cutaneous, tactile, equilibrium, thermal stimuli, rhythms, and of deep sensitivity; there are many others, of which we are not yet aware.

I

Attempts to interpret the meaning of facial expression or behavior in the neonate as we do in the adult are bound to be misleading. Of course, when in the first five minutes after delivery silver nitrate is instilled under the closed eyelids of the quiescent infant and the infant responds with violent generalized prolonged excitation and facial contortion and screaming, we feel fairly safe in calling this an expression of unpleasure.

But when a smile appears on the face of the same infant, or what looks like a smile, we may not call this an expression of tension reduction or of pleasure. The circumstances in which infants at this age smile are far too variable for that. Far too often a facial movement which looks like a smile appears in circumstances accompanied by mounting tension, a condition experienced as unpleasure at any later age. Far too rarely, not to say exceptionally, does the neonate smile in circumstances which an adult would experience as pleasurable. It is no accident that our grandmothers used to say that when a newborn smiles, he has a belly ache.

The argument could be extended. One of the simplest demonstrations of the lack of correlation between overt behavior and the quality of experience in the neonate is the series of experiments performed by Jensen (1932). He demonstrated that a large variety of stimulations, including among others hair pulling, pinching, pinpricks, and dropping from a height of one foot, elicited the sucking response.

This experiment shows that there is as yet no constant relation between a given stimulus and a response in the form of expression at birth and in the weeks immediately thereafter. It is an open question whether one can speak in the neonate of a reliable linkage between manifest behavior and the stimulus which appears to trigger it. When we find such linkages, they are very tenuous. And the behavior occurs in response to stimuli which are frequently vastly different from those which provoke similar expressive behavior at a later age. Similarly, the neonate will respond differently from older subjects to identical stimuli. We express this concisely by the statement that the neonate's behavior is neither stimulus specific nor response specific.

However, it is common knowledge that, in the course of the first year of life and later, certain forms of emotional expression become firmly linked to and associated with certain emotional experiences. The question is how this comes about. Three basic hypotheses can be formulated: (1) The developmental hypothesis, according to which the expression of emotion is *learned* in the course of infantile development; (2) the maturational hypothesis, according to which expression is *inherited* as an Anlage and will be activated in the course of development; (3) some combination of these two propositions. The second and third hypotheses obviously involve phylogenetic factors. We may wonder how expressive behavior, be it of a mimetic nature or more generalized, has come to be linked with emotion-producing experiences in the course of *phylogenesis.*

However, a discussion of this problem would go far beyond the scope of this paper. I will therefore limit this investigation to the linkage between emotional expression and emotional experience in human ontogenesis. The excitation at birth (with the character of unpleasure) is clearly a discharge phenomenon. I will speak of this as a precursor of the emotions which will develop subsequently. We should certainly not regard this as an emotion, proposing, as I do, to reserve this term for a psychological experience with concomitants of a conscious nature. It follows that I consider the external manifestations of tension-increasing experiences in the neonate as indications of discharge processes. What is discharged is physiological tension without psychological content. Such manifestations occur reliably when stimuli succeed in breaking through what Freud called the protective shield against stimuli, the neonate's high perceptual threshold.

At birth the infant reacts to the surround only if a stimulus is sufficiently powerful to break through the stimulus barrier. That is the case when stimulation from the outside is overstrong; but also when normal discomfort originates from inside, because the newborn is not protected against stimuli originating inside as he is against those coming from the surround. Elsewhere (Spitz, 1957) I have discussed my concept of the nature of this threshold. In essence, I stated that at birth the psychic representations of the neural receptor stations are not yet energized.

So far I have said little about the behavior observable in the neonate when a stimulus is strong enough to overcome the barrier against it. I mentioned that we can observe excitation of a negative kind which is manifested through discharge phenomena. These are not consistent, not limited to given systems of the organism, but in the nature of overflow activity. They appear randomly, they are unorganized, diffuse, and should be considered total responses. Among these discharge phenomena are agitation, violent spastic movements, violent facial contortions, as well as vocalizations such as screaming, wailing, and whimpering.

In all this turmoil, we can nevertheless distinguish behavioral items which at a later age would be called expressive ones. Among the behavioral items enumerated above, vocalization has a special place in view of the role it will subsequently assume as the main instrument of human communication. At the neonatal stage the forms of vocalization I have listed above are in response to tension-increasing experiences. These are experiences which might be called painful or unpleasant, were it not that these terms carry a psychological connotation. However, we lack a sufficiently neutral term to designate tension-increasing experiences which do not involve the psyche. One of the peculiarities of the neonatal stage is that vocalization appears to be restricted to responses arising in the wake of stimulation we judge to be "unpleasure" provoking. Neonatal behavior patterns which I consider the somatic *precursors* of subsequently developing *expressions* of pleasure—the most conspicuous such behavior pattern is "turning toward"—do not appear to include vocalization. "Pleasure" vocalization in the neonate is probably nonexistent.

To my knowledge no investigation has been undertaken to establish at what stage of development vocalization other than that conveying unpleasure appears.[3] Nor are there any reliable observations on what this first vocalization of gratification consists of. We may suspect that it is developed from the more or less mechanical clucking sounds occurring during nursing activity, which lead to the "Mm . . ." sound, discussed both by infant observers and psychoanalysts (Spiel-

[3] See "Goma, das Basler Gorillakind." *Documenta Geigy Bull.*, 1-5, 1959-60.

rein, 1922; Greenson, 1954). It is debatable whether a vocalization of pleasure may be derived, for instance, from panting in connection with manifestly gratifying experiences. Whether this particular vocalization might, for example, lead to the sounds of laughter ("he-he-he-he") will have to be verified through observation.[4]

II

I have not yet had an occasion to speak of the expression of emotion *proper,* for I was discussing the first six weeks of life. As stated above, emotions proper involve consciousness. During the first weeks of life conscious perception, in the sense in which psychoanalysis defines the term, is not present. At this time practically all activities of the neonate are uncoordinated and undirected, because a central volitional—that is, conscious—steering organization has not yet emerged. Physiological activities are the exception; they become increasingly coordinated and integrated into a functioning totality. But *intentional* skeletal musculature is not yet integrated under the direction of a *central steering and coordinating organization* and will only become so in the course of the subsequent months. It is this central steering organization to which we assign psychological functioning, both conscious and unconscious.

This organization, which we call the ego, will enable the infant to perceive his emotions and to relate their expression to sensations experienced and to stimuli received. It comes into being, at least in a rudimentary fashion, around the third month. Before this organization begins to function, I am unwilling to speak of emotion proper, only of its precursors. Even after the beginnings of the central steering or-

[4] To avoid misunderstanding I wish to go on record that all my statements on the ontogenesis of the expression of emotions refer to average normal children. I am aware that deviations occur; for example, neonates who respond with unpleasure manifestations to stimuli which should be pleasurable. Such instances have been described by Escalona, by Solnit and Ritvo and by others. They are the exceptions; my current task is to deal with the average. I will add that this average shows a rather wide range of individual variations which I will disregard here.

ganization are established, specific emotional expressions are still only loosely linked to specific types of experience. The infant's expression can still be interpreted (or understood) only in the context of an ongoing situation. In a certain measure, that remains true throughout a great part of the infant's first year.

It appears, then, that specific facial expressions as expression of emotions become meaningful as a result of a linkage. The linkage takes place between a specific facial expression and a specific experience, a coordination comparable to that which takes place in the conditioned reflex. The refinement and the progressively increasing specificity of the expression itself are acquired in the course of development. A great deal of research remains to be done in order to learn how this coordination is achieved. The fact that the negative expression is present from birth shows that it is inborn. It is presumably of phylogenetic origin and has survival value. The demonstration of this proposition is one of the objects of the present paper.

The expression of pleasure is the next one to appear; in the infant its most conspicuous example is the smiling response. Beginning with the third month of life this is produced in response to a Gestalt signal, which comprises certain salient features of the human face. The constituent parts of this Gestalt are the eyes, the nose, and the forehead; moreover, the whole configuration must be in motion (Spitz and Wolf, 1946).

It should be clearly understood that I am referring exclusively to the smiling *response* and not to random activity of the facial muscles, which may look like a smile. The facial movement of smiling is probably present from birth—my earliest motion picture record for such a smile is of a three-day-old infant. This smile "movement" is a discharge phenomenon which occurs randomly; it cannot be reliably elicited by repeating the specific situation in which it had been observed, nor by situations which are the opposite of those eliciting the negative "displeasurable" expressions.

Among the few positive manifestations at birth, "turning toward" is the most relevant for this discussion. I consider "turning toward" as a positive expression because of its survival value, which is demonstrated by its phylogenetic history (Spitz, 1957). It is provoked primarily by eliciting the sucking reflex. In the third month of life this turning-toward response develops into reciprocity with the adult: the infant responds to the adult's face with a smile. I have considered this to be the expression of a positive *emotion* for the following reasons:

1. After the smiling response has been established, it ceases to be random and becomes stimulus specific. Beginning with the third month of life, it will be produced reliably in situations which have the specific character of initiating a need gratification. This linking of the smiling response to certain stimuli which adults would consider pleasurable or gratifying will continue throughout life in an unbroken line.

2. Conversely, the smiling response will not be manifested in situations which would provoke responses or emotions of unpleasure, such as pain, rage, anger, or boredom, in the adult.

3. The physiognomic characteristics of the smiling response are those of "turning toward."

4. Finally, when in the third month of life the infant achieves the smiling response, he has also achieved conscious perception and has become capable of rudimentary mental operations. This is evident not only from the smiling response but also from all his other volitionally directed, intentional activities.

III

The psychological concomitants of the smiling response at the level of the third month throw a new light on my findings about some responses at birth. They permit the conclusion that, from the viewpoint of structure, negative excitation at birth is fundamentally different from the turning-toward response. Negative excitation behavior is a nondirected, random, unspecific emergency behavior, in response to any stimulus *quantitatively* strong enough to break through the stimulus barrier. The turning-toward behavior, on the other hand, is specific, nonrandom, and occurs in response to a specific discrete stimulus. It is not a response to quantitative but to *qualitative* differences. At birth this is the only directed response to stimuli qualitatively differentiated from the surround. The turning-toward response has a positive value for survival. Consequently I feel justified in considering it one of the first positive behavior patterns in the infant, though not a psychological one.

Though the turning-toward response is present already at birth, it is questionable whether this applies also to the avoidance reaction. However, we know that the latter will soon emerge in the course of development, although its phenomenology has not been investigated in sufficient detail. We do not know when manifestations of unpleasure—e.g., screaming and random violent movements, which denote negative excitation—are transformed into movements of withdrawal and flight. In other words, we are unable to say at what point of infant development expressions of unpleasure are replaced by expressions of *fear*.

The inception and the sequence in the structuring of the expression of negative emotion parallel the development of the smile. In the neonate stage, negative experience results from a break-through of the stimulus barrier (either from inside or outside) and is responded to by increase of random activity, rise of tonus, and vocalization. In the subsequent weeks, though expression of negative emotions is still triggered by the quantitative factor of a break-through of the stimulus barrier, a qualitative factor is added. The stimuli for such a break-through become ever more specific. It becomes increasingly evident that this behavior of the infant will arise mostly in the hunger situation or in situations of intestinal discomfort. These are need situations, requiring discharge through gratification to insure survival. The development which now sets in adds *secondary needs* to the primary survival-insuring ones; I will call these secondary needs *"quasi needs."*

By the third month, the circumstances leading to and accompanying need gratification proper also begin to become specific. When they are withheld, the infant responds as if he were being deprived of physiological need gratification. In concrete terms, the infant now insists on being cuddled, on physical contact, on the presence of the adult.

By the fourth month of life, the infant reacts by screaming when the gratification of this quasi need is withheld, that is, when the adult leaves after playing with him; just as he reacts by smiling when the adult approaches him. It is at this point that the precursors of emotion are transformed into emotion proper. No other object (thing) will provoke these responses at the same age, though, of course, straightforward need deprivation or need gratification will.

It is regrettable that we do not yet possess findings on physiognomic differentiation between the infant's behavior when subjected to the frustration of a quasi need (such as the contact with the adult being interrupted), on the one hand, and the expression of fear resulting from the anticipation of pain on the other (Darwin, 1872).

IV

Before going on to the subsequent unfolding of the expression of emotion in the course of the second half of the first year of life. I want to mention some of the problems which arise from what I have presented so far. They can be summarized in three points:

1. How does the elaboration of the expression of emotion proceed from the physiological process to the psychological experience?

2. What elements in the expression of negative emotion and of the smiling response are innate?

3. What, if any, is the implication of these considerations for psychoanalysis and for psychoanalytic theory in particular?

I shall confine myself to the first question, the progressive shift of the expression of emotion from a somatic process to a psychological experience. Psychological stimuli (in the sense in which we apply the term to adults) do not provoke observable responses in the neonate; we must assume that he does not perceive them. He does not *perceive* physical stimuli either, but he *reacts* unspecifically to them when they are sufficiently massive. In this statement perception is defined as a function which involves an activity of the psychic apparatus. This activity comprises, among others, the dealing with and the processing of nervous stimuli with the help of psychic operations.

Our operational criteria for the infant having achieved perception are his capacity to *recognize* a percept previously experienced, or, at the earliest level, the demonstrability of a change wrought by the percept in the perceiving organism. This last statement includes the conditioned reflex.

But the conditioned reflex partakes of two worlds. As we shall see later, it stands on the borderline, reaching into the neurological on the one side, into the psychological on the other. This is why, on the one hand, chronologically, and in regard to consciousness, the conditioned reflex begins in the undifferentiated, nonconscious stage of life. On the other hand, however, it appears to form, many weeks later, the bridge leading over into the stage in which conscious and unconscious have separated from each other. It is my opinion that the conditioned reflex at the neonate level is largely responsible for maintaining those exchanges which eventually lead to the emergence of consciousness.

Conditioned reflexes can be set up in the neonate quite early, depending on the sensory modality which is used for the conditioned stimulus. In the first days of life it would obviously be impractical to try to condition through a visual stimulus; in the first days the neonate's eyes are mostly closed, and even when they are open, they do not react to visual stimulation, unless this be rather violent; in that case it produces the startle reflex. During the same period of life, however, conditioning with help of change of position, that is, deep sensitivity involving the coenesthetic system, is perfectly possible (Bühler, 1931).

Negative excitation which at the neonatal age requires discharge of a disorganized, random nature, will retain this negative connotation also at a much later stage, when psychological[5] functioning is already in existence—witness, for instance, the proverbial irritability and ill-humor which takes possession of us when we are kept waiting for food.

This is one application of Freud's proposition that, just as the birth experience is the physiological prototype for the psychological response of anxiety which appears much later, there exist other archaic experiences which become the prototypes for other emotions. It is my contention that the discharge of negative excitation is the prototype for the expression of unpleasure. I suggest that this proposition be applied in the first place to emotions consciously experienced as unpleasure; furthermore, that somatic and physiological responses to unpleasure stimuli should be considered to accompany in varying measure the whole subsequent gamut of psychological unpleasure both conscious and unconscious.

This proposition applies equally to the expression of pleasure; it follows that the feeling tone of the newborn's somatic response to pleasurable experience also will be recalled in the feeling tone of later psychological experience. I believe that there is a direct genetic connection between the feeling tone of the turning-toward response in the early feeding situation and the feeling tone attached to, first, following the face of an adult visually, and later responding to it with a smile.

[5] This statement should not be construed as implying that psychological functioning is predicated on consciousness. Consciousness is one of its attributes; consciousness and the central steering operations performed by the psyche offer us access to the nonconscious sectors and to their function.

It would be tempting to investigate the somatic origins of the feeling tone, expansive and at the same time all inclusive, which accompanies for instance such emotions as joy. But the expression of the opposite of unpleasure in the neonate is tenuous and not easy to observe. Darwin already remarked that it is much easier to observe expressions of suffering, pain, etc., than expressions of joy. I will therefore choose the easier road and take the negative responses as my point of departure.

In the course of infant care the neonate experiences a variety of stimuli as a disturbance of his quiescence; being washed, being exposed to cold, being disturbed in his sleep—these are the most common disturbing *external* stimuli. We are equally familiar with internal ones such as the baby's being hungry; and with his response to intestinal pain. None of these experiences has a psychological representation at this stage. It is to be assumed that they will acquire one in the following few weeks. How they do that, however, is unclear. It seems to me that at this point a series of experiments performed by Volkelt (1928), in a totally different psychological sector, that of perception, and the application of his findings to the feeding situation by Frankl and Rubinow (1934) are particularly enlightening. They investigated when and how the infant, in a series of successive steps, progressively recognizes the "thing" he most frequently sees, namely, his bottle with the food. These steps are the following:

1. The neonate responds reliably to the nipple when it *touches* his oral mucosa.

2. A week later he produces what these authors have called *Flaschenerkennungsreaktion,* which we can translate into English with "food-recognition reaction." By this is meant that when the *preliminaries* to placing the bottle in his mouth are performed (whatever these may be, e.g., putting a bib under his chin), he responds by this particular reaction. The food-recognition reaction consists in a conspicuous change of the infant's behavior, e.g., the crying infant

becomes quiet; or the infant makes sucking movements; or he extends his lips, his tongue, etc. The precondition for the success of this experiment is that it must take place at the infant's feeding hour. The experiment shows that the response has been displaced from the unconditioned stimulus (food in the mouth), and that a conditioned stimulus (bib under chin) has been established. *Prolepsis* (the function of anticipation) has emerged in the form of a conditioned reflex—we may consider it the earliest *prototype* of psychological function.

3. The next step is a highly significant one. The *tactile* conditioned stimulus of "bib under chin" is replaced by a new, *visual* conditioned stimulus. The response is elicited already when a person approaches the infant's crib at the usual feeding hour. This means that the perception of a new conditioned stimulus takes place both sooner and from a greater distance. The contact receptor has been replaced by a distance receptor. Anticipation, surely a psychological function, is more in evidence; in this experiment we have been able to record two steps in its development. However, the response still depends on the perception of a process going on inside the neonate, namely, hunger and thirst. Environmental perception as such is not yet established independently.

4. In the next step the outside world as the *perceived* stimulus, independent of the inner state of the infant, comes into its own; now the food-recognition reaction occurs in response to a thing, whatever its shape, which enters the infant's visual field. In this experiment the stimulus consists of two factors, namely, of the movement and of the object. In my belief, this is the point in development at which the earliest manifestation of *psychological processing proper* can be observed. It consists, in its simplest form, of a sequence of events in which A followed by B followed by C is remembered. Whereas in the preceding stage these different modalities were united in one summative sensation, now the modalities are distinguished from each other and their *sequence* is endowed with significance. This is the process of appercep-

tion; here it consists of two or more memory traces, in the present example, of the memory of an object and of its approach. They are used in a specifically psychological process, namely, in anticipation of that which will follow the perception of the approaching object.

The response to the percept of an *approaching object* could be called an "as-if" behavior of the infant. The infant responds in the terms of the need gratification which the percept food is *expected* to provide.

The inference that anticipation proves the functioning of a psychological process is not a stringent one. After all, anticipation of a sort is involved also in the conditioned reflex. But I believe that in the unfolding of the food-recognition reaction we witness a phenomenon of a different order. The rapid shifts in the physical nature and in the space-time structure of the response-evoking stimulus just described are not characteristic of the conditioned reflex. In the first three phases of the food-recognition reaction, the awareness of the stimulus was displaced successively to percepts both more distant in space and occurring earlier in time than the actual gratification of the need. These percepts are also very different in their physical appearance. The successive anticipatory percepts were first the bib under the chin and later a person approaching the crib.

In the subsequent stages, however, a new process sets in. Instead of responding to a percept which is more distant in space and which also occurs earlier in time, the infant now disregards these previous percepts. It is as if a finer discrimination has begun, as if the three- to six-month-old infant has realized that "approaching person" could mean other things also, besides food. He now seems to wait for more "tangible" facts. Now he does not respond to the approaching person, only to the stimulus of a "thing" approaching his face, whatever the thing's general shape may be, within certain wide limits of size.

This is not the usual development in the establishment of conditioned responses; and the further steps in the unfolding of food recognition are increasingly directed toward the cognitive perception of essential attributes of the food itself; while the anticipatory recognition of the accompanying circumstances (e.g., the adult entering the infant's room, etc.) goes its own way. The subsequent steps in the achievement of food recognition are:

5. It is no longer sufficient that any object be approached to the child's face; the object has to be roughly cone-shaped and to end in a point.

6. A few weeks later the object's ending in a point is no longer sufficient; it must have a nipple at its point and must be filled with white liquid.

7. The final step, achieved somewhere around six months of life, is that the milk as such is recognized, whether in a bottle or any other container.

This sequence of steps in the development of the cognition of a visual percept also gives us the key to the ontogenesis of the expression of negative emotions—and, of course, positive ones as well. I postulated—and this certainly could be experimentally established—that in the beginning the expression of unpleasure takes place only in response to the unconditioned stimulus of experiencing pain or discomfort. In the course of the first few months of life this unconditioned response is modified. Unpleasure will be anticipated already in response to changes in the environment which in themselves, and at the moment when they occur, need not produce discomfort.

We do not possess as precise observational and experimental studies of the earliest development of negative emotions as those we have for the unfolding of the positive ones. There the meshing of the food-recognition reaction with the smiling response provides us with an unbroken genetic sequence beginning with birth. We can, however, advance a plausible hypothesis about the development of the expression of negative emotion. This hypothesis is based on direct observation as well as on the parallels between this development and that of the sequence observed in the expression of positive emotions. My hypothesis, which is presented below, is further supported by its consistency with well-established psychoanalytic propositions.

In the neonate the expression of emotion most in evidence is the one in response to unpleasure, caused by the unconditioned stimulus. This is in manifest parallel to the first stage of the food-recognition reaction, in which the response is to the nipple in the mouth. This would lead one to believe that later, more advanced expressions of unpleasure also develop in a straight genetic sequence from the original situation. But this does not seem to be the case.

In the weeks following birth the unconditioned stimulus of *somatic* pain, discomfort, etc., elicits manifestations of unpleasure, predominantly undirected and random. However, unequivocally clear manifestations of unpleasure in response to psychological stimuli do not develop in direct genetic derivation from these. To my mind, the first unequivocal psychological manifestation of unpleasure in the infant occurs when he begins to cry when left by the adult with whom he had been in contact. This behavior appears after the third month of life and is the counterpart of the smiling response of which I have spoken above.

This unpleasure manifestation can only be understood if we assume that the infant has integrated into the inventory of his need gratifications the *presence* of the adult as a quasi need. Accordingly the infant will react to the adult's moving away by expressing negative emotion in anticipation of being deprived of the gratification of this quasi need. There obviously is a parallel between this "negative" expression of emotion in response to a *receding* person, and the "positive" behavior manifested to the approaching person in the food-recognition response as well as in the smiling response.

One explanation of this paradoxical and circuitous line in the development of the expression of negative emotions may be found in the phenomenon of the stimulus barrier at birth.

The break-through of the stimulus barrier can be responded to only by an undirected total behavior, which is generalized, uncoordinated, and random. Such total behavior does not lend itself to structuring and further development within the individual ontogenesis. A gradual process of adaptation cannot be expected from a disorganized, decompensated emergency reaction, comparable to what Kurt Goldstein (1928) described as the "catastrophic reaction" in the brain-damaged adult.

However, in analogy to what I previously described for the "trauma of birth," elements of this reaction may be used for the expression of negative emotion, when at a later stage an experience of discomfort produces a shadowy, essentially physiological, recall of complete loss of control. The early physiological responses to unpleasure are random, uncoordinated, and often involve the autonomic nervous system. Some of them will enter into the later, organized expression of negative emotion. This holds true not only for infancy and childhood. Thus the adult may feel nausea under the impact of violent disgust. He commemorates, so to say, earliest infantile autonomic reactions.

Unpleasure experiences of two fundamentally different kinds will be expressed by superficially similar behavior patterns:

1. A form of unpleasure in response to the unconditioned stimulus of pain and discomfort. The response to this is an uncontrolled behavior which will change very little in the course of development.

2. A form of unpleasure in response to psychological stimuli. This response is not present from birth. It has to be acquired by developing a *quasi need* on the one hand, and the *proleptic function,* that is, the function of anticipation, on the other. Both the need and the function are developed in the framework of object relations, primarily as the result of need gratification. Once the function to anticipate pleasure is acquired, it becomes possible for the child to perform also the psychological operation of anticipating unpleasure when *losing* the object. The infant displays this anticipation through the facial expression of negative emotion.

At this level at the age of three to six months of life the anticipation of unpleasure has acquired a *signal* function, the function described by Freud in *Inhibitions, Symptoms and Anxiety.* The expression of this emotion increasingly acquires the function of communication. This communication comprises two bits of information, which are channeled in opposite directions:

1. The first is the mounting tension of the emotion. This is similar to the conditions leading to the break-through of the stimulus barrier. It is experienced as a danger signal, an information which is transmitted centripetally to the incipient ego of the three- to six-month-old infant.

2. The facial and behavioral expression of the same emotion. This is perceived by the surround as a communication. Though it is at first not intentional or directed, it nevertheless transmits information centrifugally.

At this stage the two components do not yet constitute an apparatus of the ego. They are not established as a discrete functional continuum, interconnecting with the different aspects of the personality. In the course of the following three months, these connections will be formed. They will become ever more suitable for triggering adaptive measures of the ego and for communicating with the surround. This process leads to the establishment of specific emotions firmly linked with their appropriate expression. The final outcome of this process is, in one instance, the "eight-months anxiety."[6]

The eight-months anxiety marks the inception of an important stage in the child's development. It lends itself particularly well to the exposition of several psychological processes. In the present context I am discussing that aspect of the phenomenon which illustrates the next step in the ontogenetic development of the expression of emotion. Through the study of this step we gain insight into the further vicissitudes of what originally was an undirected state of excitation. For in the eight-months anxiety we can observe how the

[6] For the description and discussion of this phenomenon see Spitz (1946, 1950).

subjective experience of emotion follows a different path from that of emotional expression. In what follows I will show how the *emotion* of anxiety (i.e., felt anxiety) assumes a centripetally directed function; at the same time the *expression* of the same emotion becomes effective in a centrifugal direction. The part directed to the inside acts as a danger signal, mobilizing the pleasure-unpleasure agency (Freud, 1926); thus the resources of the personality are marshaled in the service of defense against mental helplessness.

The other part is channeled into the efferent nervous system and sets in motion the gamut of the expressions of this particular emotion. These expressions serve as a communication to the outside: to the surround, to the libidinal object. They are perceived by the outside world as a sign of helplessness or as a signal, that is, as an appeal for help.

The successive stages of this development, beginning with the break-through of the stimulus barrier, are:

1. The unspecific, undirected, total emotional responses in the first three months of life.

2. The progressive integration of emotional responses with their facial and behavioral expression in the course of the next three months on the one hand; their serving as a communication to the outside on the other.

3. The establishment, in the third quarter of the first year, of a definitive link between felt emotion as a signal for the ego and the expression of emotion as a communication to the surround.

The process of organizing the original discharge into recognizably different expressions linked to specific emotions is initiated and carried on through the exchanges between child and mother in the course of object relations. The unfolding of the individual child's object relations parallels closely the ontogenesis of the expression of his emotions.

When infants are deprived of object relations, their emotional expression remains on the archaic level of the first months of life (Spitz, 1946). The expression becomes rigid and vacuous. But when object relations are close and gratifying to mother and child, then the expression of emotions unfolds in a variety of patterns and eventually becomes a means of communication in the framework of object relations.

The proposition of the role of object relations in the ontogenesis of the expression of emotion is further borne out by two different observations: (1) the chronological sequence in the successive stages of the positive smiling response, which parallel those of the first specifically psychologically motivated expression of negative emotion; (2) the range of expressions accompanying the emergence of the eight-months anxiety in the second half of the first year.

As to the first: the response of smiling, the expression of pleasure on perceiving the Gestalt signal of the human face appears approximately one month earlier than the response of unpleasure on being left by a partner. In other terms, a partner, at least in the form of *a pre-object,* has to be established as a result of object relations before the consequences of the loss of this pre-object can be anticipated. It is gratifying to find this argumentation confirmed by the facts of observation.

In regard to the second confirmatory evidence, we find that the phenomenon of the eight-months anxiety varies in a wide range, and is dependent on the nature of the individual child's object relations. In my observations of psychopathological deviations in the first year of life, the appearance of the characteristic anxiety was significantly delayed and even completely absent when certain forms of inappropriate object relations were present during the preceding months. On the other hand, the eight-months anxiety was replaced by uncontrollable manifestations of panic and fear in those cases in which object relations were extremely inadequate or the infant had been deprived of them altogether.[7]

[7] Two different sets of circumstances can lead to this end result. One is a separation of the infant from his object at a critical age, resulting in a mourning process with regression to earlier, and often archaic modes of functioning and adaptation. I have discussed this picture elsewhere (1946) and called it *anaclitic depression.* The second is the picture of infants raised from birth in institutions without opportunity to form any object relations whatsoever. Here the response

Eight-months anxiety of the usual kind varies a good deal in its intensity. This phenomenon has not been sufficiently explored up to now.[8] The reason for this is that it requires thorough investigation of children in private family homes, in itself a major project. Added to this is the fact that children vary in their congenital frustration tolerance and that as yet we have no instrument suitable for evaluating this tolerance in the neonate.

We may say in conclusion that the ontogenesis of the expression of emotions is a function of the nature of the individual child's object relations as much as of the unfolding of an inherited Anlage. To the psychoanalyst this finding is not unexpected. We were aware for a number of years and have been able to demonstrate (Spitz, 1946) that the expression of pleasure is developed from an innate Anlage in the course of the exchanges with the human object. We now find a similar sequence obtaining in regard to the expression of negative emotions. These also develop from an innate Anlage, from disorganized, decompensated response to the breakthrough of the stimulus barrier, through object relations to the expression of negative emotions in response to the loss of the pre-object and from there to the signal of anxiety.

I cannot discuss the further ramifications of the expression of emotions. Enumerating them as they appear in the course of the first year of life already shows that they also are differentiated in response to specific object relations. I need only mention jealousy, envy, possessiveness, demanding attitudes, anger, rage, love, amusement, laughter, boredom (yawning and fatigue), not to speak of the chronologically later, increasingly subtle expressions of doubt, hesitation, quizzical attitudes, trust and mistrust, and a whole gamut of others.

---

remains unspecific, as in response to the unconditioned stimulus—a quantitative response, be it to the experience of pain or to the interruption of quiescence. I described this condition under the name of *hospitalism* (1945).

[8] But see Benjamin's (1961) careful investigations and his distinction between "stranger anxiety" and "infantile separation anxiety."

I am aware that in the ontogenesis of the expression of emotions it would be well to follow Darwin's example and to investigate the somatic components, the neuromuscular bases of these expressions, their connections with physiology, embryology, genetics, and phylogenesis. Such an investigation is not within my competence. It would certainly require the collaboration of several disciplines. In this study I have therefore kept within the limits of behavioral observation on the one hand, of psychoanalytic dynamics on the other.

Summary

In the ontogenesis of the expression of emotions, both maturation and development, both the innate and the experiential, play their own particular roles. The innate factors in maturation are evident at birth in the two precursors of the expression of two diametrically opposed emotions, namely, negative excitation and "turning toward." These innate factors still play a major role in the ontogenesis of perception and in the inception of memory; however, both perception and memory traces are subject to the influence of development, as the latter becomes effective in the course of the formation and the conduct of object relations. At this point of my argument, I stressed a basic aspect of emotions and their expression, namely, their proleptic function. This function has survival value; hence, the potential for developing it is innate. Its unfolding, however, is predicated on a process of development taking place within the framework of object relations. This process leads to the endowment of emotions and their expression with two further important functions: (1) the signal function of emotions within the psychic apparatus; (2) the communication function of emotional expression directed to the surround. These functions, the proleptic function, the signal function, and the communication function, offer us an approach for further investigation of the subsequent stages in the ontogenesis of the expression of emotions.

Discussion

Sibylle K. Escalona, Ph.D.

We have just heard an extraordinarily condensed statement. Dr. Spitz's presentation contains so many different ideas and touches upon so many empirical issues that it will be impossible to do the paper justice. In fact, it was only with several readings of the text that I was able to understand several new formulations that are implied rather than fully stated. Among other things the paper contains the germ of a theory of affect which is compatible with but not identical to the more usual formulations in psychoanalysis. Dr. Spitz also takes a position in relation to several alternate theories of anxiety. In addition, he briefly outlines several developmental stages that are usually not so differentiated but are treated as a single phase of development. Most important perhaps, the paper contains a network of propositions which link together such diverse ideas and phenomena as anxiety, emotion in the psychological meaning of the term, object relations, and anticipation. Dr. Spitz also suggests certain mechanisms by which these developmental processes are propelled, for example, the special role he assigns to the conditioned reflex.

I have decided to limit my comments to only two points. These two issues are selected for discussion not because I regard them as necessarily the most important ones. Rather they were chosen because they seem to me important not only in relation to the ontogenesis of emotion, they are important for any developmental ego psychology.

The first concerns the organization of behavior in the neonate. Dr. Spitz described neonatal behavior as random, lacking in direction or coordination. He selected for emphasis those behavior episodes which can be described as a massive discharge due to excitation as certain intense stimuli manage to penetrate the stimulus barrier. He contrasted the chaotic nature of overt behavior with the physiological level of functioning in neonates, which possesses a reasonable degree of coordination and stability. The random behavior Dr. Spitz described is indeed observable in all neonates. However, it is not the only mode of responding to stimuli observable in this age group. Provided the newborn is in a suitable state (neither markedly excited nor sound asleep), he will respond with either partial or complete motor reflexes to many stimuli of moderate and even mild intensity. For instance, to touch, to sudden sound, to cold and to light one observes all degrees of startle, reflexes of flexion which are sometimes called withdrawal, and also local and position reflexes such as the palmar grasp, the Babinski, lid closure, the tonic reflex group, and the hand-to-mouth movement which can be observed on the first day. In other words, most neonates show coordinated, patterned movement responses to a variety of external and internal stimuli, though, as Dr. Spitz has said, cortical dominance and psychic representation are absent. What distinguishes the six-day-old from the six-month-old is not so much the degree of coordination as it is the principle of behavioral organization.

The second point concerns the problem of whether pleasure and unpleasure affects develop in a parallel fashion as Dr. Spitz has proposed. In his presentation he made it clear that it is far more difficult to observe a continuity in the development of pleasurable emotion from early states of quiescence, or from the turning-toward response, to the smile than it is to trace unpleasure from early states of excitation. A true parallel in the appearance and subsequent development of the two kinds of affect becomes manifest, Dr. Spitz stated, at precisely the point when the primarily physiological experiences observable during the early months give way to what Dr. Spitz would designate as emotion, which implies some conscious awareness of the feeling state. First, I would like to call attention to the fact that it is precisely at this point, sometime after the third month, that pleasure no longer corresponds to quiescence. The smiling response usually includes some motion and the baby's experience is best described as pleasurable excitement. Bela Mittelmann demonstrated (in an unpublished manuscript) that at these early ages the movement patterns with pleasure and with unpleasure are indistinguishable. While at age three months and beyond pleasure and unpleasure are accompanied by excitation, it remains true that excitation when it becomes overly strong does invariably turn into unpleasure.

It appears to me that our present knowledge of the phenomena is so limited that several radically different interpretations of the genesis of emotions can be made. Each of these is congruent with the facts we know, which means that each of them is inadequately supported by tested knowledge. It occurred to me that it is indeed difficult to observe in very small infants behavior that in feeling tone or overt pattern is akin to what we later know as pleasure. This is in marked contrast to the ease with which the behavior of an upset neonate is perceived by the adult observer as unpleasure. We do know a good deal, however, about stimulating conditions which in neonates and young infants remove behavioral signs of displeasure. Almost all crying newborns can be temporarily calmed by being lifted, held, and swayed. Some times firm touch or rhythmic patting will be sufficient. Another well-demonstrated inhibiting stimulus is fairly loud continuous sound. As a matter of fact, ongoing loud sound will induce in neonates a state resembling sleep. These phenomena are well known to clinicians and in fact to everyone as the bag of tricks used by mothers and nurses to comfort their charges. They are equally well known to the neurophysiologist who studies these phenomena in the laboratory under the heading of inhibition.

In view of Dr. Spitz's suggestion about the relationship between emotion and what he has called pre-object relationship, it is interesting to note that many of the effective soothing devices consist of the very activities that become important in early object relations. Being held and rocked and touched and sung to are surely common important components of the growing relationship between the baby and his mother.

If one were to postulate from the very beginning not only

direct needs requiring gratifications but also quasi needs which require merely removal of the noxious state of excitation, one could say that the gratification of this quasi need for soothing is as important a part of the mother-infant relationship as is direct need gratification such as feeding.

I am not in a position to propose seriously a theory of affect according to which both positive and negative emotion are equally rooted in the earliest physiological experiences of excitation and inhibition. I would like to suggest, however, that the facts reported by Dr. Spitz along with the phenomena to which I referred make it logically possible to do so. Schematically speaking one could say that all emotion ultimately derives from earliest physiological anxiety. At the neonatal period one can distinguish between primitive unpleasure without psychic representation and an affectively neutral state of relative quiescence. Next during several months the infant experiences patterned configurations of sensation imposed by the cycle of need distress and need gratification, excitation and soothing in many forms. These recurring patterned experiences might then be said to develop a reservoir or a matrix of feeling tones and earliest "organ memories" which gradually differentiate with respect to intensity and quality. This reservoir of recurring physiological states and feeling tones would then be the stuff of which is made both pleasure and unpleasure in the psychological meaning of the term. The transition to emotion would depend on the congruence of maturational and developmental factors which make possible among other things the function of anticipation and an early form of object relation.

Part II

LEVELS: AN ANALYSIS

Introductory Comments

It is fitting that this section begin with work by a past and continued pioneer in the study of expressive behavior. Not only has Dr. Felix Deutsch elucidated during many years the ways in which bodily processes achieve symbolic representation in states of disease, and in which language itself is suffused with bodily imagery; but he has specifically pointed out how motor activity itself serves as communication in the psychoanalytic and the psychotherapeutic situation, as well as in everyday life.

His approach to the interview, the "associative anamnesis," he describes as: "A dynamic interviewing method designed to explore the meaning of a neurotic symptom or condition in a certain sector through free associations to a key word or phrase selected by the interviewer from the patient's own verbalized material of the introductory part of the interview." Transcripts of associative-anamnestic interviews form the basis of numerous publications (cf. Deutsch 1949; Deutsch and Murphy, 1955). In these a therapeutic technique has been elaborated called "sector therapy."

Also Dr. Deutsch has made several sound films of his technique. One of these serves as the starting point for this part of our symposium. A sample segment of interview will serve as a springboard for discussion of the various levels at which emotional expression may be studied.

The sample itself was part of a separate experiment (cf. Deutsch, 1962). This was to study the associative anamnesis by introducing sensory stimuli of various sorts into an interview to see whether they had a facilitating effect upon associations and the emergence of important material. In Felix Deutsch's words, "Exposing a patient to an external sensory stimulus given without preparing the patient for it and before he is actually interviewed has the advantage that it will lead more quickly to deeper unconscious material. . . . If we use an initial sensory stimulus, not consciously object-related, the patient has no cognitive defenses lined up against the responses. He can, therefore, associate more freely and the introductory part of the interview can be bypassed." A number of different sensory stimuli, such as changes in light or in temperature, have been used by Dr. Deutsch. For the interview to follow, he used a strong olfactory stimulus, cat dung soaked in ammonia, placed out of sight under the patient's chair.

The following chapter consists of a case summary, a typescript of the first twelve minutes, which were filmed, then a digest of the remainder of the interview.

The succeeding chapters begin with a detailed analysis of this interview. "Analysis" means, in the dictionary sense, "separation into constituent parts," not psychoanalysis, although the first paper consists of psychoanalytically oriented observations, wedded to the meticulous experimental technique of Dr. Mahl. In the discussion, psychoanalytic understanding is elaborated by three other experienced clinical investigators, who show how complex a clinical situation can be when scrutinized by well-trained eyes, as well as how complex can be the content and meaning of emotional expression.

The argument moves toward more uncharted areas. In Chapter 6 the kinesicist shows us what magicians have always known, that the hand is quicker than the eye. Dr. Birdwhistell also warns us in his opening parable to beware of magic. Since sleight of hand can be caught by a net of film, there is danger in thinking that we have imprisoned the unconscious. The unperceived gesture, like the unnoticed vocal modifier, tells us about one aspect of emotion. Or, if, as Renneker says, it is discordant with conscious utterance, it informs us of one aspect of a process that is unconscious. It is not a new *via regia.* We may still find out about other unconscious processes from the dream, dreamed while lips and hands are still.

A further move takes us from the clinical to the laboratory study of emotion. The last chapter of this Section is one of a series of brilliant papers by Dr. Lacey and his colleagues. Lacey completes the analytic demolition started by the psychoanalysts. "Emotion," the simple unitary humor which Galen set in motion and Cannon found to consist largely of adrenaline, evaporates not only under our eyes but under those of our instruments. Not only psychic but somatic complexity grows. Students' hearts, we find, race to intellectual stressors as well as to cold pressors, and slow down to heart-rending drama. Student bodies react differently when they are hostile to peers at their Alma Mater than when hostile to their dear mothers. Dr. Lacey's hypotheses are exciting, particularly the one which suggests contrasting physiologic processes in states aimed at environmental exclusion and environmental inclusion. Regardless of whether or not they are ultimately verified in their present form, they challenge old complacencies with new experiments. They may even hint at points of contact between those two figures, hitherto so widely separated, the psychoanalytically oriented clinician and the experimental psychologist. To speculate a little about Dr. Lacey's speculations, his experimental findings may ultimately be fructified by such apparently remote notions as "attention cathexis," "mobilization for activity," or even, since he brings in the mother, "unconscious sense of guilt." At the very least, his stimulus specificity suggests that stimuli to adult human subjects have predictable, generalizable, and observable *meaning.*

CHAPTER 4

Sample: An Experiment with the Associative Anamnesis

FELIX DEUTSCH, M.D.

A. Case Summary. The patient was a thirty-four-year-old, white, male, married laborer, who entered the hospital with a one-and-a-half month history of jerking the head backward and to the right. The symptom first occurred while he was walking to and from his work, and increased gradually in severity and duration until he had a constant, uncontrollable, steady pulling back of his head, which caused him to pull his head down forcibly with his hand. Later, after manipulation from a chiropracter, the steady pulling changed to sudden jerking movements of the head backward and to the right in dramatic spasms. These became worse if he was upset or if he was with other people.

The patient was born in Maine and reared on a farm. He was the third of four sons born to a rugged, quiet, upright, and religious country woman and a hard-working laborer father, who was away most of the time. As a boy the patient did not take part in sports or other activities, was shy with children his age, and totally unable to stand up for his rights in any sort of fight or disagreement. He spent most of his time with his brothers at home. The mother never approved or tolerated conflict within the family and stopped arguments abruptly before they really began. She "could take care of the boys," and demanded immediate obedience.

When he was fourteen years old, the patient began masturbating alone, finding a secluded place, feeling increasingly guilty about it. He frequently concealed himself in a dense apple tree next to the road by his house, peeping at women going by, hoping to see their dresses lifted by the wind. Anal fantasies appear to have entered his voyeuristic excitement. In high school, by the time he was eighteen years of age, he was going out occasionally with a girl, but making no sexual advances.

After the patient graduated from high school at eighteen, he joined the Army. During two years in England, he gradually developed nervous shaking of the head and hands, especially when he was mixing with people, going into strange places, or especially when addressing officers. To his dismay, friends began to nickname him "Shaky." At the end of his tour abroad he became seriously disturbed, and was hospitalized. He remembers nothing of his disturbance except that he was given insulin coma treatments and saw a diagnosis of anxiety state on some of his papers. Finally he was sent back to the U.S. and given his discharge from the hospital after three months.

After his discharge the patient returned home to Maine and began working in the cotton mill where his father was employed. He lived at home for about six months and then roomed out. He recalls a traumatic event at this time, when he was about twenty-one years of age. A cousin, with whom he was hunting, accidentally shot himself through the head with his hunting rifle (which for some unexplained reason had a filed hair-trigger). The patient, shaken by the gory sight, left him with other members of the family and did not even attend the funeral. After that, his fear of violence and death became an obsession.

When the patient was twenty-two, he married for the first time. However, he started running out to bars and drinking excessively. He lived for short periods with a woman who later became his second wife; she was a heavy drinker and, he says, a "ripper." She had been married and had two children. His first wife divorced him. The patient and his present wife lived together for four years before they married. The marriage, which resulted in two children, was one of constant fighting, yelling, and drinking.

The most serious issue between the patient and his wife became her drinking. They might get along well for a few weeks, and then the patient would come home to find the house in shambles and the wife drunk. He persuaded her to drink at home rather than alone in barrooms; yet they often went to taverns to drink together. At times he threatened to leave home or actually did for a few days; but he always returned.

During the four years prior to admission, the patient became more anxious and self-conscious in public, sometimes wondering if he was going crazy. Once or twice he requested help from a minister or doctor, but failed to follow up with his appointments.

The patient's father died three years before admission and his older brother died two years later. At that time a neighbor in the apartment building was asphyxiated with his five children because of a gas leak. The patient was aware of some kind of tragedy there, but refused to go near the scene and was disturbed by feelings of anxiety and by bad dreams afterwards.

Some months before admission, while walking to and from work because he was too nervous to take the bus, he again reported voyeuristic excitement similar to that he had known in adolescence. This time, however, he felt extremely guilty, "almost cheap," about looking at the women's legs. Often he felt an urge to masturbate at these times, too. He had also had erotic sensations from looking at his thirteen-year-old stepdaughter in various stages of undress at home, and wondered if he was a "peeping Tom."

Also, just before the onset of his illness, the patient began doing a different kind of work at his job, cutting steel with a power saw. He had to look to his right frequently on this job and when he did would often notice an elderly man watching him. He wondered if this man were scrutinizing his work critically, to be sure he did it right. He volunteered that his head was pulled upward and to the right, to glance fearfully at this man, just as it was in his illness.

B. The Interview. The interviewer having seated the patient in a chair under which, beneath the carpet, has been placed cat manure soaked in ammonia.

Dr. How do you do. I am glad to see you. It is a little smelly here, no?

Pt. Yes, it's smelly, like a disinfectant, or something. I don't know what it is.

Dr. Do you mind it?

Pt. No, I can stand it. It's all right.

Dr. It's all right! You like it?

Pt. No, I don't like it, but it's all right.

Dr. You don't like it?

Pt. No, I don't like the smell of it, no.

Dr. What? You never liked?

Pt. I don't know what—I have smelled it before. I don't know what you call it.

Dr. What do you call it?

Pt. I was trying to think what it is. It's [pause] I can't even think of it. I know what it is. I think I do.

Dr. It reminds you of something unpleasant?

Pt. I am trying to think. It reminds me—I have smelled the same thing before. I think—.

Dr. But you never minded it, you were always a little sensitive to it?

Pt. Oh, yuh, I don't like it but it don't hurt me. I can stand it. That's all right.

Dr. Have you ever been in a place which was bad smelling from something, that you minded?

Pt. No, I don't think so. I have smelled something like this here before, but I don't know where. It wasn't anything.

Dr. In the past?

Pt. Yuh, I was trying to think. It might have been in high school when I had chemistry or physics. It might have been there. I don't know. It wasn't too much.

Dr. You were in chemistry?

Pt. I took physics. Yuh, I think I took one year of chemistry too. I was in a small country school down in Maine, a little small school. We didn't have much, but I took one year of physics and one year of chemistry.

Dr. And you liked?

Pt. I didn't like school. I didn't like to go to school. The only thing I liked, if you could say I liked any of it, was Math, figures. I didn't mind that. I could figure pretty well.

Dr. So you became a chemist?

Pt. Oh, no. I'm nothing. I've got a trade in the cotton mill, a slush attendant. That's all I've got and I don't work at that now. The cotton industry went to pieces so my job went to pieces.

Dr. Did you like to work with chemicals?

Pt. No, I haven't worked with them except when I was in high school.

Dr. But you remember the smell?

Pt. It seems to me I have smelled it before but I can't place it.

Dr. You said high school.

Pt. Pardon?

Dr. You said high school.

Pt. Well, I was thinking maybe that's where I smelled it. I don't know. I honestly can't think. I don't know where it's from. I know the smell [long pause]. I can't tell what it is.

Dr. But you remember?

Pt. Yes, I know I have smelled that before, or something similar or awfully close to it [long pause].

Dr. In high school?

Pt. I don't honestly know. I don't know where else I would have smelled it.

Dr. At home?

Pt. I wish I could recognize it and I could tell you. All I can think of—my mind don't work—bleach. It ain't bleach.

Dr. What do you mean?

Pt. Bleach water. I mean I hate the smell of that. *It stinks every time my wife does* a washing you know, but it doesn't smell exactly like this.

Dr. Your wife?

Pt. Yuh, when she does a washing with bleach. It *stinks,* but it doesn't smell like this.

Dr. What does she wash?

Pt. What do you mean? She washes clothes. When she does her washing.

Dr. Your wife?

Pt. Yuh.

Dr. It makes you angry when she washes and makes such a—?

Pt. I sometimes holler at her. I mean I don't actually holler at her. I ask her why she has to do it when *I'm home.* I don't like the smell of it. She don't too often but the kids —that's what it smells like. It smells a lot like my kid's diapers, stale diaper, strong. That could be it. I think that's just what it smells like.

Dr. Diaper?

Pt. Yuh, it smells like an old stale diaper. What do they call that stuff in a person's *urine?* Some kind of a stuff there, what do they call it?

Dr. Hm? Yes.

Pt. There's a strong smell to it. A lot of people mention it. What the devil it is now I can't remember.

Dr. You holler and shout?

Pt. No, not really about that. Oh, I've argued with my wife

about other things, but I ask her why the devil she has to use it when I'm at home. I tell her forget it that time and next time I'm not at home use the bleach. She don't use it every time anyway. So that's about it. We ain't had a fight over it.

Dr. But you said you fight about something else?

Pt. Oh, I'm a very jealous person, very jealous. I don't know —my doctor downstairs wanted to know where it started from. I honestly can't say. I don't know, but, well, my wife ever since I have known her, well, before we got married, put it that way, she used to step out on me. I don't know if she—there are no women around here, is there— I don't know if she got laid or not, but whether she did or not, I used to think she did. I'd blame her for it anyway. I mean I'm that kind of a person. It would make me mad and it built up through the last ten years. This was the only reason that I—I don't think this put me in here to start with, but then when they thought something was in my mind bothering me, or something, well, it's the only thing that has really bothered me. I figured it must be that. I don't know. I guess they don't seem to think so. But I get so mad with her, well, I almost can't see straight. I mean I'll use that for a figure of speech. I just *get blind mad* and I want to leave her but I won't.

C. The remainder of the interview elaborated the themes already started. The bulk of it was spent in the patient's account of his marital frictions and the vicissitudes of his symptoms. He could not, so he said, tolerate being at home; yet when drinking with his buddy, he told the interviewer, "My head is as steady as you are." He reminisced about his first wife: "She was good, clean, a very nice woman." He had been unable to stay with her, but found himself "drawn" to his present wife, a fellow employee, a drinker, and a flirt, who had been "kissing all the guys" at a Christmas party when she first took the lead in seducing the patient.

Three quarters of the way through the interview he shifted the topic again and talked briefly about the hunting trip of the previous December when his present symptom had first clearly manifested itself. He had started on this trip at a time when things actually were peaceful between him and his wife. Though he had cut the trip short by a day, he had gotten along well with his wife, who had accompanied him. Another psychiatrist, he stated, had tried to establish a connection between the trip and previous hunting experiences with his father. With some vehemence the patient protested that he was bewildered, unable to understand any rhyme or reason for his illness.

The interviewer returned him to the topic of his jealousy, and the conflicts over drinking. He mentioned that his father used to drink surreptitiously. He also recalled the only fight he ever knew his father to have with his mother. Again he grew vehement: other psychiatrists had tried to infer that he had suspected his father of behaving improperly toward the patient's own wife, patting her rear. In his very denial he managed to confuse wife and mother in several speech slips. Furthermore, he protested angrily, others implied that he was "queer"; he had challenged the doctor to "go outdoors" and settle the matter.

After mentioning in passing that he had hoped to find something wrong that could be helped by an operation, he ended on a note of effusive gratitude, saying to the interviewer: "Thanks a million for coming in anyway. Bye."

CHAPTER 5

The Lexical and Linguistic Levels in the Expression of the Emotions

GEORGE F. MAHL, PH.D.

In his introductory remarks, Dr. Knapp asks the question: to what extent are words alone and particularly their formal changes, useful in the study of emotional expression? My presentation deals with the question in so far as one emotion, anxiety, is concerned. I will refer to studies we have made of the lexical and nonlexical expression of anxiety in the adult human, and will apply some of their concepts and methods to Dr. Deutsch's interview. This contribution to the symposium will not result in final answers to Dr. Knapp's questions, but I hope it will suggest some fruitful leads and useful premises for investigation.

The original purpose of our research was to develop objective measures of the patient's anxiety during psychother-

The preparation of this paper and the research from which it derives were supported by a United States Public Health Service Research Grant (M-1052), "The patient's language as expressive behavior."

apy interviews, and it is from this standpoint that I will summarize that part of the work relevant to this Symposium. The goal was to develop techniques for inferring moment-to-moment changes in the patient's anxiety as they occurred during the interview itself. We were not interested in over-all assessment of the patient's general anxiety state outside of the interview. For various reasons, we wanted to base these measures on the patient's verbal behavior rather than on physiological changes. Further, we required a high-fidelity sound recording of this verbal behavior instead of reconstructed notes.

A recorded interview presents a wide array of phenomena, including both the verbal or lexical content, and the many nonlexical aspects. These parallel, roughly, Reich's distinction (1933) between "what" the patient says and "how" he says it. The nonlexical comprise both linguistic and extralinguistic aspects. The nonlexical, *linguistic* features include, for example, the primary phonemes (our vowels and consonants), phonemic stress, intonation patterns, the grammatical construction, etc. The *extralinguistic features* include, for example, the paralinguistic vocal modifiers described by Pittenger and Smith (1957) and Pittenger (1958), rate of speech, general pitch and volume changes, silences, interaction patterns, etc.

The literature dealing with the reflection of psychological states in verbal behavior is growing rapidly. Sanford's review (1942) covers a great deal of the early research. The last two decades have witnessed increasing investigation of verbal behavior in the interview situation owing to improved sound-recording procedures. The kind of research initiated by Lasswell (1935, 1936) and by Earl Zinn's recording of a psychoanalysis in the early 30s has flourished. Today there is a background of research into a wide variety of aspects of verbal behavior in the interview and related situations. This literature will only be briefly indicated here.

The single aspect of verbal behavior that has received the most attention is *manifest verbal content*. Carl Rogers, his students, and colleagues stand out as the pioneers and continue to produce a great deal of this research. Dollard and his collaborators (1959) have also contributed significant work in this area. The reviews by Snyder (1947) and Auld and Murray (1955) contain detailed references to investigations of manifest verbal content. The book *Trends in Content Analysis* (Pool, 1959) presents a variety of methods and applications of content analysis, further references to the literature, as well as critical discussions of the theoretical and methodological assumptions involved in the use of manifest-content analysis for making psychological inferences.

The relationship of *nonlexical, linguistic* aspects of verbal behavior to psychological states has been persistently a matter of interest. Earlier studies (for example, Sanford, 1941-42; Lorenz, 1952, 1953a, 1953b, 1955; Lorenz and Cobb, 1952, 1953; Boder, 1939-40; and Balken and Masserman, 1940) investigated the *grammatical aspects of language* as a function of a variety of psychological states. Gottschalk and his collaborators (1955, 1956, 1957, 1958) have continued this line of inquiry, as part of their broad investigations that deal with other verbal behavior measures as well. *Vocabulary diversity* has also been investigated as a method of studying psychological states. The earlier work (for example, Whitehorn and Zipf, 1943; Johnson, 1944; Zipf, 1949; and Lorenz and Cobb, 1952, 1953) is represented today in psychiatric interview research by Jaffe (1957, 1959). Recently, *microscopic linguistic analysis* of recorded interviews, using the techniques of descriptive linguistics, has been proposed, and illustrative material indicates the potential fruitfulness of such detailed investigations (see, for example, Pittenger and Smith, 1957; McQuown, 1957; and Pittenger, Hockett, and Danehy, 1960).

Objective investigations of recorded interviews have also included studies of the *extralinguistic, nonlexical* aspects of verbal behavior. These studies have treated verbal productions from the purely behavioral standpoint, dealing with

(a) temporal aspects of talking, such as rate of speech, duration of utterances, etc.; and (b) the interaction of talking by patient and interviewer. There has been a continuous thread of this approach from the early work of Lasswell (1935), through the pioneering by Chapple (1940, 1953) with his interaction analysis, the early studies by the nondirective therapists, the research by Lorenz and Cobb (1952, 1953), and into the more recent extensive investigations by Saslow, Matarazzo and co-workers (Matarazzo et al., 1956; Saslow et al., 1957, 1959) and by Goldman-Eisler (1958).

Our own starting point was the assumption that the most generally useful indicator of anxiety would be in the nonlexical area. We have investigated something in this area that was within our clinical and everyday experience, the phenomenon of flustered, or confused speech, which earmarks areas of anxiety and conflict in the speaker[1]

Our preliminary study of tape recordings (Mahl, 1955) carried out in collaboration with Dr. R. Karpe, revealed two important things. First, there are identifiable, discrete categories of disturbance which constitute "flustering" or "roughness" in expression. The terms "flustering," "garbled," etc., are too indiscriminate. Secondly, these categories appear at varying rates. When there are many of them bunched together we perceive transitory episodes of disrupted speech. Actually, many disturbances take place below this threshold of clinical observation. These two findings suggested that by scoring interview typescripts for the speech disturbance categories and then making serial counts of the disturbances throughout the interview we might have a useful, sensitive indication of the patient's changing anxiety level.

[1] Unbeknownst to us at the time, in a brief passage in *Psychopathology of Everyday Life,* Freud (1901) had already called attention to this dimension as the result of internal conflict and the work of the "inner critic," and Sanford (1942) had pointed out the possible fruitfulness of investigating "roughness" in speech. Dibner (1956) included the enumeration of these phenomena in his method of "Cue Counting." Eldred and Price (1958) also included such phenomena in their "break-up" category.

Table I lists and illustrates the disturbance categories: "ah," sentence change, repetitions, omissions, stutters, tongue-slips (three types), sentence incompletion, and intruding incoherent sounds.

Table 1

Definitions and Illustrations of the Speech Disturbance Categories

Category	Examples
1. *"Ah."* Wherever the "ah" sound occurs it is scored. Less frequent variants are "eh," "uh," "uhm."	Well . . . ah . . . when I first came home.
2. *Sentence Change.* A correction in the form or content of the expression while the word-word progression occurs. To be scored, these changes *must be sensed by the listener* as interruptions in the flow of the sentence.	Well she's . . . already she's lonesome. That was . . . it will be two years ago in the fall.
3. *Repetition.* The serial, superfluous repetition of one or more words—usually of one or two words.	Cause they . . . they get along pretty well together. He was . . . he was sharing the office.
4. *Stutter.*	It sort of well l . . . l . . . leaves a memory.
5. *Omission.* Parts of words, or rarely entire words, may be omitted. Contractions not counted. Most omissions are of final one or two parts of words and are associated with sentence change and repetition.	She mour . . . was in mourning for about two years before. Then their anni . . . wedding anniversary comes around.

6. *Sentence Incompletion.* An expression is interrupted, clearly left incomplete, and the communication proceeds without correction.

   Well I'm sorry I couldn't get here last week so I could . . . ah . . . I was getting a child ready for camp and finishing up swimming lessons.

7. *Tongue Slips.* Includes neologisms, the transposition of entire words from their "correct" serial position in the sentence, and the substitution of an "unintended" for an intended word.

   We spleat the bitches (for "split the beaches")

   He was born in their hou[se] . . . hospital and came to their house.

   The reason that I don't . . . didn't seem to feel the love for him [son] that I felt for J . . . [daughter].

8. *Intruding Incoherent Sound.* A sound which is absolutely incoherent to the listener. It intrudes without itself altering the form of the expression and cannot be clearly conceived of as a stutter, omission, or neologism (though some may be such in reality).

   If I see a girl now I'd like to take out I just . . . dh . . . ask her.

This set has been used in the analysis of the speech of some two hundred varied individuals in varied situations: patients in intensive psychotherapy interviews, outpatient clinic patients in initial interviews, hospitalized schizophrenic patients during TAT-like storytelling behavior, medical patients and elementary-grade school children under similar conditions, undergraduate college students in investigative psychological interviews and in role-playing situations, and faculty members of psychiatry and psychology during heated seminar discussions. Judging from this experience, the category set described is a generally useful one.

Some of the salient purely quantitative aspects of the disturbances are the following (Mahl, 1956a):

1. They occur very frequently in our materials. The median rate for all the categories, based on a substantial portion of the material, is one disturbance for every five seconds spent talking.
2. There are significant interindividual differences in the over-all levels of disturbance. There are also significant intraindividual variations, both from interview to interview and from moment to moment within individual interviews.

In spite of the relatively great frequency of them, the vast majority of the disturbances escape the awareness of both speaker and listener. When presented with the evidence of their disturbances, individuals have shown the gamut of responses typically evoked by abrupt confrontation with something they have been doing without realizing it: interest, surprise, concern, self-criticism, anger, dismay, etc.

Four lines of evidence have converged to show that the variations in the frequency of disturbance categories, *other than "ah,"* are correlated with variations in the speaker's immediate anxiety level. Initially, we made detailed *ad hoc* clinical estimates of changes in the patients' anxiety during psychotherapy interviews to see if these estimates could account for variations in the disturbance level (Mahl, 1955). Apparently positive findings led to a more refined study. In this second study (Mahl, 1956b), a judge, who had been the therapist, evaluated clinically the typescripts of six psychotherapeutic interviews from one patient. On the basis of detailed knowledge of this case and of the immediate context of these six interviews in the psychotherapy, he classified phases of interaction in the six interviews into either an "anxiety-conflictful" category or into a "low anxiety-successfully defensive" category. The typescripts had been carefully edited so that they contained no speech disturbances, nor references to pauses or silences, which could have contaminated these independent criterion judgments. Speech disturbances were scored in the original records by another person who knew nothing of the nature of these phase judgments nor their identity in the typescripts. The speech disturbance level was significantly higher in the "anxious-conflictful" phases of the interviews than in the other.[2] A third study (Mahl, 1956c) correlated the speech disturbance levels of thirty-one psychiatric outpatients in their initial interviews with global anxiety ratings of the interviews made by independent observers. For the twenty women patients in the sample there was a significant positive correlation of +.59 between the two measures, but ambiguous findings resulted for the eleven male patients. A fourth study (Kasl and Mahl, 1958) clarified matters for males and also supplemented the correlational approach of the three preceding studies with the direct experimental method. We determined the speech disturbance levels of twenty-five experimental subjects during a control and a subsequent specially designed "anxiety" interview. There were also ten control subjects who had two successive control interviews, but no "anxiety" interview. All thirty-five subjects were male college students. The anxiety interview increased significantly the subject's speech disturbance level.

In short, the findings just summarized have led us to conclude that a measurement of the speech disturbance level, as defined by the category set presented earlier, is a sensitive, at least partial, indicator of the speaker's immediate anxiety

[2] Boomer and Goodrich (1961) attempted to replicate this study with interviews from two patients. They improved the method by having independent judges identify the motivational phase units and then classify them into the two categories. The judges consisted of the therapists who treated the patients and other experienced therapists as well. Boomer and Goodrich obtained ambiguous results. In one of the cases, using the therapist's judgments of the motivational phases, our findings were confirmed. But when the nontherapist judgments were used in this case, there was no difference in the speech disturbance levels in the two types of phases. In the second case, there was no difference in the disturbance levels for the two types of phases for either the therapist's or the nontherapist's judgments.

Panek and Martin (1959) investigated the relationship of some of these disturbance categories to skin resistance changes. They found a positive relationship between the two phenomena.

level. Furthermore, preliminary data have indicated that this measure is not unduly influenced by degree of hostility, educational level, intelligence, age, or rate of talking (Mahl, 1956c).

A concrete example will illustrate some functional relationships of the speech disturbance level. This is taken from a symposium on the program of the Regional Meeting of the American Psychiatric Association held in New York in November, 1959. A group of workers interested in objective methods for studying psychotherapy interviews applied their various techniques to two recorded interviews for the same patient, from the Research Program directed by Dr. Milton Greenblatt.

Figure I shows the course of the patient's speech disturbance level during successive two-minute intervals of his 18th interview. It also shows the parallel skin temperature measurements. The latter were recorded continuously during the interview as part of Dr. Greenblatt's study and the present data on skin temperature were determined by DiMascio, one of the investigators in that project. This figure is taken from DiMascio's presentation at the A.P.A. Symposium (DiMascio, 1959).

It is immediately apparent that from the 16th to the 36th minute of the interview there is a progressive rise in disturbance level followed by an abrupt fall. Notice that there is an abrupt fall of two degrees in the skin temperature during the peak of the disturbance curve. Over-all there is a moderate negative correlation of —.38 between the two measures (—.33 in the other interview). In a previous paper, DiMascio and his colleagues stated they "had analyzed the skin temperature changes in relation to the ego functioning (on a gross clinical basis) of this patient and had drawn the conclusion that '*when anxiety was expressed, the skin temperature fell or remained low*' " (quoted from DiMascio, 1959).

Now something was definitely going on in the middle of this interview. What was it? We certainly do not know all we would like to about it, but we do know some relevant facts.

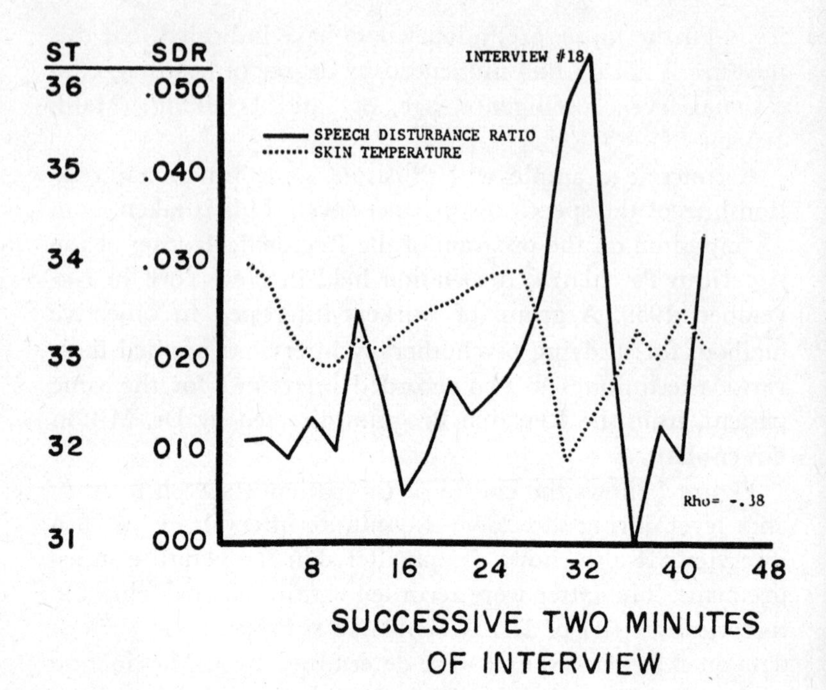

FIGURE I

The patient is a young professional worker in the behavioral sciences whose obsessive-compulsive character disorder had manifested itself partly in work inhibition including procrastination. The therapist's progress notes which were available to us showed that keeping his appointments on time was an emotionally charged matter. The patient was often late and in the past had failed to notify the therapist adequately of absences. This man's handling of time had all the signs of symptomatic behavior or resistance or both. The patient started this interview by being late. He made references to this fact at the outset of the interview, but then avoided talking further about it. The therapist was quiet, biding his time, until he intervened, starting at the 18th minute point in the graph, by stating "You seem not to want to talk about the motivation for your being late today," and "I wonder if we could go into it." Throughout the time when the disturbance curve is rising the therapist maintained a steady, active pressure on the patient to explore his lateness.

Hans Strupp was also a participant in the Symposium and had independently applied his method of analyzing therapist activity to this material. The following are excerpts from his conclusions about the therapist's communications in this interview (Strupp, 1959):

> . . . more than one-half (58 per cent) of his communications were classed as interpretations. . . .
> His interpretations . . . focused very markedly on the transference relationship (41 per cent).
> The degree of initiative displayed by the therapist was consistently high.

The majority of the therapist's communications took place during this period of the rise in the speech disturbance curve and the marked fall in skin temperature. Knowing the situation, it seems pretty clear that the therapist actively touched on an emotionally charged topic. He energetically and persistently disrupted the patient's defensive avoidance of that topic. This caused the patient's anxiety to mount steadily, and this was manifested in the progressive rise of the speech disturbance curve and in the skin temperature changes.

When the disturbance curve first dropped the patient seemed to me to have become defensively angry; it is objectively a fact that he cried and experienced an insight during the entire drop. When the curve was at and then near the base line, the therapist's communications consisted only of "What about the tears?" "Why would you find it difficult to be observed crying?" and "When men have strong feeling, they can cry too." Strupp's system scored the latter words as communicating "a measure of empathy."

In short the clinical facts—the patient's lateness, his defensive avoidance of this matter, the active and persistent intervention by the therapist, the patient's crying and insight, and the therapist's empathic understanding—explain what was going on when the patient's speech disturbance level and skin temperature showed the marked changes in the middle of this interview. The three sets of data "fit together" meaningfully.

With this background about the functional relationships of the speech disturbance measure, I would like to apply it to Dr. Deutsch's interview.

In the actual scoring of the disturbances, it is necessary to use simultaneously both a verbatim typescript and the tape recording. A useful measure for investigating anxiety is a ratio of the total of all disturbances, excepting "ah," to the number of words spoken:

$$\text{Disturbance Ratio} = \frac{\Sigma \text{ ``Non-ah'' Disturbances}}{\text{N words}}$$

This ratio is independent of the actual size of the language sample. Another alternative, of course, is to hold the language sample size constant and use the raw count of the disturbances. I will refer to both types of measures here.

The reliability of the "Σ Non-ah" is uniformly high—interscorer reliabilities having been .86, .88, .90, .91, .96, and .99 in our studies. The scorer of Deutsch's interview was one of the independent scorers in all but two of these studies. While the reliability of his scoring in this particular interview was not determined, the best estimate of it is his average in the above studies—.93.

All of the patient's speech in the entire interview with Deutsch (the first twelve minutes of which were presented in the film) was scored for speech disturbances. Then we determined his Non-ah Ratio for successive one-minute and also two-minute intervals of the interview. His average two-minute ratio is presented in Figure II, along with the averages of the thirty-one patients in the initial interview study mentioned earlier. Only six of the initial interviews equal or exceed this man's average level in this interview. His relatively high level of disturbance would thus indicate that in this interview he was quite frightened. This assessment is consistent with three known things:

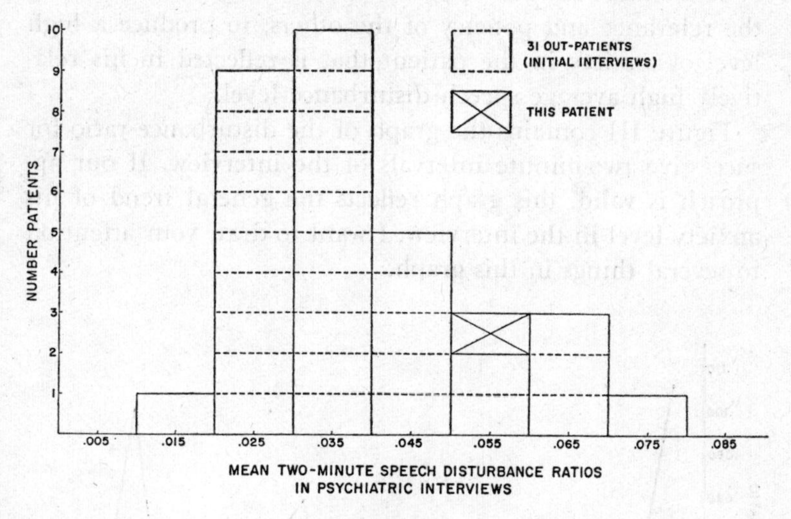

FIGURE II

1. The patient's symptomatology which included marked chronic anxiety and self-consciousness; and phobic anxiety when mixing with people, going into strange places, as well as public stores or restaurants and buses—seemingly in public generally.

2. The fact that a sound-film was made of the interview with the patient's knowledge. Unless Dr. Deutsch supplied some unintentional cues after we saw the film end, the patient assumed that the filming continued throughout the interview. The sound recording, of course, did continue throughout.

3. The fact that the interview was conducted in the presence of the "distinctive" sensory stimulus. By itself this stimulus, in this setting, would probably be disturbing to a large number of patients. In addition, Dr. Deutsch intentionally made reference to the stimulus during the interview and made rather direct connections between the odor and the associative material of the patient, guided by his psychodynamic formulation of the patient.

These three factors are seen as interacting, each increasing the relevance and potency of the others, to produce a high level of anxiety in the patient that is reflected in his relatively high average speech disturbance level.

Figure III contains the graph of the disturbance ratio for successive two-minute intervals of the interview. If our approach is valid, this graph reflects the general trend of his anxiety level in the interview. I want to draw your attention to several things in this graph.

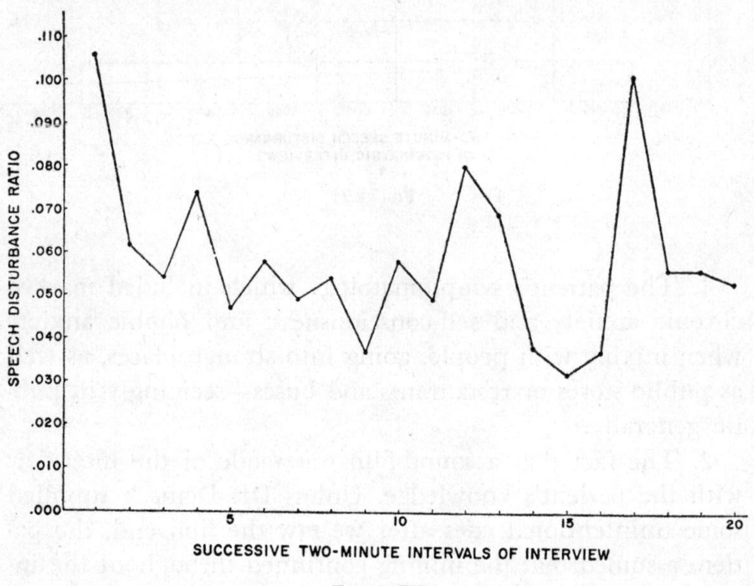

FIGURE III

First, there is the high level in the opening minutes of the interview when the patient is confronted *en masse* with the disturbing features of this situation—the constellation of factors I just mentioned has its most powerful effect now—producing a "breech in the stimulus barrier." The extent of this breech is apparent if you keep in mind that this man's average disturbance level is high, and this is among his very high points.

Second, the filming ended during the sixth two-minute interval. It is of some interest that the speech disturbance level is essentially the same before and after this point. While the patient was not told that the filming would stop at this point, there were two factors that changed at this time which could conceivably have affected him. One was a distinct change in the audible noise made by the camera when the film ran out and which was picked up by the mike. I had listened to the tape recording before the film arrived and had marked the time of this change in the background noise. It coincided exactly with the time the filming ended. Another factor was that Dr. Deutsch knew when the filming stopped and it is likely that this caused some change in his overt behavior, however slight. The disturbance measure indicates that these two potentially influential factors did not by themselves cause a significant change in the patient's anxiety level; they do not tell us whether or not he perceived them and correctly interpreted them.

The third factor to be noticed in this graph is the sustained but moderate increase in the disturbance level from the tenth to thirteenth two-minute interval, inclusively. During this eight-minute period, the patient was speaking almost exclusively about the conflict he has over being separated from his present wife. Essentially what he was saying about it consisted of a description in his own words of his conflict.

Finally I want to point out now the abrupt rise in the seventeenth two-minute interval.

Figure IV contains a graph of the disturbance level during successive one-minute intervals of the interview. It brings out *some* marked variations in the disturbance level that were "smoothed out" in the two-minute measures. These changes are especially noticeable in the opening minutes and again in the closing minutes of the interview. The sustained phase of moderately increased disturbance level when describing his inability to leave his second wife is still portrayed, and the abruptness of the marked rise in the thirty-third minute is brought out even more clearly.

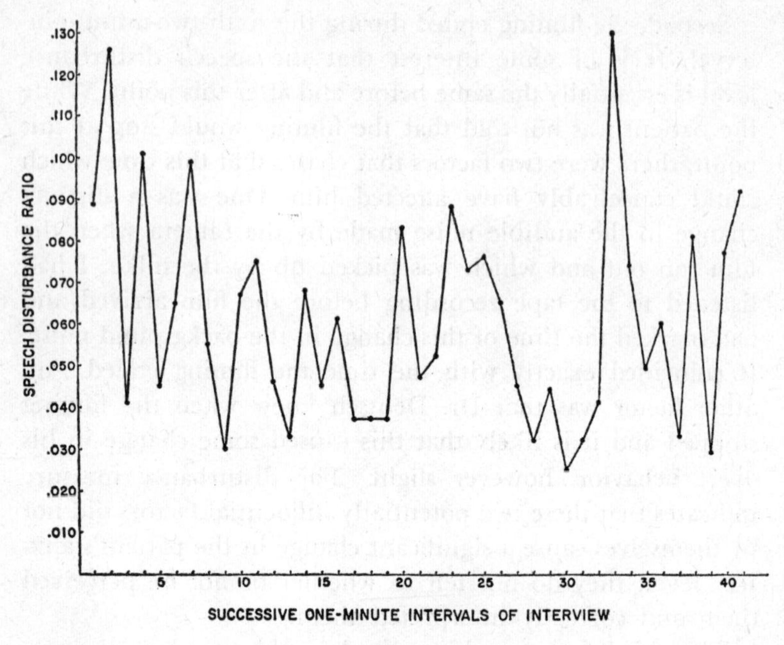

FIGURE IV

Concerning the opening minutes of the interview, this graph shows both the high level of disturbance at the outset and also considerable change at the same time.

A still more refined analysis was done to see how the disturbance measure was reflecting the details of the interaction in these opening minutes, through and after the sudden recognition of the odor by the patient.

Taking the sudden recognition of the odor as the reference point, we counted off successive 100-word samples—first, backwards to the beginning of the interview, and then forwards an equal number of segments past the recognition point. The procedure produced a segment containing twelve consecutive 100-word samples. Then we determined the number of speech disturbances in these 100-word samples. Figure V shows the results.

The immediate confrontation with the odor as part of the

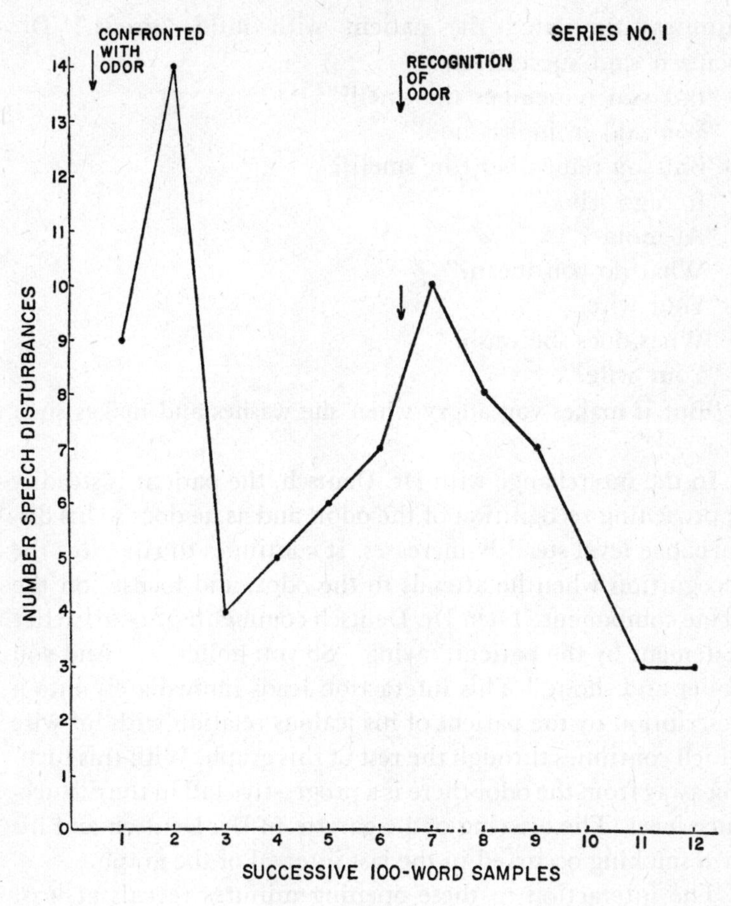

FIGURE V

total interview situation, preordained by the patient's psychodynamics to be threatening, starts the patient out at a high level of disturbance. As he and Dr. Deutsch continue to talk about the odor the level of disturbance rises further. Then Dr. Deutsch briefly changed the subject by asking the patient a few questions about his occupation and school. As the patient responded to these "diversions" his disturbance level fell abruptly. But then Dr. Deutsch again brought up the matter of the smell and within about two and a half minutes stimulated the patient with mild "prods." Dr. Deutsch said successively:

"But you remember the smell?"
"You said in high school"
"But you remember [the smell]?"
"In high school?"
"At home?"
"What do you mean?"
"Your wife?"
"What does she wash?"
"Your wife?"
"But it makes you angry when she washes and makes such a . . .?"

In the interchange with Dr. Deutsch, the patient is steadily approaching recognition of the odor, and as he does so his disturbance level steadily increases. It continues to rise after the recognition when he attends to the odor, and focuses on the urine component. Then Dr. Deutsch commented on an earlier statement by the patient, saying, "So you holler. . . . And you holler and shout." This interaction leads immediately into a description by the patient of his jealous relation with his wife which continues through the rest of this graph. With this turning away from the odor there is a progressive fall in the disturbance level. The offering of a cigarette to Dr. Deutsch and his own smoking occurred in the last interval of the graph.

The interaction in these opening minutes reveals at least one clear gradient of activity, one side of which has as its goal "the approach" to the recognition of the odor, but this "approach" to the goal is conflictful for the patient and is pushed by Dr. Deutsch. On the other side of the gradient, the patient can "avoid" the odor and its most direct associative responses. The disturbance curve during this period can be interpreted as revealing the gradient in anxiety that one would expect if this view of the interaction is correct.

But one can be dubious about such a "neat fit." It is possible that this disturbance curve reflects a cyclical tendency inherent in the patient and that it bears no relationship to the presumed gradient of interaction concerning the odor. If this is so, then by repeating exactly the procedure followed in this observation, we should find similar "cycles" of disturbance measures in succeeding sequences of twelve 100-word samples. We made these control measurements and they are shown in Figure VI. As you can see, none of them show the same pattern as the first sequence. The first two are patternless and the last two show patterns of their own. These control observations increase my belief in the original interpretation, but there is one other important control that should be made. It is possible that the first pattern is characteristic of the way this patient would open all his interviews. Since there are no other recorded interviews available for this patient, this check could not be made.

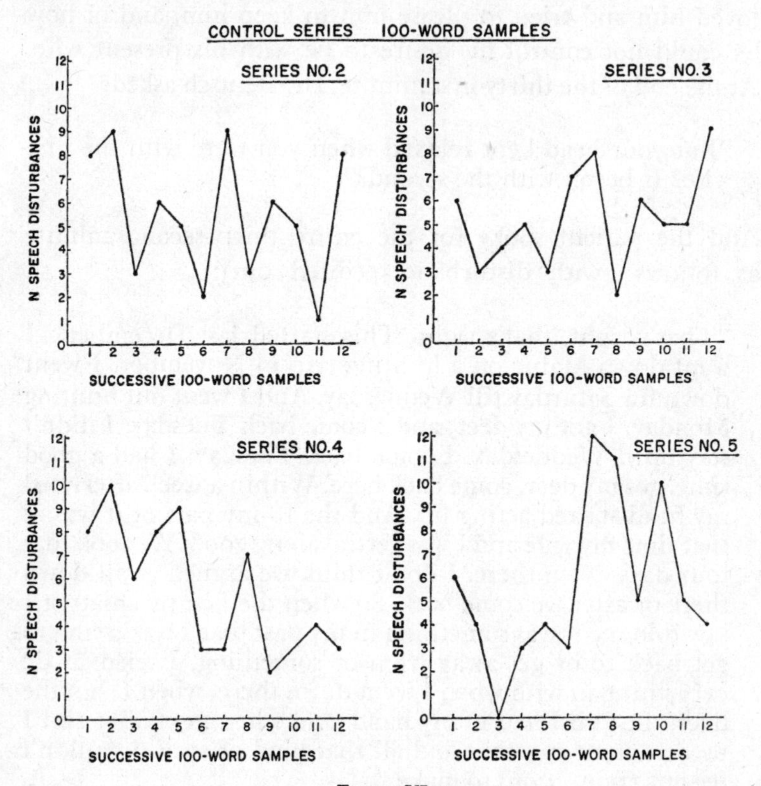

FIGURE VI

I would like now to return to the abrupt peak toward the end of the interview. How does this peak fit into the context of the interview and the case? Is it an expression of an increase in the patient's anxiety?

First I will describe the context in the interview of the peak in disturbance. The patient described his conflict over leaving his present wife during the period of the interview where the disturbance curve is moderately elevated (20-26th minute). Dr. Deutsch then asked if this was his second marriage. The patient replied that it was, and during the twenty-seventh through thirty-first minutes—where the disturbance level remains relatively low—he spoke in detail about his first marriage: of the positive attributes of his first wife, of his meeting his present wife, how his first wife loved him and tried to please him to keep him, and of how he could not control his desire to be with his present wife. At the end of the thirty-first minute, Dr. Deutsch asked:

> "But your head kept relaxed when you were with the first wife? It began with the second?"

And the patient spoke for the entire thirty-second minute as follows (with disturbances edited out):

> "That's right, that's right. This started last December. I went down Maine on a hunting trip in November. I went down for Saturday till Wednesday. And I went out hunting Monday, I got my deer, and I come back Tuesday. I didn't stay until Wednesday, I come back Tuesday. I had a good time, got my deer, come back here. Within a week afterward my head started acting up. And the funny part of it was at that time my wife and I was gettin' along good. We took that four days down there. I don't think we argued at all down there or after we come back. So when the first psychiatrist I saw told me it was something in my past that I was trying to get back to or get away from or something, I tried to tie everything in with when I went down there, when I shot the deer, the gun I had in my hand, and when my father and I used to hunt together and all that kind of stuff. I couldn't see any connections to make."

Then in the thirty-third minute, when the abrupt rise occurs, the patient continued with the idea of the last utterance, but in a way that abruptly changed the subject:

"I don't understand psychiatry that's all. I can't understand it. I wish I did."

Dr. Deutsch: "You mean if you would understand. . . ?"

Patient continuing:
"I might be able to see what I'm looking for. I keep pestering my doctor about it; I shouldn't, but I do, for some string to get ahold of, to start me on my way out of this. I don't know what I gotta do when I find it. I don't know nothing. And when you ain't got no start, you can't do nothing about it, as far as I'm concerned. I can't help myself."

I'll stop at this point, for this is the essential part—the patient has said 80 per cent of what he did say in this thirty-third minute and 80 per cent of the speech disturbances in the interval have occurred by now.

To see how anxiety has been manifested in the "peak" under consideration, I want to work backwards from the peak in the disturbance curve. We should find anxiety looming very prominently.

With such a dramatic rise in the disturbance level, I suspected it was part of a sudden increase in anxiety that was either in response to something or in anticipation of something. Now the rise was part of a response in which the patient had abruptly changed the subject; it occurred when he was rapidly withdrawing from something. This was most likely to have been something connected with what he was talking about immediately before the withdrawal. And *that* was about *the hunting trip,* and associated material—his shooting the deer, the gun in his hand, when his father and he used to hunt together. Is there any evidence that the "gun-hunting-shooting" leads us to *anxiety?* The case material provides unmistakable confirmation, for it includes a statement:

> (The patient) . . . "recalls a traumatic event at this time, when he was about twenty-one years of age. A cousin, with whom he was hunting, accidentally shot himself through the head with his hunting rifle (which, for some unexplained reason, had a filed hair-trigger) and the patient, shaken by the gory sight, left him with other members of the family and did not even attend the funeral. Since then, his fear of violence and death has been an obsession."

Recalling that the patient's conversion symptom involves the head, that it started after the recent hunting trip, and that this traumatic event consisted of his cousin's being shot through the head, it appcars that the speech disturbance peak has not only led us directly to a large quantity of anxiety but perhaps to a memory of an event significantly involved in the conversion symptom itself. This brings up the "father" topic, too, for the psychoanalytic theory of conversion hysteria would emphasize that behind such a traumatic event is a repressed, active unresolved oedipal complex. The case material does not contain any unequivocal evidence on this matter; but five minutes later in the interview, after the point under consideration, the patient provides it when in the space of a few seconds he commits the classical slip of the tongue in saying

> "Then he (a doctor) said, 'Did you ever see your father pat your *wife* on the ass? . . . Or your mother.' "

and

> "Any time my father went to work or left the house he always gave my *wife,* my mother rather, a quick kiss and he was gone."

It seems very likely, then, that when this patient spoke of the recent hunting trip, the memory of the traumatic hunting trip with his cousin was associatively aroused, evoking intense anxiety which was both "expressed" in the abrupt peak in the speech disturbance level and also motivated the abrupt change in topic. It also seems likely, though it is much more inferential, that the hostile component of his repressed, unresolved oedipal complex was also associatively activated by the discussion of the recent hunting trip and the mention of earlier hunting trips with his father, and that this contributed to the production of the intense anxiety reflected in the speech disturbances.

The responses of the patient in the early minutes of the interview and in this last episode have illustrated the way his anxiety was manifested in an expressive dimension of speech.

How was his anxiety expressed in verbal content, in *what* he said? The last episode is particularly instructive. It is noteworthy that at no time in this episode, neither in the references to hunting nor in the abruptly introduced topic, was there any manifest content referring to "anxiety" or "fear." Although presumably very anxious, he did not report this fact to Dr. Deutsch; he did not say he felt nervous, or upset. In short, he did not name or label his emotional state. Nor did he produce *displaced* references, such as references to having been frightened in other circumstances, at other times, or to other people having been frightened. The fact that the patient *did not* do any of the preceding things deserves emphasis, for most studies of emotional states via content analysis score just such direct and indirect content.

One of the characteristics of his verbal content during the peak in the disturbance level was a high frequency of sentences that included the expressions: "I can't . . ." and "I don't know . . ." ("I couldn't see any connections; I can't understand psychiatry; I don't know what I'm looking for; I don't know what I gotta do when I find it; I don't know nothing; you can't do nothing; I can't help myself"). This content characteristic was first noticed in this episode just listening to the recording clinically. It was also noticed clinically at several other points in the interview when one sensed that the patient's anxiety was mounting. I had first the vague awareness and then the distinct impression that verbal content resulting from completing the sentence frames "I don't know . . ." and "I can't . . ." was this patient's idiosyncratic verbal content response to anxiety whenever it increased, regardless of the source. That is, it seemed to be part of this patient's *characteristic defensive and adaptive techniques for coping with stress in the interview.* Such an interpretation would be in keeping with the view I have presented elsewhere (Mahl, 1959a, 1959b) that valid assessment of emotions by content analysis must treat verbal content as instrumental behavior—interpersonally and intrapsychically—and use "tailor-made" categories appropriate to individual patients and situations.

If the preceding observations and reasoning about the "I don't know . . ." and "I can't . . ." categories are valid, then there should be a positive correlation between the frequency of such utterances and the speech disturbance measures. We tested this hypothesis by obtaining an "I don't know . . ." and "I can't . . ." ratio for one-minute intervals of the interview. This ratio is analogous to the speech disturbance ratio, being the number of utterances completing these two frames divided by the number of words in the sample. To avoid erroneously building a correlation into the data, repetitions of these two expressions due to speech disruption itself were not counted.

Figure VII presents the one-minute interval curves for comparison. You can see that there is considerable, though of course not perfect, agreement between the two measures. The product-moment correlation between them is a relatively strong one of $+.60$ ($p < .001$). An inspection of the scatterplot of the two measures indicates that this correlation is lowered because the content measure tends at times to stay at zero when the disturbance measure is varying. You may be able to detect this trend in the graph, although it is more apparent in the scatterplot. As high and significant as the correlation is, it still appears to be kept down because the content measure is less sensitive than the expressive measure.

I have run one control observation to check on the interpretation of this correlation as confirming my views. One alternative explanation is that *"negative expressions"* by this patient are the things correlated with speech disturbances,

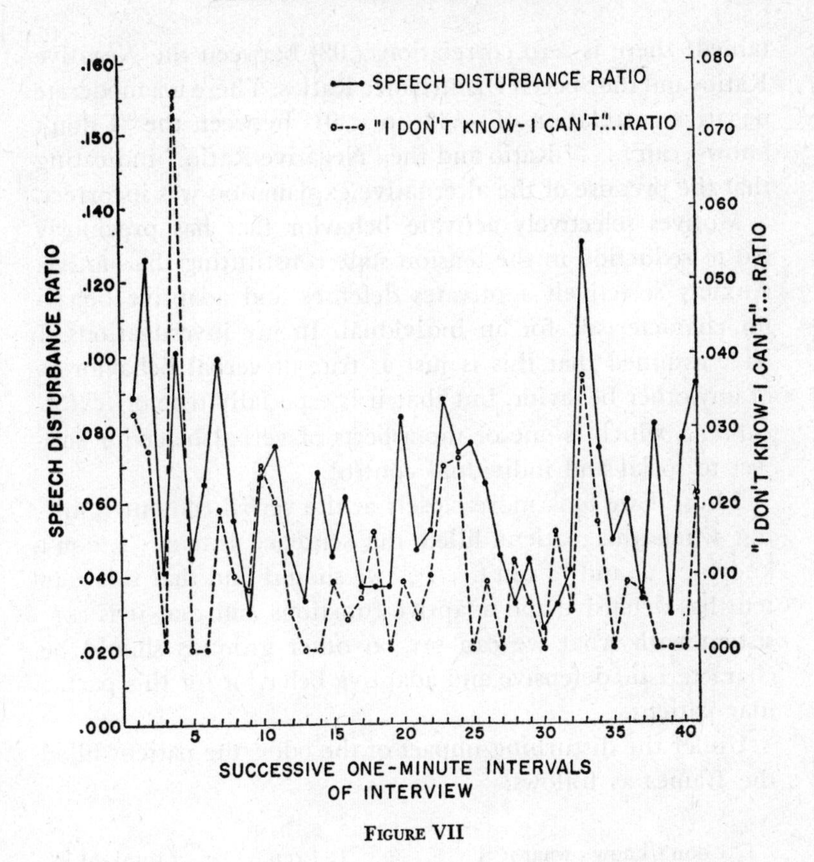

FIGURE VII

and that the "I don't know-I can't . . ." correlation merely reflects this more general relationship. If confirmed, such an alternative explanation would require considerable revision in the thinking presented here. I tested the alternative by obtaining a "Negative Ratio" for the one-minute intervals—a measure of all *other* negative expressions *besides* "I don't know" and "I can't." These included all other expressions containing the "no, not, never, none" forms.

If the alternative explanation is correct, the one-minute "Negative Ratios" should be positively correlated with the one-minute Speech Disturbance Ratios and also with the "I don't know-I can't . . ." Ratios. These results are not obtained: there is zero correlation (.02) between the Negative Ratios and the Speech Disturbance Ratios. There is a moderate negative correlation of $-.38$ ($p < .01$) between the "I don't know-I can't . . ." Ratio and the "Negative Ratio," indicating that the premise of the alternative explanation was incorrect.

Motives selectively activate behavior that has previously led to reduction in the tension state constituting the motive. Anxiety selectively motivates defenses and adaptive behavior characteristic for an individual. In my investigations, I have assumed that this is just as true of verbal behavior as of any other behavior, but that it is especially true of *lexical content,* which is one of the aspects of verbal behavior subject to social and individual control.

Thus, if we look more closely at the verbal content resulting when this patient filled the sentence frames "I don't know . . ." and "I can't. . . ," we should find that this content has defensive and adaptive functions and that it is consistent with what we can say on other grounds should be characteristic defensive and adaptive behavior for this particular patient.

Under the disturbing impact of the odor, the patient filled the frames as follows:

1. I don't know	what it is	1. I can't	even think of it
2. I don't know	what you call it	2. I can't	place it
3. I don't know	if it was in chemistry or physics	3. I can't	think
4. I don't know	if it was in high school	4. I can't	tell what it is
5. I don't know	if it was in high school		
6. I don't know	where else I could have smelled it		

During the later very anxious episode, he filled the frames in the following ways:

1. I don't know	what I'm looking for	1. I can't	see the connections to make
2. I don't know	what I gotta do when I find it	2. I can't	understand it
3. I don't know	nothing	3. I can't	do nothing about it, if I ain't got no start
		4. I can't	help myself

The outstanding characteristic of the statements in both episodes, it seems to me, is *the denial* of the perceptions he has made—of the recognition of the odor and of the connection between the hunting trip and his head symptom—and *the repression* of *the thoughts* evoked by these perceptions. Denial and repression are characteristic for hysteria, which is the outstanding diagnostic feature of this patient.

Another prominent feature of the statements, it seems to me, is the sense of *impotency* they imply, and also convey to the listener, which was especially noticeable in hearing them in the tape. There is *intellectual inhibition:* he "doesn't know" on a grand scale, he "can't think," "can't see connections" and "can't understand." There is also more *general impotency* implied, however, for he also says he "doesn't know what he has to do when he finds out," he "can't do anything," and he "can't help" himself. I speculate that these statements are the verbal reflections of the *inhibition of initiative* considered by Erikson (1959) to be the residue of the unsuccessful solution of the developmental crisis that includes the oedipal crisis, a feature I have already mentioned in connection with both this patient and hysterics. Regardless of this speculation, it is noteworthy that the *sense of impotency* and *inhibition of initiative* appear prominently throughout his case material. They characterized his relation to his mother, brothers, peer males and females, from childhood to the present, and his present marriage.

Under usual conditions of human interaction the "I don't

know-I can't . . ." class of verbal content may elicit a nurturing response from the other person. He would *tell* the speaker what he thought the smell was, and would *give* him his ideas and understanding. He would "help out" the speaker. This would seem to be an interpersonal function of this verbal content in this case, for the patient concluded the second series of statements by saying openly, "I can't help myself."

I believe there is evidence here that the increased anxiety selectively activated characteristic defenses and "adaptive" behavior, that is, that the "I don't know-I can't . . ." content is consistent with other indications of his character, serves the intrapsychic function of repression and the function of denial, and is an automatic attempt to arouse desired activity from the interviewer that would subserve these defenses and reduce his state of anxious helplessness.

Some people under some circumstances will be able and motivated to report on their inner experience of anxiety or will react with displacement substitutes. In such cases the manifest content would refer directly or indirectly to fear or anxiety and would reflect the emotional state. It is an important problem for investigation to discover the factors resulting in this type of emotional expression. I do not believe they are sufficiently known at the present time to rely heavily on manifest content analysis for the assessment of emotional states.

This patient did not behave in this way when his speech disturbance level was so high. This isolated observation is consistent with what we have found in two previous studies. One of these studies (Mahl, 1957) compared the anxiety ratings made for the initial interviews with the Discomfort Relief Quotient introduced by Dollard and Mowrer (1947). There was no correlation between the two measures for either men or women patients. Further, there was no difference in the speech disturbance level when the manifest verbal content referred to Discomfort, or to Relief from Discomfort, or was manifestly Neutral. In the second study (Schulze,

Mahl, and Murray, 1960), we investigated the same kind of relationship, only with the more refined content analysis system devised by Murray (1956). Murray's system consisted of the following major categories of patient content: sex, affection, dependence and independence drive categories; categories of hostility due to frustration of each of these drives; a nonspecific hostility category; categories of sex anxiety, affection anxiety, dependence anxiety, independence anxiety, and nonspecific anxiety. The materials used in the study were series of recorded psychotherapy interviews for three neurotic patients. In no patient was the speech disturbance level higher in the anxiety categories than in the others. However, the speech disturbance level did vary significantly across the categories, in different and meaningful ways for the three patients.

I have shown how one emotion—anxiety—is manifested in one formal aspect of speech and how it may be expressed in verbal content. I have attempted to illustrate methods and ideas which may be useful in investigating the expression of other emotions, as well as anxiety, in verbal content and in the many nonlexical "expressive" dimensions of language.

CHAPTER 6

Remarks and Interpretations: Discussion of the Papers of Drs. Deutsch and Mahl

MORTIMER OSTOW, M.D.

The study of the nature of affect is primarily a biological problem. It is the obligation of clinicians to become skillful in recognizing and detecting and assessing and estimating affects for use as guides in their clinical work. As a clinician, working primarily with psychoanalytic problems, it seems to me that my most useful contribution would be to review Dr. Deutsch's clinical material, merely underscoring the affective inferences used in making clinical assessments. It should be emphasized that the discussions of all of the panelists were prepared quite independently and aside from an abstract of Mahl's remarks, none of us knew what the others were going to say.

Here we have a thirty-four-year-old married man whose childhood was characterized by disinterest in school, seclusiveness, avoidance of fighting with boys, shyness with girls, more than compensated for by voyeuristic practices. In the Army at the age of twenty, he had tremors so pronounced that he was called "Shaky" by his friends. He was hospitalized for a while in the Army and received a series of insulin-coma treatments, from which I assume he was probably psychotic, since ordinarily insulin-coma is not administered for anything but real psychosis. When he was twenty-two years old he was married to a woman whom he called in this interview a "clean" woman. She was a nurse, who seemed to be rather intelligent in view of her subsequent behavior, namely, leaving the patient and remarrying. He began to be unfaithful with an alcoholic woman, his present wife, whom he calls a "ripper." He sought a divorce. I am sure from the clinical material that he had probably had a bad sexual relation with his wife and from the clinical data my guess was that it was premature ejaculation. I was interested to learn informally from Dr. Deutsch today that he really did suffer from premature ejaculation. He left his first wife when she became too "hot" for him, and began to seek a degraded woman in an effort to resolve his oedipal conflict. With his second wife there was a great deal of bickering and quarreling, but he was unable to leave her. Before the onset of his present symptom of hysterical torticollis there were other symptoms. He had a fear of going crazy, quite common in hysteria and also in catatonics in remission. He was anxious and self-conscious in public. He had claustrophobia. He would not use buses. He was pathologically jealous of his wife, but nevertheless clung to her. His presenting symptom followed an outburst of voyeurism on the streets, and at the same time worry about being watched and supervised by an older man.

Therefore, in order to formulate our diagnosis we have to take into consideration the following elements: first, conversion symptoms including recent neck twisting, and in addition, tremors occurring in his Army service; second, phobia; third, pathological jealousy perhaps to the point of paranoia; and fourth, the occurrence of some sort of psychotic breakdown approximately twelve years previously. The current diagnosis then would be conversion and anxiety hysteria, but there is evidence of a past psychosis which was probably a catatonic psychosis or possibly a paranoid schizophrenia. Several dynamic patterns are evident in this material. Unconscious homosexual trends are manifested by his pathological jealousy, by his pleasure and symptom relief obtained from drinking with his buddy. Second, we see a regressive resolution of the oedipus complex. He replaced the clean wife by the dirty wife and he shifted from genital to anal strivings. Third, there are certain projection mechanisms. He projects his sexual excitement upon the street girls. He projects the responsibility for his marital discord, he projects his guilt and shame—his anality and his dirtiness, as well as his homosexuality—upon his wife.

I shall now attempt to reconstruct the pathogenesis of his present illness. It turns out that in November, 1959—and I did not have Mahl's discussion when I reconstructed this—the patient went on a hunting trip with his wife. He says that at that time he was on good terms with her. We must insert here the memory of the cousin's mutilation and death by accidental shooting—premature ejaculation with the rifle if you like. His symptoms started within a week after this pleasant hunting trip, which incidentally was cut short. He was supposed to come home on Wednesday, but he finished shooting on Monday and he went home immediately. He had left while he was still on good terms with his wife. One month before the onset of the symptom, there had been the onset of claustrophobia while on a bus, and at the same time a great interest in voyeuristic excitement. What may we conclude? We may conclude that the patient was unable to satisfy his sexual desires either with his first wife or with his second wife. So long as his wife quarreled with him, he obtained sadistic and masochistic gratification from his pathological jealousy, and drinking with his wife. He obtained heterosexual gratification at a distance by use of voyeurism. When his wife stopped quarreling with him, *he had to turn away from her in some other way.* On the hunting expedition, perhaps stimulated by the memory of his cousin, he probably developed a fantasy of killing her, and we may wonder to what extent the symptom of cocking his head back has to do with an aversion to aiming a gun. What we may assume is that he has succeeded in turning away from her, by a narcissistic innervation of his body musculature, very common in hysteria, namely, a spasm of his neck. In other words, then, the patient's symptom represents aversion from oedipal sexual gratification by a narcissistic genitalization of the neck musculature, which symbolizes the wish to be potent, the wish to be erect, the wish to look, the wish to look away, the wish to kill, and the wish to be punished for looking and killing.

What I have discussed so far is the reconstruction of the pathogenesis of an illness, but what can be said about this interview? What do we see in this interview? We see guilt. The patient says he got a "cheap thrill" out of his sexual activity, condemning himself. He expresses guilt anxiously. He deprecates himself. He says at one point, "I got myself and my wife into one hell of a mess." At another point, talking about his affair with his second wife, he says, "It wasn't right, but I did it just the same." Second, we see a great deal of self-observation, to some of which Dr. Mahl has already called attention. There are three aspects to this self-observation. First of all, it is primarily derogatory. He keeps saying, "I am nothing; I've got nothing; I can't understand anything. We didn't have anything in our school; it wasn't much of a school. Nothing attached to me is any good." Second, his self-observation is primary—that is, concerned essentially with his feelings rather than his appearance. He says, "I am a jealous person. My mind don't work. I get mad. . . . The jealous part of me figured that about her." Third, and most importantly, we are seeing here a sense of despair and depression, much concealed by the pleasant aspect of his face. He says, "I'm not as good as I was before treatment. I'm scared now. I can't help myself."

Finally, we have to take cognizance of certain observations that Dr. Schafer and Dr. Kepecs might mention, and that is his attitude toward the psychiatrist—toward the treating psychiatrist and Dr. Deutsch. Let me repeat to you some of the things he said about his relation to the psychiatrists. He said,

"I'm not as good as I was when I came here. I don't understand psychiatry, that's all. I can't understand it. I wish I did." And you know when a patient says that, he is repudiating your interpretations. He said, "I've got to believe it's in my mind. I can't hardly believe it." He says, "I'm not a doctor. That's something for you fellers to figure out. Psychiatry's for the doctors; it's not for the patients." At another point he mentions that his neck becomes relaxed in the presence of his buddy; he clearly states that it is not the presence of his buddy that makes his neck relax, it is the drinking. He says, "The alcohol relieves me, psychotherapy does not." At another point in talking about his neck, he says to Dr. Deutsch, "My head is just as good as you are." He does not say, "Just as good as your head." He says, "My head is just as good as you are," showing a certain amount of disrespect, a sort of presumptuous identifying of himself with the psychiatrist. Lastly he reveals that he really came to the hospital hoping that something organic could be found, so that he could be cured by an operation.

What may we now conclude about the state of the patient at the time of the interview? Following the hysterical crystallization of the oedipal conflict in the physical symptoms, the patient is left without a love object, without gratification. Finally, he becomes depressed. The disability from which he suffers also decreases his self-regard and enhances depression. This depression leads to an impoverishment of the ego, which is accompanied by feelings of guilt, of despair, which evoke still further decrease in self-regard, and a clinging to his wife for help, as well as to the psychiatrist. When he is threatened by the uncovering of the homosexual nature of his relation to the doctor, he blames the psychiatrist for his failure to improve. We have to distinguish, I think, between two separate categories of affects. The current affects include depression, anger, discouragement, pessimism, and guilt; and the historical affects include jealousy, anxiety, disgust, and rage.

Three conclusions follow: (1) It is necessary to distinguish between the important historical roots of this illness on the one hand and the patient's current affective and dynamic state on the other. (2) Depression is the most prominent current affect. This is confirmed by Dr. Mahl's note that the major indications of concern are associated with expressions of self-deprecation and self-degradation, which are characteristic of depression. (3) In assessing current affective status, it is important to attend to the form in which the material is presented as well as to its content. By form I do not mean simply slips of speech. I mean the status of his object relations, the amount and quality of his narcissism, the amount and quality of his self-observation, his sensitivity to affects and especially to guilt, the prevalence of projection and identification, and the nature of his self-regard—that is, the wide clinical context in which affect is expressed.

ROY SCHAFER, PH.D.

Of Dr. Deutsch's material, including the typescript of the entire interview and the life history data which have been made available to the panelists, I would say first that, listening as a clinician listens, there is little to be found in the way of directly experienced and communicated affect on the patient's part. This is so for intensity, variety, and shadings of affects. What little affect is discernible sounds shallow and well-worn with rehearsal and repetition. It is obvious that, except for some irritability which must be viewed as secondary and ego syntonic in nature and far removed from primary rage, the patient is highly resistant to spontaneous affect. I infer that his massive symptom is a great help to him in this respect, for it is well known that it is a major function of a symptom to ward off or deviously discharge painful affects. Most noticeably the patient succeeds in avoiding the affect of disgust in response to the foul smell in the room. In fact, initially he cleans up the smell, as it were, by associating it with school, disinfectant, and bleach rather than excrement. Yet, he indicates that at home he can be disgusted by a similar smell. I ask myself: why the difference?

This question leads me directly to consider what the present interview situation probably meant to this patient. Of course, with the data at hand, I can only conjecture, but it is part of the clinical method of investigating affects to set up tentative hypotheses without committing oneself to them, and in the first section of my remarks I would like to illustrate this method. In particular I will examine the structure of the present situation as it might be perceived by this patient in order to define its inherent stimulations, gratifications, threats, and deprivations, and to arrive at a formulation concerning affects, which is only one of a number of necessary formulations. This can be only a very incomplete examination.

I am struck by the patient's general compliance in the situation. He does not mind the smell. He does not even ask why in the world he is being subjected to this sensory assault. In this connection, his saying he can stand the smell bespeaks pseudo manliness only. Further, he makes no self-conscious, direct references to sound movies being made of the interview. He complains not at all when with seeming arbitrariness Dr. Deutsch keeps bringing up the theme of smell, even though he obviously knows that Dr. Deutsch is grinding an ax of his own, as evident in one comment near the end of the interview: Dr. Deutsch had referred abruptly to the smell of the anal zone and the patient retorted that he was now quite used to the smell in the room. With apparent earnestness the patient tries to figure out the reasons for his symptom, being stimulated in this respect, I suspect, by a somewhat intellectualistic therapeutic approach during the preceding months.

I ask myself: how does this behavior serve the resistance and how does it express transference? Concerning resistance, I would say the patient tries to remain essentially impenetrable, i.e., to ward off the dirty intrusion of the smell and the doctor. He will intellectualize about his past life and have his symptom, but he will shut out the present, live situation with all its affective potentials. His last remark is,

"Thanks a million for coming in *anyway*," and, shortly before that, when Dr. Deutsch suggests that now they know where to look for an understanding of his symptom, he blankly responds, "Where?" He is saying, in other words, "You got nowhere with me, doctor."

Concerning the transference, I would point out first that the patient has been taken over by a senior expert—a change that could well signify, if we remember his family context, moving from a brother (his young therapist) closer to his father (Dr. Deutsch). Since this new figure brings with him an ordinarily unacceptable odor, and keeps talking about it as he does about other "unacceptable" matters, he provides an additional transference link to the father who himself practiced and smelled of secret vices in some contrast to the clean, anti-instinctual mother. Moreover, this father figure is having the interview filmed, thereby putting the patient in the passive-feminine position of being exposed and observed. I connect this with the patient's obvious voyeuristic (and implied exhibitionistic) interests; I refer particularly to his remarks mentioned in his case history about trying to look at women in cars with their skirts pulled up. The patient himself is aware that *he* is now being observed with his skirt pulled up, so to speak; he indicates this awareness, for example, in his question whether there are any ladies around before he feels free to speak of his wife having sexual relations with other men. Thus, his voyeuristic activity is now reversed to passivity and being exhibited himself. And just as he denied his father's smell in the past (at least partly out of love, I suspect), he now denies Dr. Deutsch's smell; in fact, he even credits Dr. Deutsch with a steady head at one point in the interview while he is trying to deny that four quarts of beer could impair his own game of whist in the least.

Altogether, in these respects, the patient gives the impression of beginning to form a passive-feminine transference to an idealized Dr. Deutsch. In this context the foul smell and the entire present situation are likely to signify forbidden intimacy and excitement involving dirty secrets and revelations. In part, it is a sensory assault devoutly to be desired, not one to complain about.

Returning to the resistance for a moment, I would now conjecture that it represents a pseudo-masculine defense, expressing stubborn opposition to the father figure, but without a show of hostile affect. The end result is an agreeable distancing of himself whereby he may have his unconscious homosexual relationship and deny it and intellectualize it at the same time. I believe these considerations point to part of the explanation of the shallow affective quality of this interview as described above.

I also ask myself whether this material suggests one or more leading affective potentials implicit in the symptom. The answer to this type of question may provide the therapist with a much needed point of emotional contact with the patient. Such points are not readily available in this interview. For purposes of the present discussion I single out one possibility, though I do not claim for it prepotent influence. I regard the affect, or mood, in question as a *potential*—preferring, with Freud, to reserve the term affect for felt experience and to speak of potential affect in those instances where defense and symptom formation have forestalled developments that would lead to feelings. The affect I refer to is nostalgia—the longing for the affects and objects of the past, the way things used to be and feel, and the unhappy feeling of having lost something precious in the present and future. In speaking specifically of nostalgia, I emphasize one affective component of what we otherwise frequently refer to generally as a regressive tendency. I submit that nostalgia and defensive efforts to ward it off are at work in this material.

What is the evidence for this conjecture?

(1) His symptom forces him to look back. (2) He associates looking back with seeing himself observed by an older man while at work. (3) He refers repeatedly to the wish to return to his first wife, who like his mother was clean and the mother of sons. (4) In his ambiguous comment that his mis-

take was to marry, he even indicates a longing for premarital times. (5) He mentions how, with changing industrial conditions, his job has gone to pieces so that he is without work now. (6) He makes two slips where he substitutes wife for mother; in addition, he is uncertain at one point, when Dr. Deutsch clearly asks about his wife, whether the question is about his wife or mother. (7) There is the recent resurgence of his adolescent masturbation ritual involving looking at women's legs in cars. (8) He refers to his buddy, with whom he can no longer be very intimate because on the one hand his buddy has seven or eight children and on the other the patient feels compelled to take his wife along when he visits the buddy. (9) Perhaps there is evidence even in his devoted attention to the past in this interview, whatever else may be determining that. In the longed-for past he was with his father, mother, and brothers, and was close to them, being otherwise relatively asocial; it was a time of hunting with father, sex play with brother, preferring to masturbate, and conspiring unconsciously with his father to deny the latter's vices while the mother was busy with the grocery store and service station. It was perhaps not much of a successful adaptation and family integration, but it was home.

In the last part of my remarks, I will turn to some problems of theory and method in the presentations of Dr. Deutsch and Dr. Mahl. Regarding Dr. Deutsch's assumptions in using his method of sensory stimulation, they seem to ignore the advances that have been made in psychoanalytic ego psychology. We now think of wishes, feelings, defense, etc., as being re-represented during development on progressively higher levels of organization. That smell will have its preverbal, basic significance may be accepted; that a present smell cuts right through to these significances and the primary defense against them is, however, questionable. Sensory experience, like values and self-concepts, takes on new or modified meanings in the course of psychosexual and psychosocial development, and patient clinical investigation is required to trace these meanings back, layer by layer, so far as possible. My reference is not just to ego development but to drive development and transformation as well.

Also Dr. Deutsch's method is not clean. I will mention only that, strictly speaking, the smell did not lead directly into the significant past; it was Dr. Deutsch who explicitly brought up and emphasized the past.

Of Dr. Mahl's speech analysis, I would say that his previous work as well as his present data, despite their precision in certain respects, have not convincingly shown that it is only or necessarily anxiety that produces speech disruption. They do show the association of speech disruption and subjectively uncomfortable affects, including (along with anxiety) guilt, disgust, horror, embarrassment, puzzlement, and other affects which one may infer from his published illustrations and Dr. Deutsch's data. Speaking generally, the correlation is with states of conflict, and it is regrettable that Dr. Mahl has dropped the reference to conflict in his formulations and refers now only to anxiety. In states of conflict we may think of contrary impulses competing for command of the approaches to motility and conceptualization, including thereby speech, with resulting difficulty in achieving smooth, synthesized expression. I propose the following as an alternative theoretical formulation to cover Dr. Mahl's findings: any depletion of the ego's freely available energies, as in states of fatigue or emotional excitement, or any great concentration of these energies in reinforced countercathectic distributions, as in the heightening of defense in a pressing conflict situation, will impair the automatization of certain ego functions, such as speech, and bring about the many halting, fumbling, unsteady, and indecisive behavioral phenomena with which we are familiar. From this standpoint, anxiety, even when present, is neither the central nor the most direct correlate or cause of speech disruption; it is merely one trigger among many to set off an automatization-disrupting redistribution of the ego's energies.

Also, as Dr. Mahl has recognized, anxiety need not express itself in speech disruption. There is, for example, the expressive realm of verbal content; this has been considered in detail, though not quantitatively, in some places in the literature on projective testing as well as on psychoanalysis. Consequently increases in speech disruptions do not necessarily mark the only or most significant anxiety reactions in the interview. Further, there is no certain or promising road from Dr. Mahl's present research design to studies of the gamut of more or less complex affects such as we typically encounter in clinical situations. Thus, in this report we have a precise examination of a limited sample of total interview behavior; moreover, this sample is to a significant degree inherently more ambiguous than is recognized. The regularities or patterns demonstrated by Dr. Mahl should be viewed in this light.

JOSEPH G. KEPECS, M.D.

There are many interesting questions raised by the film and the discussion. I propose to limit my comments to some observations in regard to the nature of the stimulus. I understand that Dr. Deutsch also used cold and darkness as stimuli; I think they, too, will fit in with what I have to say.

The first question I would raise is: what does "entering the mind through the sensory gateways" mean? The concept of sensory gateways, especially with a smell stimulus, or cold stimulus, as used here suggests an emphasis on the so-called "minor senses"—such as touch, kinesthesia, and smell—in other words, those whose receptors respond to mechanical or chemical stimulation. The use of cold is certainly an example of this. I do not know how one would classify darkness, whether as sensory stimulation or as sensory nonstimulation. I imagine it would be somewhat akin to isolation experiments and would tend to facilitate interoception. In many people the proximal receptors and proximal perception predominate over perception through distance receptors (sight and hearing). J. O. Wisdom (1953) and Jurgen Ruesch (1957) have emphasized proximal perception as predominant in patients with psychosomatic disorders. (This predominance is also to be noted in many other types of clinical disturbance.) A shift from proximal to distance receptors accompanies maturation. Stimulation of proximal receptors may thus be considered to evoke or be related to "regressive" phenomena, because they comprehend relationships at short distances, thus dealing perhaps with more primitive matters than do the distance receptors. Relationships at a distance permit a higher level of abstraction, and a more cognitive approach. So, in the present context, we could perhaps say that entering the mind through sensory gateways is a description of an attempt to arouse feelings by bypassing cognitive defenses through the stimulation of chemically or mechanically activated receptors.

Another question: was the smell of the (now perhaps historic) cat's dung the stimulus *per se,* or was it the idea of smell, so often reiterated by Dr. Deutsch. (Parenthetically, a possible explanation of Dr. Mahl's observation that the anxiety or tension level increases as recognition of the odor is approached, followed by a drop after recognition, might be that the patient thought his task in the interview was to recognize the odor, that he became tense under this requirement and relaxed when he had achieved it.) The perception of a bad smell reinforced the concept of smell; but was it the odor of the cat's dung or was it Deutsch's statement, "It's a little smelly here," which served as a stimulus? We know that the idea of a stimulus can be very powerful, as in the allergic person whose nose begins to run when he sees artificial flowers. It might be possible to test the role of the smell stimulus by interviewing when the patient, and perhaps the interviewer, too, is not told about the presence of a smell. To avoid the cognitive confrontation, we used smell, skin, and muscle stimulation in a group of psychosomatic patients (Kepecs, et al., 1958). That smell stimulus was a mixture of jasmine and skatol. After smelling it, subjects were requested to draw and then to associate to their drawings. Since they did not consciously connect what they drew with the stimulus, and since there was good evidence that what they drew and their associations to the drawings were influenced by the stimulus, the connection between stimulus and drawings was considered to be preconscious; in other words, a sort of olfactory Pötzl experiment. Our findings most relevant to the present discussion are: the conscious perception of the stimulus, for example, smell, aroused less affect than the preconsciously effected elaboration in drawings and associations. The emphasis on conscious awareness of the stimulus thus seems to damp down affect. This, I think, is a particular example of the defensive or screening-out nature of consciousness. This is illustrated by an asthmatic lady who described our jasmine skatol stimulus as smelling like mothballs or disinfectant presumably in reaction against dirt. She showed no marked feeling as she described the stimulus and then made a drawing. When she described and associated to this drawing, a few minutes later, it evoked weeping and sobbing verging on an asthmatic attack. I think if the dung could speak for itself, to mix a metaphor, rather than having its advocate in the interviewer, there would be more likelihood of bypassing the cognitive defensive sphere.

As Dr. Deutsch recognizes, there is no evidence that smell is of any particular significance to this man. Nor for that matter do we know how good a sense of smell he has. It is very possible that the smell stimulus tends to influence the modality of expression, not necessarily the predominant affective state. For example, if with this patient Dr. Deutsch had used a taste stimulus, the patient's wife might have been a disgusting rather than a smelly woman. If a skin stimulus had been used, she might have been an irritating woman, an itch.

Finally, our own observations suggest that there are some individuals in whom a particular sensory modality is intimately related with a particular kind of affective expression, for example, the smell-asthma complex. The affects to which these particular sensory modalities are linked, or of which they may be considered part, vary. Two factors have a part in determining the variation. One is the nature of the stimulus. For example, smells, especially bad ones, tend to stir up anality, destructiveness, reaction formations—in other words, the complex of the anal phase. Second, the emotional state of the individual at the time he is tested will have a good deal to do with how he responds to a stimulus. For example, a patient of ours who suffered from a severe dermatitis was tested with a skin stimulus to elicit drawings and associations. When this person was first tested, she was in a very regressed state and her drawings were all connected with food and eating. When she felt a little better and her skin was better, she responded to skin stimulation with heterosexual fantasies.

EDWARD A. KENNARD, PH.D.

I would like to discuss some of the specifically linguistic aspects of the speech of this particular patient, features of his speech pattern that were apparent to almost everyone who watched the film and listened to *how* he spoke as well as what he said. Dr. Mahl paid special attention to the lexical items (words), the number of words in each utterance and the number of hesitations and other interruptions in his flow of talk, and sought to correlate these with other aspects of the verbal content bearing upon the patient's anxieties. Let us suppose that we did not have all the detailed data on his social and clinical history, that we knew nothing of the social and economic background of the family in which he was reared. What help would we get from listening to the phonetic characteristics of his speech? How much could we learn merely from listening to the patient talk?

We might not have known that he was from the state of Maine, but we would have known beyond any doubt that he was from the northeast coast dialect area of New England. We would also have known that he came from a stratum of society that spoke substandard English. Several specifically quoted remarks of his indicate that. If we accept this information in the light of the survey done on the New Haven population by Hollingshead and Redlich (1958), which showed how psychiatric difficulties were distributed through the population, stratified on the basis of a number of sociologically relevant criteria, we would not be surprised that the patient's emotional problems were somatized. Their data showed that organic manifestation of symptoms was most frequent in the lowest social class. Thus, linguistic inferences confirm data which were gathered clinically.

In addition, we find through Dr. Mahl's analysis inferences concerning the patient's emotional conflicts, as reflected by the number of pauses or hesitations in relation to the total number of words in the utterance. From a linguistic point of view a word is a unit of print (or typescript, in this case) and cannot be satisfactorily defined as a unit of speech. Therefore, the linguist deals with the utterance or sentence, and analyzes it into a hierarchy of component elements both in terms of sounds and in terms of grammatical structure. In each utterance there are different kinds of pauses, technically called "junctures," that perform essential functions in signaling to the listener. For example, it is by means of juncture that we distinguish between "nitrate" and "night-rate." Therefore, I would suggest that there are probably better units than words to use in measuring frequency of hesitations in the flow of speech.

Those of us who have never had the traumatic experience of hearing our own speech played back to us on a tape recorder probably imagine that each of our utterances flows out naturally without a pause or a break, unless we insert one for rhetorical reasons. Actually, this is rarely the case, and it is only skillful transcribing by our secretaries that makes us *look* good, no matter how we *sound*. Therefore, it would be helpful if we had samples of the patient's speech obtained when he was not emotionally disturbed to use as a standard for him, to compare with the recorded interview. These are merely suggestions of the ways in which the clinician can utilize techniques developed by modern linguistics to assist him. The essential features of American English speech patterns have been outlined by Pittenger and Smith (1957) and an analysis of one patient's speech has been made by McQuown (1957).

I should now like to turn to a more general problem related to human speech. It is certainly the most distinctively human attribute of man, and the capacity for speech and the use of symbols was most significant in the evolution of the human brain. This is related to what we learned earlier in this Symposium about the evolution of the mammalian and the primate brain, and to what Dr. Spitz said about the role of learning in the human individual's experience. This capacity was essential both for the growth and development of culture, and for the development of personality.

Yet, during the six years that I worked in psychiatric hospitals, I was struck by how little attention was paid to the manifest content of patients' utterances. There was a tendency to be exclusively concerned with meaning at a personal idiosyncratic or symptomatic level. I believe that in many cases, the manifest content may be very important. Frequently, people can and do communicate a great deal about themselves on a fully conscious level which is of significance, but may be ignored.

As an anthropologist and a linguist, it seems to me that the acquisition of his native language by the child; the time in his development at which it is learned; the ability it gives him to share in the objects, relations, and meanings which are part of his heritage—all are essential to the growth of personality. It is the means by which he becomes an object to himself, and becomes a person both to himself and to others. The individual's consciously learned and developed speech is one of the most important expressions of himself, and one to which, so far, we have paid too little attention.

CHAPTER 7

The Kinesic Level in the Investigation of the Emotions

RAY L. BIRDWHISTELL, PH.D.

An unscheduled tribute. I want to preface my remarks by a tribute to a great and sensitive clinician, Dr. Deutsch. In so doing, I may also indicate how a piece of behavior will tend to carry on and find and identify a large stretch of behavior far beyond the particular piece.

In the film of Dr. Deutsch and his patient, there is a very important little bit at the beginning which escaped the attention of almost every viewer at first viewing. It occurs in only the first seconds.

Dr. Deutsch is a familiar figure with his very fragile body, the characteristic thrust of his head, his mobile features, and his uniquely expressive hands. It is very easy for the clinician to look at the patient. On the other hand, it is often very difficult to look at the therapist. I would like to speak very briefly about the therapist and what the therapist does in the very beginning of the scene, these actions cross-referencing what happens later in this film.

At the start of the discussion the therapist asks the patient whether he notices the smell and at the same time holds his fingers and carefully cleans them off. Apparently, the patient does not respond to this. Next Dr. Deutsch cleans his hands, wiping them on his white coat. The patient does not seem to get these signals completely. Finally, Dr. Deutsch is more explicit. He puts his hands together and slowly, gradually brings them down in front of the genitalia. Thus he gives the patient a series of alternative statements about what the odor is about. I think this is tremendously important. It occurs so rapidly that it takes the average audience one or two viewings, even on the slow-motion analyzer, before they really "see" it. As the audience at this Symposium can testify, once it has really been "seen," it is unmistakable.

The human being picks these things up very quickly out of awareness. They are a way of making a statement of introduction. In any encounter between two human beings there are a large number of these phenomena which we call markers. They are separate from what we call gestures. For instance, in the discussion of Dr. MacLean's paper you will remember that there was a suggestion that a motion of the arm with outstretched palm is a universal gesture meaning peace. It means "peace" only if the remainder of the context goes with it. This is a bound morph, a stem form in body motion, in English and, I think, also for the French and German. If to this you add the infixes, the prefixes, and the transfixes from the remainder of the body, it can be correctly received. We have thus far been unable to locate any universal gestures.

But enough of unscheduled preface. I hope it will strike a theme and allow me to progress to a prologue.

Prologue

It has been said that a great *guru* was approached by one of his students who requested that the master tell him how to discover the nature of human feelings. The *guru* replied that the student must first demonstrate his readiness for such a task. He gave the student a butterfly net and instructed him to catch an elephant. The student was dismayed, but feeling great respect for his teacher he took the butterfly net and went away to meditate on the size of elephants and of butterfly nets. After months of thought he took the net and went into a jungle frequented by elephants. With the net he carefully scooped up a patty of elephant dung and took it home to analyze and to reflect upon. After months the student returned to the *guru* to tell him all that he had learned of the elephant. The *guru* was secretly pleased by the perspicacity of his student but decided to test him further. "You have made good use of the net, but," he asked, "what did you discover about the essential nature of the elephant?" Without hesitation the student replied, "I discovered that the essence of the elephant is not in his dung." "Good," said the *guru*, "you have passed the test. Take your net and begin to discover the nature of human emotions. But do not be surprised if you see a fellow student with a knife working on the same problem. He too has learned not to seek essences in part of the elephant."

Introduction

As a student of human behavior particularly interested in the structure of communication it seems essential that I take this parable to heart. Kinesics is the systematic study of those patterned and learned aspects of body motion which can be demonstrated to have communicational value. As such it is only indirectly concerned with the physical or chemical states within a physiological system. When emotional and affective states are defined as direct idiosyncratic responses to particular electrochemical balances *within* the physiological system, they are of little direct concern to the kinesicist. I have neither the butterfly net nor the knife to gather data of consequence for the understanding of states which do not have *patterned* behavioral transforms at the interactional level. However, if it is possible to demonstrate or reasonably hypothecate social and, thus, communicational transforms for such states, the methodology of kinesics becomes relevant to the problem.

As an anthropologist I am devoted to the proposition that

generalizations about the behavior of man must take full cognizance of his biological substructure. When I first became interested in studying body motion I was confident that it would be possible to isolate a series of expressions, postures, and movements that were denotative of primary emotional states. In fact, in 1945 when I first began to think about these problems I anticipated a research strategy which could first isolate universal signs of feeling that were species specific. It seemed to me that once these were isolated it would be possible to delineate the body behavior characteristic of particular societies and, finally, to use the analysis of body behavior as a device for establishing particular personality patterns.

As research proceeded, and even before the development of kinesics, it became clear that this search for universals was culture-bound. Even the most preliminary survey made it clear that the list of ten or twelve emotional states that seemed so "natural" to me were culturally defined categories. However rigorously defined, these categories did not provide us with psychological or physiological base states characteristic of the species. All societies do not abstract their emotional lives into the same subdivisions of feeling. It appears likely that the rich variability of the patterning of human cognition is paralleled by comparable variability in affective organization.

The recognition that there are probably no universal symbols of emotional state or tone should not lead us to an atomistic position. That is, the alternative to species universals is not simple individual difference. To maintain some degree of predictability and order in social life, men within a given society must not only have comparable emotional experiences but must be able to share information about these experiences with their fellows. If such experiences and their expression are not exclusively biological, we can expect them to be learned and patterned according to the particular structures of particular societies. It is at this point that communication theory and research seems most promising. It is our hope that in the years to come we will be able to isolate and describe these learning and developmental processes. Such information should open new vistas for the student concerned with the relationships between character and culture.

Kinesics is not a methodology for the study of the expression of individual personality syndromes. Its findings may implement such studies, but the measurement of individual personalities is not its central aim. This is not to abjure the responsibility of kinesics to contribute to the study of personality. Through research on the nature of communication it should become possible to derive objective profiles of behavioral expectancy. The projection of individual behavioral systems against such profiles should reveal the special structures of idiosyncratic behavior. This research strategy seems particularly well suited to provide safeguards for the delineation of such loosely defined behavior as that called "emotional." This is all the more necessary when we are concerned with the definition of pathological behavior and its amelioration.

Much of our present knowledge about the emotions is based upon research with the abnormal. It is impossible to deny the tremendous progress of the last century in recognizing the intimate relationship between man's emotions and the rest of his behavior. However, the nature of research centrally concerned with the abnormal personality has left us with but the crudest instruments for investigating the etiology of even the most manifest aberration.

We get very special answers to our questions about the emotions when we investigate a sample selected for the aberrancy of its membership. Such a sample is skewed toward the communicationally successful. It contains only the behavior of those who have been successful in communicating their distress to those whose task it is to deal with this order and degree of communicative success. We are, thus, always studying communication about pathology as well as the pathology itself. In fact, the present interest in schizophrenia leads to the study of therapist-patient communication about pathological communication of emotional states. It may very well be that further knowledge about these complex processes will reach resolution in a simpler focal point of scientific and clinical concern about communication and its pathologies.

The discussion to follow is predicated upon the assumption that the communication of feelings is patterned, social behavior whether pathological or normal. Such behavior is learned and ultimately analyzable, much of it by methodologies recently developed in linguistics and kinesics. It is my hope that these operations will provide configurations against which to project individual performance for the discovery of that behavior which is private and idiosyncratic.

Communication

Before I turn to the relationship between kinesics and research into affects, some statements must be made about the process of communication itself. I wish that there were another word for the particular aspect of the interactional system with which we are concerned. Several neologisms have been suggested as substitutes for "communication," but most of these have been either too barbaric or too awkward for serious consideration. Other words in our vocabulary seem even less appropriate while equally infected from past usage. Perhaps by clearing some of the underbrush from "communication" we can retain it.

Communication is not a process made up of a total of individual expressions in some action-reaction sequence. It is a system of interaction with a structure independent of the behavior of its individual participants. One person does not "communicate to" another person; he engages in communication with him. A human being does not invent his system of communication. He may make additions to it, and he may vary the direction of its formulations. However, as a system, it has been in existence for generations. He must learn it in order to be a member of his society.

Communication is multifunctional: it not only composes

the primary relations of interaction but maintains the rules for the regulation of these relationships. There are some who would go so far as to make communication coterminous with culture. I would not. But I would say that communication provides the means of sustaining the patterned interpersonal relationships without which culture would be impossible.

Communication is made up of the interdependent activities of a series of abstractable subsystems emergent from the patterning of the several sensory modalities. Kinesics is not the study of communication any more than is linguistics. Both are sciences which investigate subsystems of communication. This point deserves further amplification here. There is nothing particularly novel about the idea that the noises men make, their facial expressions or their body movements have something to do with the way in which men or animals signal their preparedness to play, to fight, to make love, or otherwise to coordinate their activities. However, because of particular cultural traditions scholars, or at least those coming from Occidental societies, have tended to assume that one could distinguish the cognitive from the affective by separation of the modalities. For many, words and sentences (at least when "properly" used) carry the cognitive messages. How such words or sentences are said and what the body and face do during their saying have been seen to convey the affective definition of these messages. There is probably sufficient truth in these generalizations to make the attack upon them a complicated task. Yet it cannot be avoided if we are to meet the challenge of this Symposium.

In a society which stresses literacy as does ours, it is easy to assume that words accomplish the cognitive functions of interaction. We are all too inclined to believe that verbalization provides the kernel of interactive behavior and that body movement simply frames or provides modifiers for such behavior. Part of this belief rests upon the assumption that certain kinds of behavior are closer to the emotions because these behaviors can be found earlier in the history of the species, earlier in the life of the individual, or simply because such behavior is less in awareness. This is an unfortunate assumption because it carries with it the companion assumption that these nonlexical behaviors are somehow closer to "nature," more instinctive and less susceptible to transformation and systematization in communicational practice. Conceptions such as these have tended to be maintained by the clumsy and misleading phrase "nonverbal communication," a phrase which, from the point of view represented here, has about the same amount of meaning as "nonvisceral physiology."

We do not yet know exactly how the linguistic and kinesic systems fit together. All of the evidence indicates that they are inextricably related in the communication process and have priority of function only in limited contexts. Both systems or their derivatives are necessary to the communication process; and they are only heuristically separable. Furthermore, until we can systematically study the tactile and olfactory modalities, already demonstrable as contributory to communication, we can do little more than predict the composition of the communicational stream. It should be noted that the terms "tactile" and "olfactory" stress the activity of sensory *reception*. We know a little about the activity of producing variant palpability or emitting odor, we lack terms for the interactive systems involving these processes. However, even the present limited evidence indicates the importance of these other modalities in human interaction. Our experience with kinesics should warn us against the overeasy assumption that these carry only expressive signals. It seems likely, too, that there are still other modalities, not yet isolated, which contribute to the communicational system. We should guard against any theoretically reactionary system which prematurely limits our investigations by dichotomizing ideation and emotion, until such systems are isolated and until we have some notion as to their structure and have organized interactional research on the co-functioning of these subsystems. At present only prejudice suggests that these are discrete systems emerging from discrete areas of the physiological system and remaining discrete in the communication system.

The fact that there is still much that we do not know about the structure of communication and its subsystems should not be discouraging. A quarter of a century ago Edward Sapir (1951) and G. H. Mead (1934, 1938), with differing emphases, focused attention on our ignorance of these processes. The progress made by behavioral science in the location, if not the solution, of these problems during these past twenty-five years is exciting. Descriptive linguistics has undergone considerable development, particularly in the investigation of American English (Bloch and Trager, 1942; Trager and Smith, 1957; Pike, 1946; Wells, 1945). This makes possible the objective examination of problems which were earlier hardly more than matters for conjecture. Kinesics has developed to the point that systematic structure of visual-motor communication is recognizable.

Developments in paralinguistics and parakinesics are giving us control over a body of behavioral data which are probably of special importance here. Since they have been extensively described elsewhere (Bateson, et al., 1962; Trager, 1958; Joos, 1950) and are discussed in other papers contributed to this Symposium, perhaps a summary statement will suffice here. As linguists described language more exhaustively, there appeared a considerable range of patterned audible behavior which was integral to speech even though its internal relations and units did not seem to be patterned in the *same* way as were phonemes, morphemes, and syntactic sentences. Paralanguage must be understood if we are to comprehend the role of speech in the communicational process. As I worked with kinesics, parallel phenomena emerged in the body-motion material. When kines, kinemorphs, and complex kinemorphic constructions (comparable to phonemes, morphemes, and syntactic sentences) were isolated, other behavior extending over varying lengths of kinesic material was revealed. Analogic to the linguistic material, parakinesics, although differing in structure from the microkinesic particles, was patterned and communicational. Parakinesics is not to be understood as unstructured residue remaining after the abstraction of the recognizable kinesic particles. In certain contexts such behavior could be analyzed as modifying particular sequences of kinesic and vocalic behavior. In others, it could be seen indicative of the relationship between the particular actor and the interaction or as relating the interaction to the larger contexts in which it appeared.

Kinesic Design

Although we are not concerned here with the particulars of kinesics, it may be profitable to pause to review the design, as Martin Joos (1950) uses the term, of body-motion communication. From the point of view of the physicist the phenomena with which the kinesicist deals are constituted of reflected patterns of light which remain continuous as long as we have a light source and reflecting surfaces. As a kinesicist I have no direct concern with questions relating to the physical nature of this light, whether it is to be described according to a wave or a quantum model. The technology of kinesic analysis requires that I have some idea about the strength of variant light sources, lenses, the excitability of films and the like. I have to attend to the technical difficulties involved in representing the reflecting qualities, the different textures and colors of skin and clothes. And I must guard against utilizing projection devices which mask significant materials. In the description of my analytic techniques, these technical details relating to light must be as explicitly stated as any other laboratory operation utilized in scientific procedure. However, I must not be led into the technophilic delusion that my units in kinesics are made up out of light.

Comparably, if we shift our sights, the kinesicist must not act as though his data were constituted of muscular, epidermal, and skeletal bits. He does not ignore physiological data but recognizes that such data are prekinesic. The behavioral scientist who intends to do kinesic research must be sufficiently conversant with physiology not to allow himself to be misled by malfunctioning systems. Before working with any pair or group of informants or subjects he must discover by inspection whether any observable behavioral deviation is significant to the problem which he is investigating. We must carefully observe his informant in a number of contexts to ascertain the extent to which hyperfunctioning or hypofunctioning influence the interactional relationships of his subject. Much later in the research, after he has had an opportunity to abstract kinesic structure, he will have further opportunity to recheck the reliability of his screening operation. Furthermore, he must take care to observe the relative visual acuity of his subjects. A myopic informant or one with tunnel vision will obviously behave in ways which will distort the data. However, access to physiologically normal subjects is a primary condition of investigation. Once the conditions are stipulated, kinesic analysis is unconcerned with segments of epidermis, of muscular tissue, of skeletal or joint arrangement, or with the anatomy of the visual apparatus. Although for convenience in recording I have chosen to utilize symbols referring to body parts, the kines (H) or (n) are arbitrary and do not signify anatomic units any more than the phoneme /p/ signifies a pair of closed lips or, incidentally, a particular shape of a sound wave.

Kinesics is, thus, but laterally concerned with the physics, physiology, or anatomy involved in the production of the continuous stream of data detectable by appropriate instrumentation. It is concerned with orders of discontinuous particles which emerge from the analysis of these streams when observed in the social context. Its subject matter is constituted by the derivation of ranges of customary behavior with demonstrable functions in the communication process. This must be understood if we are to proceed with our discussion. Furthermore, kinesics is no more concerned with specific body movements than it is with specific body parts.

It is concerned with the derivation of ranges of movement with equivalent function. On the articulatory level no two body shifts are ever identical, but kinesic analysis reveals that it is possible to derive variants of behavior which can be used interchangeably. Usually such variants are located within a given region of the body.

It can be demonstrated that the head-nod kine //Hn// is a kinesic unit covering a class of down and up movements of the head. This class is made up of a series of movements which are called *kine variants.* In a population of American movers in comparable contexts, it is possible to show by contrast analysis that the kine //Hn// covers a range of kinic variants $(Hn)^{1,2,3\ \text{etc.}}$ These kinic variants differ from each other along two axes, breadth and velocity. Our present measurements indicate that informants respond to any down and up movement of the head (in the median sagittal plane) utilizing any portion of an arc extending from approximately 5° to about 15° as "meaning" the same thing. That is, the structural meaning of (Hn)5° ≡ (Hn)8° ≡ (Hn)13° ≡ (Hn)15°. Comparably, clocking has revealed that a similar population of movers will make a full 15° nod in moments which can extend from about .5 seconds to around 1.5 seconds. While we have not exhaustively clocked the intermediate arc utilizations, the evidence indicates that velocity not duration is significant here. That is, we have kinic variants (Hn) with a velocity range of from about .8° per frame (or $^1/_{24}$ of a second) to around 3° per frame. When kine variants of this velocity range have been checked out in their structural contexts, they may be recorded as the kine //Hn//. As such //Hn// stands in contrast with head movements with higher and lower velocity and incidentally with movements of greater and lesser breadth. The role of //Hn// as combined in kinemorphs and kinemorphic constructions of varying size can now be investigated. The fact that we have abstracted //Hn// from our kinic variants and do not need to attend at this level of analysis to the particular breadth or velocity of these variants does not mean that we ignore such variations in behavior. The fact that such variation is *kinesically* insignificant does not mean that these variations are *communicationally* insignificant. We carefully store our descriptions of such data as reminders for parakinesic analysis. Investigation of the American movement system has revealed that it is possible to isolate a series of ranges of variation which "modify" the kinesic structures and which have an analytic identity separate from these structures. These variations I have termed the *motion qualifiers.* This category includes:

Intensity, which delineates the degree of muscular tension involved in the production of a kine or kinemorph. It has been possible to subdivide intensity into five relative degrees of tension: overtense, tense, N, lax, and overlax. It is obvious that intensity variation in //Hn// is a function of the activities of the neck muscles. (For American movers it is possible to record a //Hn/ /as having degrees of tension without referring to the neck where we are recording //Hn// as a single kine kinemorph. If, however, a full kinemorph, including eyebrows, eyes, etc., is structured, the degrees of intensity must be recorded as occurring in the neck.)

Range: width or extent of movement involved in performance of a given kine or kinemorph. Range is subdividable into narrow, limited, N, widened, and broad.

Velocity: the temporal length (relative to the range) involved in the production of a kine or kinemorph. Thus far we have been able to isolate only a three-degree scale for duration, staccato, N, and allegro.

Although it is possible to get absolute range and velocity measurements, such measurements give us little more than central tendencies. The ascription of "overtense," "staccato," or "broad" to a piece of behavior is assigned only after the base line of the interactors has been established and the general qualifier behavior of the actor has been noted. Thus, while informants tend to react to head nods of .8 to 1 degree movement per frame as allegro and to 2 and 3 degree movements per frame as staccato and to 1 to 2 degree movements per frame as normal, these velocities shift in value depending upon whether the over-all movement pattern of the interactor is slow or fast. Comparably, an arc of from 5 to 8 or 9 degrees is reported as limited and from 12 to 15 degrees is regarded as widened. The viewer in terms of his own diakinesic system makes his judgment of these depending upon the normal range of movement in the actor.

It should be clear from the foregoing that the communicational units are not absolute bits of articulations but are always parts of larger cross-referencing contexts. The system of which they are a part is sufficiently ordered that its patterning can be internalized by all members of the social system who must interact through it. At the same time the values of its particles and forms must be sufficiently flexible to permit adaptation on the part of the viewer to both individual and situational variation.

I have elsewhere (1959a, 1959b) discussed at length the fact that communication as a system must not be seen as a device primarily designed for the transmission of new information. It must be sufficiently *productive,* to use Hockett's term (1960), to deal with novelty, but we have every indication that its central function is that of giving continuity and predictability to the social system. As we worked with the films used in the research for *The Natural History of an Interview* (Bateson, et al., 1962), it became clear that the communicational activity of vocalic and body-motion behavior was not exhausted by the linguistic and paralinguistic, the kinesic and parakinesic behavior. We attempted to deal with this material under broad categories which were sufficiently flexible to guide, not limit, further research.

The communication system must be learned and shared by all members of a given society. However, a society is not made up of equivalent units. Within its membership it has the young, the maturing, and the old, males, females, and the nonreproductive, the very ill, the handicapped, and so on. Nor does it exist in a closed and absolutely repetitive surround and the society itself is changing. The communication system must be sufficiently flexible and productive to permit its particles to have differential meaning depending upon the state of the actor, the interactors, and the special context of interaction. Rigidity or disorder would occur if some devices were not built into the system identifying these special circumstances to the communicants.

Activity occurs throughout every sequence of interaction which operates to relate the communicants to each other and to the contexts in which the interaction occurs. Since such behavior cross-references other communicational activity and is made up from all of the sensory modalities, I have called them the *expectancy identifiers*. These are of special interest to the investigator of affects since, if their performance is distorted or misunderstood, all behavior modified by them becomes somehow ambiguous and inappropriate.

We have thus far isolated eleven subdivisions of these expectancy identifiers which have behavioral constituents from the vocalic and body-motion areas. Exigencies of space preclude the adequate discussion of these categories, but a listing of them will give some idea of the directions of research anticipated in these areas.

We have subdivided the body-motion aspects of this category into two paired groups which are termed the *body base* and the *body set*. *Body base* is a cover term for those cultural expectancies which the individual member of the society must internalize if he is to be able to recognize the particular *body sets* which occur in particular situations; that is, body base is that diagram about the behavior of other human beings which the individual must internalize to be a predictable and predicting member of a particular society. Body set thus represents the special behaviors which are measured against the body base zero.

Body Base	*Body Set*
Position	Status
Sex	Gender
Age	Age Grade

Status of Health	Health Image
Body Build	Body Image
Rhythm Phase	Rhythm Image
Territoriality	Territorial Status
Mood	Mode
Toxic State	Toxic Image
N-State	N-Status

Columnar listing of these categories of behavior is deceptive. Such a presentation device suggests that each of the bases or sets is distinct from each of the others within that column. Thus far we have no evidence to suggest that these are more than heuristically separable. That is, there are probably no occasions on which it is possible to transmit only a single one of these eleven categories. For instance, at the moment of delivering remarks like these I am cross-referencing my presentation here with at least ten of the eleven categories. However, let us be clear. In the presentation of this material, unless my reception is quite pathological, it should not be said that I am *expressing* these behaviors. I am in a social situation. The analysis of the body-set activity experienced by me and my audience must recognize the interactive quality of this behavior. In the presentation of such a paper we both have sufficient time to change our relationship from mere encounter to full interaction. The body set which we would describe in an analysis of this behavior emerges as a joint communicational endeavor.

As this discussion is part of a symposium on affects, I must attempt in my summary to relate the foregoing to affects research. What I have been attempting to say is that the communication of affect is an integral part of all interaction. It is thus calibrated into the communication system and cannot be understood apart from it. If emotional disturbance occurs within an individual, it is highly likely that some statement *about* this disturbance will be entered into the communicational stream. Whether this disturbance is reacted to appropriately, is damped out of recognition by one of the interactors, or is hypertrophied to the point of system destruction will depend upon the sensitivity, the knowledge, and the skill of the communicants.

Kinesics and linguistics research methodologies are only useful as tools in affects research if they are used appropriately. Without the safeguards of systematic data exhaustion provided by microanalysis the categories do not assist in objectifying observation. We know too little about how humans or even those particular humans, Americans, communicate to utilize kinesics as a shortcut. However, if the progress of the past ten years is prognostic, we can anticipate that within twenty years we may know enough about the communication system and how it is learned to make a contribution to the analysis of human affective systems. At present, questions concerning the expression of the emotions seem to me to be inextricable from other questions about the nature of the communication system. Perhaps in the future we may find them separable. In either case we may then be able to develop a definition of "emotion" or "affects" which is not lost in an interlevel never-never land.

CHAPTER 8

Kinesic Research and Therapeutic Processes: Further Discussion

ALLEN T. DITTMANN, PH.D.

I wish to continue the discussion by reporting two investigations of expressive movement in psychotherapeutic interviews, one study carried out in a semirational fashion, and the other in a more purely empirical way. The results are neither all-encouraging nor all-discouraging, and give pause for thought about where to go next.

First let me tell you why our project[1] is interested in studying expressive movement. We want to be able to "read," through some channel of communication other than words, how a subject feels at a given time. This information should be separate and independent from the words for two reasons: the first is that we are convinced that nonverbal messages are often different from verbal ones, and that congruences and discrepancies between the two can give clues about

[1] The Psychotherapy Research Project (carried out at the National Institutes of Health) includes as investigators Drs. Robert A. and Mabel Blake Cohen, David Shakow, and Morris B. Parloff. For a general discussion of its aims and possibilities, see Shakow (1960).

what is happening in interviews. Our second reason for wanting to have nonverbal information is that we are convinced that it can give clues faster than words can, that people often react sooner than they are willing or able to say. Thus timing of reactions is just as important to my research as form. Many of our investigations, then, will be of moment-to-moment events in interviews, so that we can relate these events in turn to other things such as stage of psychotherapy, interplay between the participants, subject matter under discussion, and so on. And we look to the interrelationship among different ways of communicating for a more complete picture of the process.

The first study I have already referred to as semirational—"semi-" because the underlying theory does not lead to deducing hypotheses in a very rigorous way. The general notion was this: some modes of expression are controlled very easily, that is, can be made to express what one consciously wants to express. The best example of this is content: one can choose words carefully so as to get across a simple, unambiguous message. True, over a period of time such control is not complete; witness the various preoccupations people have, and the parapraxes they produce. But at a given moment, content is subject to what I call intentional control. There are probably other modes of expression which cannot be controlled so easily, and through these channels messages other than what one "intends" are transmitted. Some of these the observer has been trained not to "notice," but others just happen so fast that he cannot possibly have time to formulate them. You will recognize this thinking as coming from many sources.

This first study took two of the less easily controlled modes of expression, disturbances in speech, as defined by George Mahl, and movements of the feet of a patient in psychotherapy.[2] The possible relationships between the two

[2] The actual coding of speech disturbances was carried out by Dr. Donald S. Boomer and Mrs. Janet C. Barclay, to whom I wish to express appreciation for this painstaking work.

might be many: they could appear simultaneously; they could substitute for one another; they could each be related to some third variable and not to each other; or they could fluctuate among these sorts of relationships. We hypothesized that they would occur at the same times.

Since in this patient foot movements occurred infrequently, it was possible to sample by interview, taking *all* of the movements from each interview selected. Experimental excerpts of speech surrounding foot movements were selected as well as control excerpts in which no movements occurred. Experimental and control excerpts were matched for length and location in the interviews. The first sample showed the predicted relationship: there were significantly more speech disturbances among the excerpts surrounding the foot movements than among the controls. On replication with two subsequent samples, however, no relationship was found; and for the total of the three samples, speech disturbance counts for the experimental and control excerpts were about equal. In all there were 215 foot movement excerpts and the same number of controls, drawn from 18 interviews from the 5th to the 100th in the same patient.

Negative results may be explained in many ways. The first thing one usually looks to is the measurement methods which were used. Identification of foot movements is not very vulnerable because it was done by looking at motion picture films of the interviews, and these can be gone over repeatedly in case of doubt. Measurement of speech disturbances is also easy, at least for some of the categories, and no single category or combination of categories differentiated in this study.

So if the measurement methods were solid, the theory must not have been. Let me list a few of its shortcomings: first, the notion that foot movements and speech disturbances are modes of communication is not a "salted-away fact." They may be under some circumstances, but in designing the study, I was assuming that they *always* were. Boomer and Goodrich (1961) of our Institute have tried to replicate Mahl's original study relating speech disturbances to episodes of anxiety in interviews, and have not come up with results as clear-cut as the original research. To be more specific, in some four years of work with speech disturbances, they have found a number of isolated instances of relationships, each intriguing at first, but none of these held up when more material was studied for comparison. In other studies of paralinguistic phenomena (Dittmann and Wynne, 1961), we were not able to differentiate contrasting affects in one patient, or indeed to differentiate one person from another. As for foot movements, the expressive nature of these has been shown only in isolated, specific situations.

Another theoretical shortcoming of the present study is the hypothesis that the two measures should be related. I have already mentioned some alternative hypotheses. It may well be that the two are not related simply, but only in some complex way which single-variable studies can never sort out.

We turned, then, to look at some more movement data from an empirical approach. Using the method of criterion groups we selected material in which we should expect to find contrasts in movement patterns, namely, samples of different moods in a single patient. There were several moods which recurred frequently in the interviews, and which the patient referred to consistently by the same names. We made up two separate samples of excerpts representing these moods, each sample having four excerpts of each of five moods. Selection was based on the double criterion of content and "tone of voice." In looking at the films we hoped at first to study the form or style of movements, but this turned out to be impossible to quantify, and we ended up making gross movement frequency counts of the only body areas which moved very much for this patient—head, hands, and legs. The two independent samples were not different from each other, but the frequencies of movements were different for the different moods; furthermore, they varied differently for the three body areas. So *for this patient,* information about mood accounted for a significant amount of the information in the frequency of body movements. But one thing sobered us: while the information accounted for was "statistically significant," the best combination of body area and mood made up only about a quarter of the total movement information, and this with moods which were selected to be pure examples so that differences should be thrown into relief! A further sobering fact: in looking at other subjects in experimental interviews, we find that patterns of movement in the three body areas vary tremendously from one person to another; and for some people one or another area does not lend itself to frequency counts at all, since movement is almost continuous, while for others one area may remain motionless under all experimental conditions.

Why should these results be sobering? If from a few variables one can find significant relationships with events as elusive as moods, perhaps we should be encouraged. For one thing, the interview setup is restricting to begin with, especially one in which the patient lies down on a couch. Many body movements which serve as excellent cues elsewhere are missing in an interview. Style and variation of gait, for example, can be observed only briefly at the beginning and end. Posture variations, too, are limited for a person sitting in a comfortable chair, and almost entirely eliminated if he lies down. So it may be that because of the physical structure of the interview, we are bound to get a smaller proportion of the total information out of body movements than out of content.

I can see two lines of further work based on what we have achieved so far. The first is to go into more detail, include additional movement or other noncontent variables into the matrix to increase the amount of information we can account for. Such an approach has merit only if each new variable is checked out systematically with good criteria before it is entered into the matrix. We must know the reliability of measurement in each case, the degree of relationship with all other variables, and then decide whether the addition of the variable is worth the work of getting it. The work itself requires enormous expenditure of time and energy of personnel to get even preliminary results. As I see it, we must look for the most efficient variables, seek the most economical ways of measuring them, then go for help to electronic computing techniques for handling the data. Otherwise we will never analyze enough interviews to generalize our results beyond merely a particular patient-therapist pair or even a particular interview.

The other line of future work is the more basic one, that of developing a conceptualization of expressive movement so that we may choose our variables on a more sensible basis. I believe first we need to think in some detail about what we mean by expressive movement. What do body movements express? I have already alluded to this problem in discussing the first study. In the second study we were assuming that to some extent they express something of what happens inside a person, call it mood, emotion, degree of tension. Body movements may also be viewed as instrumental acts of communication in the same sense that words are, but transmitted via a different channel. Seen in this way, body movements could tell us only indirectly about emotional states or moods. But these are not the only possibilities: body movements may also be idiosyncratic expressions of specific conflict (Krout, 1935). Or, in more general terms, they may be responses to internal and external stimuli in all their combinations. A person may uncross his legs because his foot is beginning to tingle. Or his foot might not actually be tingling yet, but he moves it now because the other person in the room has just said something surprising or stimulating in some other way.

A related problem for our conceptual task is what sort of information we can get from the study of movements. Most of what is in the literature from the early days, for example, Allport and Vernon (1933), deals with characterology, long-standing predispositions which show up in gait, stance, and the like, and early ingrained indicators of sex role or of other status classifications. These relatively unvarying characteristics, descriptions of the sort of person the subject is in general, comprise one sort of information one can derive from the study of movement, and is closely allied to what one hopes to get out of a diagnostic interview or set of projective tests.

Another sort of information is the more transient overlay to character, mood swings, for example, and reactions to specific situations. This is what I was searching for in both the experiments I reported earlier. It is more difficult to get at, because it relies on finer cues, or smaller variations of the more outstanding characteristics. But in psychotherapy process research—our project's original goal in this field—it is precisely what is needed.

I should like to point out one more difficulty in the study of expressive movement, one which occurs in any field being newly explored. We derive our hunches of what to concentrate on from our experience in living with people, and from watching interviews and making other observations. In these situations, we make global judgments of what the people are feeling and of what they are doing to each other. Then we ask ourselves, "What are the cues that led to these judgments?" Since we are inventive, we can usually point to things that have been happening as the bases for our conclusions, along with plausible reasons for following them up. But in a field such as emotional expression, where conscious and unconscious factors intermingle so freely, the actions we point to as "cues" may consist merely of those we have been able or willing to put words to, and we may not in our follow-up studies be concentrating on the right cues at all.

An example from another field may help clarify this point. A famous teacher of the Rorschach technique was once asked to make judgments of intelligence level from the Rorschach protocols of a group of subjects to whom standardized intelligence tests had been given. His judgments correlated with the test I.Q.s almost as highly as the reliability of the test itself. When he was asked to state the Rorschach factors on which he had based his judgments, he gave a list consisting of movement responses, whole responses, and the like. But none of these, either individually or in any pattern, could match his global judgment in predicting the I.Q.s. The question was: did he base his original judgments on the cues he had listed, or was he also influenced by other cues which are really extraneous to the Rorschach technique, such as verbal facility ?

We are trying to tackle this problem in one study now by allowing judges to look repeatedly at short sequences of film. We hope that in the process they will be able to report things that they did not originally identify or formulate as possible cues, discrepancies among different movements and postures, for example, that happen too fast to "see" on first viewing. We will then check out each of the findings systematically to see which are worth retaining. It is only through such painstaking exploration that we will be sure enough of our cues to use them as tools in studying interviews.

RICHARD RENNEKER, M.D.

The study of the extraverbal information contained within body movements in psychotherapy hours is an important potential source of new knowledge about emotions in man. Thus far, unfortunately, we have had to work with kinesic theorizing instead of kinesic knowledge, since research about kinesic phenomena is still in its infancy. These remarks, therefore, are directed toward: (1) identifying and discussing some of the methodological problems of kinesis and process research responsible for prolonging this phase of kinesic infancy; and (2) presenting some observational impressions about the "meaning" of expressive human movements.

This paper is based upon a four-year experience of studying body movements within the framework of therapeutic

---

The investigative work on which this discussion is based was supported in full by National Institute of Mental Health Grant M2556.

Systematic descriptions were recorded while observing through a one-way viewing window; also, participant movements were studied by frame analysis of silent and sound films made of several sessions.

process research. The thoughts leading to these remarks were stimulated by asking myself: "All right, so after trying to extract information from patient and therapist body movements by using different methods of systematically observing and describing approximately 150 hours of psychoanalytic psychotherapy—what have you learned? And what theoretical and methodological factors would you emphasize strongly to someone beginning to work in the same area?"

Remarks about the Nature of Therapeutic Process Research

The recent upsurge of investigative interest in the communicative significance of external body movements has arisen in part as a natural concomitant of therapeutic process research. Process research requires us to have the potential techniques for identifying every informational stimulus to which the interacting participants are exposed at any given moment. This means that we must have ways of tuning in to the interpersonal communication channels;[1] and, further, of separating out within each one its coexisting levels and types of messages and meanings.

All process research to date, whatever the beliefs of individual investigators to the contrary, has been exploratory. Our intentions were willing but our methods are weak. The serious methodological problems encountered sobered investigative enthusiasms, frustrated research hopes, engulfed projects, and finally confronted us with an unpleasant reality—the time was not yet (and still is not). Between us and precise "scientific process" investigations are many years of hard work. We must develop refined techniques for overcoming the obstructive research problems inherent in the nature of psychological variables, subjects, personnel, instrumentation, data collection, data processing, and data analyzing.

Ultimately, in order to be effective in a reliable sense,

[1] Movements of striated muscles represent one such channel.

process research has to be able to achieve the following things:

1. To record, recognize, and differentiate each bit of information contained in the words, sounds, and movements of both listener and speaker during a therapy session
2. To account for this information through fitting it together as a cohesive explanation of the listener's and speaker's conscious and unconscious behavior (i.e., the psychological interrelationships between self-image, image of others, values, needs, feelings, motivations, goals, plans, actions, and experiencing reactions to the internal-external environment)
3. To develop, thereby, in time, a thorough awareness of an individual's patterns of psychological functioning, with their component behaviors
4. To understand each pattern historically and chronologically by discovering and reconstructing its phases of development; included are the environmental, emotional, and psychological circumstances concerned with its origin, and the subsequent modifications in its component behaviors and in its functions
5. To evaluate the behavioral components of these patterns along a more-less mental health continuum
6. To identify component changes during therapy
7. To determine cause (s) of change
8. To differentiate extratherapy causes from intratherapy ones
9. To identify the specific intratherapy causative factor (s) responsible for change
10. To connect a specific causative factor with the change variable in a manner congruent with the scientific method requirements for establishing significant cause and effect relationships.

A body movement is both a source of information and a channel of communication. Psychiatrists assume that at least sometimes a patient's perception of a therapist's movement must be the predominant causative factor responsible for his next action; also, that such a perceptual event occasionally becomes the evidential basis for altering a neurotic misconception.

Most psychological systems of therapy hold that when a personal belief (about self, others, world) is altered, behavioral change necessarily follows.

Body movements within therapy are:

1. A source of information about the person moving
2. A channel for sending messages
3. A stimulus producing reaction (possible) in the viewer
4. A therapeutic experience leading to change in the viewer.

On all counts, therefore, it is clear that kinesic variables are active agents in therapy; and as such, essential variables to recognize and cope with in therapeutic process research.

Some Methodological Considerations Regarding Kinesic Research

The Use of Moving Pictures

Using motion pictures is essential.[2] Tape-recorded observational data from a one-time viewing of a therapy hour catches less than 50 per cent of the total movements. It favors the speaking movements and often misses the listener. It is static in its finality, since there is no way of getting back to check recorded observations against the actual movements they are supposed to replicate. The multidetermined nature of a movement requires (ideally) repeated re-viewings and multiple observers before it can be understood and extracted. Movies make this possible.

Frame analysis is basic to kinesic research, since some kinesic manifestations (of adaptive functioning, neurotic defensiveness, and immediacy reactions) take place from one frame to another (i.e., a time span of less than 1/24 of a second). Frame analysis is an accepted technique for kinesic

[2] Both filming and technical advising were well handled by Churchill-Wexler Instructional Films, 758 N. Seward Street, Los Angeles 38, Calif.

study of motion picture film. The picture is observed one frame at a time. There are 24 frames per second, or 1,440 frames per minute. Frame analysis is done by using a movie-editing machine. A Movieola is the optimal equipment, but expensive to rent and prohibitive to purchase. A "poor man's Movieola" is the film industry's way of describing an efficient construct-it-yourself film-editing machine, which costs less than $100.00 to make. It consists of two manually operated spindles mounted at opposite ends of a ¾″ piece of wood (1′ x 3′). Each is large enough to take a 2,000-foot 16 mm. reel. The film is cranked through a Craig Kalart Viewer that has been supplemented by a frame counter. Adding sound to the system is optional; however, a relatively inexpensive unit is available.

Movements were studied on film in two steps: (1) without sound; (2) and then with sound. This procedure separates the auditory and visual channels and allows for explicit identification of the contents of one channel as opposed to the other. Sound-film analysis allows a movement to be tied into the exact syllable upon which it was initiated, altered, and terminated. The moment of movement initiation can also be placed in its sequential relationship to other movements. Here film supplies a way of anchoring everything in the hour into a time relationship framework.

The movement variable to be studied must be meticulously described and differentiated. Failure to do so makes it easy to draw false conclusions, since the data represent an unrecognized and undifferentiated "blob"; for example, the use of undifferentiated "head movements" as the crucial kinesic variable. Such a selection would ignore the complexity of human movements (i.e., a therapist-patient pair used 87 different variations of head movements in one forty-three-minute session).

There are two basic training experiences for evaluator observers of human movement studies, and for residents in psychiatry. First is to take one minute of a silent film of therapy and to examine each person's every movement by repeated re-viewing, and to ask oneself about each one: "What does it make me think of? Why? Is that its message? Or is it rather a bit of information about the mover's psychophysiological state at the moment? If so, what would be going on inside of me if I moved like that? What could have stimulated it? What immediately preceded it? What is its homeostatic function? How do my speculations about this movement fit into those already made about this person, and about his current interactive relationship with the other individual?"

The essence of evaluating communication movements is an attempt at understanding the observed behavior through reconstructing states of inner experience which could have given rise to the same behavior in oneself. The question is: what does the movement communicate to me, the viewer? It is not: what did the mover mean by that movement? The vast majority of communicative movements originate beyond consciousness and are not part of the mover's awareness.

The second step is to repeat this process about the same minute, but this time as part of a group. Now an awareness of the fantastic informational richness of the minute is experienced as group members begin to identify new kinds of information, levels of meaning, and connective patterns of intermovement relationships—all previously unsuspected by the one who had been convinced till then that his hours of individual viewing and analysis had undoubtedly exhausted the material. Each new experiencing of this sequence of individual frame analysis, followed by group frame analysis, has continued to startle and impress us with the realization of how much can be learned from microanalysis of one minute of film data, and of how much can be predicted or postdicted: about transference, parent personalities, special life experiences, and undisclosed neurotic symptomatology. A group serves as control for our common tendency to bog down after finding our first explanation of the thing observed. This could be called the "Aha! I understand" phenomenon.

Single observers inevitably possess quantitative and qualitative limitations in their capacity to grasp the complex totality of the variety of informations contained within one movement.

A group experience of analyzing human movements in one minute of a silent motion picture film brings awareness of the rich spread of information extractable when movements are passed through filters provided by the many eyes and minds of the group. It takes a human to read a human. Each observer can therefore be calibrated for his observational gaps and proficiencies. An observational team could thus be selected systematically, so that in its final composition perceptual capacities would counterbalance perceptual limitations. A group also helps to avoid the individual's occasional tendency to focus on a "tree" instead of seeing the "woods."

Just as a painting is more than the sum of its physical ingredients, so truc meaning is often found only in the Gestalt of a total communicative action; that is, in the combined effect of its words, sounds, and movements, but not in the communication significance of any single element by itself.

Be sparing in filming. It is expensive and time consuming to analyze. Until there are automata to do film processing, we should confine ourselves to filming very few total clinical sessions, and to filming a few separated minutes in carefully selected others. Extraction of movements by frame analysis of a forty-three-minute therapy film required eighty-four hours of viewing. Group analysis of one silent film minute takes a minimum of two hours. One minute is almost an optimal work unit; one sentence is another.

Perceptual Domination of Auditory Over Visual

We are word bound. Our observing energies are dominated by verbal auditory stimuli, or by anticipation of them. Visual perception of another person's movements appears predominantly to be preconscious, or unregistered. In order for perception of a movement to reach consciousness, something special must occur to focus an observer's attention upon it, and away from speech.

This seems strange only if we forget the conclusive findings of communication research from the early days of radio—that auditory perception of speech dominates visual perception of the written word, while learning from the former is greater than from the latter. Certainly this fits psychotherapy. All those words! In addition, visual information is recalled less well than auditory. For example, immediately after a therapy session while two psychoanalyst observers recalled 1 per cent of its relevant visual data, the therapist recaptured only .03 per cent. By comparison, recall of verbal manifest content by a therapist hits around 40 per cent immediately after a session, and drops to around 20 per cent within two days.

Such findings threaten our unrealistic image of the therapist as someone who is particularly sensitive to extraverbal expressive phenomena. It might be more accurate to say that therapists usually notice only the most frequent and major movements; and even then only after long periods of perceptual blindness.

From a methodological standpoint the concept of auditory domination means that (1) the therapist's kinesic observations are grossly incomplete; and, (2) kinesic evaluators of a movie should first observe its silent version.

Selection of Therapist Subject

An important aid in future investigations would be selection of subjects capable of high degree of openness about communicating to an investigator the actual content of consciousness around a movement's occurrence, or during his repeated observations of it on film. This simple procedure would eliminate much guess work. This would allow us to separate out from the observer's inferences those meanings which were part of the subject's awareness, or were so accessible in preconsciousness that they were recallable by the subject during the process of observing himself on film. The remainder would represent "beyond consciousness" meanings about the mover, or idiosyncratic information peculiar to the viewer. It is impossible to place confidence in such a procedure unless the subject's openness is "beyond question." Such openness theoretically occurs after "thorough therapeutic analysis"; however, I would add to this that the subject should be younger rather than older, less experienced rather than more, and should show a preanalysis history of possessing the habit of openness to communication.

Investigative Impressions about the Informational Nature of Human Movements

1. *Every external movement in human beings is a source of information about the psychophysiological state of the person moving.* As nearly as I have been able to determine from speaking to colleagues no one seriously doubts the probable truth of this assumption, nor seems to feel the need for confirmatory evidence. Perhaps this is because everyone has experienced bodily movement as an extraverbal source of information, both as sender and receiver. If this is so, then:

2. *Common to humans are the learned abilities to interpret movements and to use them for communicative purposes.*

3. Kinesic behavior can be evaluated along a continuum of more-less healthy ego functioning, since the efficiency and appropriateness of movements are in direct proportion to an individual's integrative capacity at the movement of moving.

Example: Speech-accompanying gestures ordinarily do not compete with the spoken word. Such gestures rather seek to complement, modify, and dramatize the meanings of words; thereby, they help in capturing and communicating the subtle overtones and colors of a multileveled message.

Using a large number of speech-accompanying gestures[3] or inappropriate ones is often associated with miscommunication rather than message clarification. Apparently, "too

[3] In the psychotherapy films studied, eye-area movements were first in frequency, head movements second, and other speech-accompanying gestures third.

many" gestures distract attention from the verbal message by acting as "noise."

4. *Kinesic skills in sending and reading information vary quantitatively and qualitatively with different individuals, times, and situations.*

"Skillful" implies that a movement is tailored to fit both the true nature of the information communicated and the cultural movement vocabulary of the person for whom the message is intended. "Skillful" also implies that the movement is easy to read, graceful, and dramatically effective in timing and execution.

5. Ineffectiveness in movement "reading" and "sending" reflects a neurotic communication disturbance, since neurosis expresses itself kinesically in various ways: as errors in interpreting the movements of others (i.e., projection, displacement, denial, selective psychological blindness, and inability to discriminate a movement's type and degree); as a relative failure to develop and use our movement interpretative skill; as a relative inability to use movements for interpersonal communication, or to use them with accuracy and skill.

A movement's grace depends upon fluid progression of the simultaneous contraction and relaxation of the opposing muscle groups involved in the action. Psychic conflict produces muscular tensions of more generalized, or specific types, depending upon the nature of the problem. A generalized state of muscular tension interferes with necessary reciprocal relaxation of antagonistic muscles, and therefore decreases motor grace and skill. Generalized muscle tension represents an indiscriminate increase of tonus in both sides of a reciprocal group. The muscles are in a precontractile state of "too great readiness." Specific muscular tensions are surface markers for inhibited impulses to action. In such an instance, the impulse to act is transmitted to the appropriate muscles. However, the antagonist muscles not only fail to relax but oppose the action through an increase in tonus. Muscular tension influences movements by reducing their range and number. Tension also leads to awkwardness, to interruption in movements already initiated, and to attempts at substitutive discharge.

6. *Each movement is a reaction to an internal or external stimulus, which frequently says: "Help is needed here." Useful information about the mover results from comprehending the nature of the stimulus behind the movement and of the help needed.*

Movements are stimulated by changes in the self and in the nature of the animate and inanimate environment, or by the harmful consequences of exposure to changes in the external environment. These *self-productive movements* are adaptive and goal directed or their neurotic equivalents. They are homeostatic actions concerned with warding off either imminent or distant threats to the existence of our biological and psychological selves. *Self-providing movements* are directed toward getting things that we need or want. They can also be part of a plan to develop an externally presented opportunity to secure need gratification.

Stimuli originating from inner biological structures, from cell to organ system, convey the same message of: "Hey! Something is needed here, something which requires the initiation of goal-directed action beyond local capabilities." "Somethings" are: an internal need for fuel, fluid, alleviation of mechanical pressure, rest, stimuli, functioning, or aid in overcoming a threatening invader. Such stimuli produce external movements when the thing required has to be gotten from the outside. We can sometimes meet the inner cry for help without going to the outside, as the pregnant woman's shift in body position to alleviate pressure from a displaced uterus; however, inevitably the inner needs also lead to interactions with the environment. These usually originate as actions designed to secure something which exists outside of the self (i.e., oxygen lack drives a person to seek a fresh supply).

There is an intermediate phase between perception of inner needs and initiation of goal-directed action in which a different kind of movement takes place. These are the inhibited, restless movements associated with an unrelieved tension state—unrelieved because the individual has put off (inhibited), for internal or external reasons, taking the necessary homeostatic actions; generally because past actions in this area have been unsuccessful or because a present action impulse seems unlikely to succeed.

7. *The partial movements of unrelieved tension states represent interrupted goal-directed actions, or their symbolic equivalents.* These are the *inhibited movements* or the residual motion fragments of inhibited impulses toward action. Example: a patient had to urinate and was too embarrassed at first to say anything about it. His increased eye and feet movements under conditions of mounting bladder pressure were viewed as inhibited action impulses stimulated by an adaptive need to escape a condition of mounting physical discomfort. The multiple, restless feet movements represented inhibited impulses to get up and leave the room. The same was the probable meaning of the many fleeting glances toward the door.

8. *Immediacy reactions are unconscious and instantaneous movement reactions to whatever is happening at that second* (e.g., the listening facial expression of approval). They reflect a person's values by disclosing how he is experiencing something on a feeling level; as such, immediacy movements are signals giving information about the subject's inner emotional state. They are the surface reflections of his psychophysiological feeling state of the moment.

The reactions can be categorized and quantified by placement along three 7-point continua: (1) nonthreatening—threatening; (2) pleasing—nonpleasing; (3) interesting—noninteresting. Relating the category and degree of the immediacy reaction to the nature and intensity of the stimulus provides information about the person's values, his freedom to react, the intensity of his need, and his state of relative well-being or discomfort.

9. *Communicative movements have the conscious or unconscious intent of sending a message, or of facilitating communication. They are predominantly interpersonal and re-*

lated to the presence of people. Note sometime how much you do not move when alone. Notice too that movements when alone tend to be reactions to internal images of external situations involving interpersonal experiences or physical activities. Communicative movements are often called "body language." They can accompany, amplify, clarify, dramatize, or replace the spoken word. Head movements and gestures are predominantly communicative types.

10. *The communication effectiveness of a movement is directly proportionate to its informational specificity.* Specificity depends upon the number of informational possibilities eliminated in the viewer by the movement. Explication in kinesis is thus achieved by using movements, which elicit the narrowest range of different meanings.

Constant and absolute verbal specificity of movement is probably not achieved very often, except in relationships of long standing or of great intimacy. Verbal specificity of movement is a situation in which movements are used to replace words, as in Churchill's two-fingered V for victory.

Informational specificity for movements is probably higher and more common when movements represent surface indicators of inner states of psychic and emotional experiences (i.e., when they are noncommunication, as opposed to communication, movements).[4]

Summary

Movements can be divided into two major categories depending upon whether they are intended (consciously or unconsciously) to serve a communication function.

1. "Communication" movements
2. "Noncommunication" movements

Protection-providing movements

[4] "Communication" and "noncommunication" are here used in the sense of "conscious or unconscious *intent* of sending a message" to another *person* or *persons.* This contrasts with the broader use of "communication" from one as transfer of information organism or "environmental subsystem" to another *regardless of intent*—as Birdwhistell uses the term.—(*Ed.*)

Inhibited movements
Immediacy reactions

The multi-informational character of movements illustrates the creative working of the unconscious: the magnificent ability to condense so much and so many things into *one* movement, word, or dream symbol. Therefore, if we want to continue learning about behavioral phenomena, it seems essential for us to accept the inevitable multi-informational nature of movements.

It is easy to find a meaning, and evidence to substantiate it, but this does not mean that different meanings and evidence cannot be found. We cannot stop with the first, usually the most obvious, explanation. Doing so has been the curse of our thinking habits in the behavioral sciences. We tend to forget a basic tenet of the scientific method: that validation requires finding and ruling out all other possible explanations. In our field, validation is possible if we view that which is validated as a part of the truth and not as all of the truth.

CHAPTER 9

The Visceral Level: Situational Determinants and Behavioral Correlates of Autonomic Response Patterns

JOHN I. LACEY, PH.D.
JEROME KAGAN, PH.D.
BEATRICE C. LACEY, M.A.
HOWARD A. MOSS, PH.D.

In common with many other investigators of the psychobiological significance of autonomic responses, we are dissatisfied with the traditional view that links autonomic response automatically and exclusively to such concepts as stress, emotion, and homeostasis. These associations obviously exist, but we feel that more specific concepts are necessary. We suspect

The psychophysiological research dealing with autonomic responses was supported by grant M-623 from the National Institute of Mental Health, United States Public Health Service, and was conducted by John I. Lacey and Beatrice C. Lacey; the more purely psychological research was supported by grant M-1260 from the same agency and was conducted by Jerome Kagan and Howard A. Moss.

that neither "emotion" nor "arousal" constitutes the sole key to the understanding of the variegated physiological display that seems to accompany all behavior.

In accordance with the plan of this Symposium, our communication is a progress report, in which we will continue the development of some speculative notions that we proposed in a critical survey of the application of psychophysiological measurements to the study of psychotherapy (Lacey, 1959). We will present some results of several studies in which an attempt is made to establish *differential* significance for different physiological functions that are commonly used in the study of autonomic correlates of behavior.

Patterns of autonomic response. The amount of reaction shown in one physiological function cannot be predicted with accuracy from the amount of reaction shown in another function. In other words, the coefficients of correlation among autonomic responses are never +1.00, and all too frequently are startlingly low. As a consequence, patterns of autonomic response appear in which, for example, overreactivity in one variable can be accompanied by underreactivity in another. The low correlations among autonomic responses are not due solely to attenuation by errors of measurement or to other sorts of unreliability. We have established the fact that there are reliable individual differences in patterns of autonomic response to a given stressor (called "intrastressor stereotypy of response"), and even to different stressors (called "interstressor stereotypy of response"). These investigations have been reviewed in detail elsewhere, and the interrelationships among the several varieties of stereotypy have been discussed briefly (Lacey, 1959; Lacey and Lacey, 1958). The main facts of interstressor and intrastressor stereotypy have been verified by other investigators (Dykman et al., 1959; Wenger et al., 1961; Engel, 1960; Speisman et al., 1961; Schnore, 1959). Wenger and his collaborators (1961), however, in trying to specify the experimental conditions in which interstressor stereotypy appears, caution "against overgeneralizing the significance and pervasiveness of autonomic response specificity"; and Schnore (1959) maintains that there is sufficient communality among responses to justify the use of a single autonomic variable, say heart rate or skin conductance, as a measure of a hypothetical unitary continuum of "arousal." Both of the last-cited papers, nevertheless, also verify the basic fact that autonomic responses are patterned.

We have practically no clues to understanding the behavioral significance, if there is any, of response patterns. What does it mean when an individual shows a large increase in heart rate but only a small increase in skin conductance? In what ways is he different from an individual who shows the reverse pattern? An indirect approach to answers to these questions may be provided by studying a third type of stereotypy, which we called "stimulus or situational stereotypy of response" (Lacey and Lacey, 1958). By this is meant consistent differences in the modal or average response pattern produced by different objective stimulus conditions. By establishing principles or generalizations to explain situational determination of response patterns, some clues might emerge to help understand individual differences in response patterns to a given stimulus condition. Even if this is a false hope, the study of stimulus stereotypy should go far toward providing a more specific understanding of the behavioral significance of autonomic activity than is provided by our more traditional concepts of "emotion" and "arousal."

The modern experimental studies of situational stereotypy, those of Ax (1953), Schachter (1957), B. T. Engel (1960), and of Davis and his collaborators (Davis, 1957; Davis et al., 1955, 1957), lend some support to an elusive and often-challenged concept long cherished by clinicians, that at least some "emotions" will be found to have a characteristic pattern of physiological activity. The studies of Davis and his collaborators, however—in which different patterns of response are found for such activities as looking at pictures, being cutaneously stimulated, and tapping telegraph keys—

give warning that more than the concept of "emotional" specificity is involved.

Many of the changes in response patterns that are produced by stimulus changes are simple quantitative modifications: one physiological response is greater in one stimulus condition than in another, while another response shows the reverse effect. In several situations, however, there occurs what we have called "directional fractionation." These are instances in which the direction of change in one physiological variable is contrary to what might be expected from the still-persistent Cannon-like view of over-all sympathetic activation by "stress." For example, Davis (1957) has described the P-pattern, characteristically and most clearly obtained when males look at sexually suggestive pictures. The P-pattern consists of digital vasoconstriction, increased palmar conductance, and cardiac *deceleration*. The vasoconstriction and the sudomotor response both are sympathetic-like changes. The heart-rate deceleration is a parasympathetic-like response. Unless it can be explained as secondary to a momentary hypertension, it is a phenomenon which poses many questions to the psychophysiologist who is accustomed to think of a massive sympathetic-like discharge in response to a variety of situations.

We reported, in the already-cited review (Lacey, 1959), that in pretesting stimulus situations for a longitudinal study of interstressor stereotypy we stumbled quite by accident on some extremely suggestive examples of directional fractionation of response, in which heart rate decelerated, but skin conductance increased. The decelerations occurred when the subject was required to attend to visual and auditory inputs. The heart accelerated, on the other hand, when the subject was solving mental arithmetic problems, or when he was painfully stimulated by the cold pressor test. The differences among situations were so clear and decisive that a high significance level was found for a small sample of fifteen subjects. Based on a brief review of relevant psychophysiological and neurophysiological evidence, we proposed that cardiac deceleration accompanied and perhaps even facilitated ease of "environmental intake," whereas cardiac acceleration accompanied or facilitated "rejection of the environment." Among other things, we pointed out that there is considerable psychophysiological evidence to support the notion that pleasant stimuli (those that the organism wants to take in from the environment) produce cardiac deceleration, whereas unpleasant stimuli (those that the organism wants to reject) produce cardiac acceleration. We also reviewed the fragmentary neurophysiological evidence for the notion that cardiac deceleration (especially if accompanied by arterial hypotension) would have the effect of facilitating sensorimotor integration. This effect is mediated by visceral afferent mechanisms. Increases in pressure within the carotid sinus that result from sympathetic-like cardiovascular changes stimulate the baroceptors within the carotid sinus. The resulting increase in impulses along Hering's nerve produces inhibition of cortical electrical activity and of sensorimotor activity.

For the past few years, we have engaged in several studies designed to test these ideas. In the first study, we tried to clarify the differential conditions which determine whether cardiac acceleration or deceleration occurs.

An experiment on directional fractionation of response. Three different samples of subjects were exposed to a wide variety of stimulus conditions. We recorded a variety of physiological variables. The data of this experiment, however, are too voluminous to present here in detail. We will present some of the results for two of the groups of subjects, concentrating primarily on two popular response systems, namely, palmar conductance and heart rate. The full details of this experiment will be reported elsewhere.

The first aim of the study was to ascertain whether heart-rate decelerations would be obtained in different stimulus situations, which have in common sustained attentiveness by the subject to the incoming stimuli. These situations, however, differed among themselves in other important ways, as will be seen.

In contrast, we desired to present a variety of situations in which it at least seemed reasonable to speculate that selective "rejection" of stimuli is called for. We hoped to establish that cardiac accelerations would occur in these situations. We called to mind here the common-sense notion that preoccupation with the "mental" solution of problems is frequently accompanied by inaccessibility and unresponsiveness to external stimuli, and often by deliberate attempts to reduce environmental inputs, e.g., by closing one's eyes. Several of our stimulus conditions, therefore, require "mental" problem solving, involving the retrieval and internal "manipulation" of already-acquired information.

We hastily admit the dangers and oversimplifications involved in asserting the existence of a single continuum from "environmental acceptance" to "environmental rejection." Having admitted them, we proceeded to attempt to establish in a preliminary way that something like this bipolar factor does exist. This was the second aim of the study. To accomplish this aim, we used one stimulus condition in which the demands for attention to environmental input and the demands for internal storage and manipulation of information would be balanced, and another in which the subject was asked to attend closely to an unpleasant stimulus.

Two radically different populations were sampled, in an attempt to establish the generalizability of the results. One sample consisted of a large group ($N = 94$) of male college freshmen, who were nonvolunteer subjects. By arrangement with the Antioch College administration each freshman, when called upon, is required (barring extraordinary circumstances which arise only very infrequently) to serve as a subject at the Fels Institute. In this way we avoid any potential volunteer error in our studies of autonomic psychophysiology. Many of these subjects arrive as strangers in a threatening laboratory atmosphere, uncertain and anxious about the forthcoming ordeal, and, many times, rather hostile.

By contrast, our second sample consists of 30 adult males who are subjects of the longitudinal study of human development carried on by the Fels Research Institute. All these subjects are well known to us and know us well. They have been in the laboratory repeatedly, are well acquainted with the sorts of manipulations and measurements we make, and have been committed throughout their lives to participation in the longitudinal study. On this occasion, they were being subjected to a series of medical, biochemical, physiological, and psychological studies. They are a sample of our so-called "graduates," individuals over eighteen years old, for whom routine annual and semiannual visits have ceased, although periodic contact is still maintained. Their ages range from twenty to thirty; many are married and have children of their own; most are well launched in their adult careers. They are completely described in a forthcoming publication of the results of a longitudinal study of their psychological development (Kagan and Moss, 1962).

The results of the study on directional fractionation are summarized in Figure I. The data for the college freshmen (Group C) are presented by solid lines, and those for the Fels subjects (Group F) by broken lines. In these graphs are shown the group averages of heart rate and palmar conductance at three critical times in each of eight stimulus situations. The times of measurement are indicated by the letters "b" (for base), "a" (for alert), and "s" (for stressor or stimulus). The "base" values for heart rate are the averages of the twelve fastest cardiac cycles in the one minute preceding an alerting announcement, by which the subject was informed what the next stimulus situation would be. (Previous to the onset of the experiment he had been drilled in the specific requirements and the nature of each of the tasks.) The "alert" values for heart rate are the averages of the twelve fastest beats for one minute following the alerting announcement. The "stress" values are the averages of the twelve fastest beats for the stimulus situations, which were

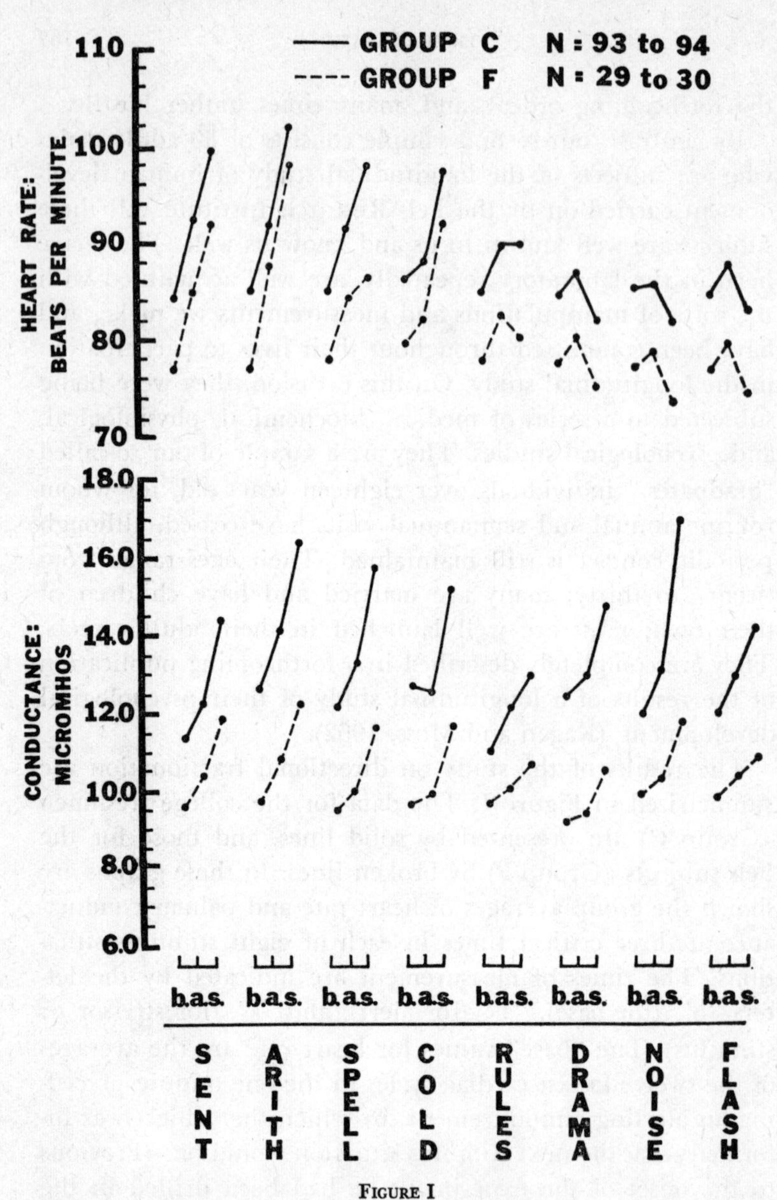

FIGURE I

These graphs are average response curves, for heart rate and palmar conductance, for two groups of subjects, under eight different stimulus conditions. The stimulus conditions are described in the text, and are indicated in the figure by single words or abbreviations, e.g., "Sent," "Cold." Each graph consists of three points: "b," for base level, is the average prestimulus or resting value; "a," for alerted level, is the average value during one minute of anticipation of the stimulus condition; "s," for stress or stimulus level, is the average value during the administration of the stimulus condition. See text for details of the measurement of maximum sympathetic-like activity in the two physiological variables.

timed to last for one or two minutes. For palmar conductance, the highest conductance in the minute before the alerting announcement was taken as the "base"; the highest value during the minute of waiting for the next stimulus situation was the "alert" level; and the "stress" level was the highest value attained during the performance of the task. For both variables, then, maximum sympathetic-like activity was measured.

The order of presentation of the stimuli on the graph does not correspond with the actual order of presentation. Indeed, the order of presentation was different for the two groups of subjects. The obvious similarity of results for the two groups, then, is not attributable to any order effect.

Perhaps the first thing to note in Figure I is that directional fractionation of heart-rate response did, indeed, occur. A cursory glance reveals that all the stimulus situations were effective in increasing palmar conductance. However, heart-rate changes from alert to stress were bidirectional, increasing in some situations, but decreasing in others. For clarity, we will first discuss the results for the stimulus conditions which produced alert-to-stress accelerations, then those which produced decelerations.

In the Mental Arithmetic test ("Arith." in Figure I), the subjects were required to solve simple multiplication and addition problems "in their heads." After solving each problem, they announced the answer aloud, and another problem was immediately given to them. Heart rate increased from base to alert, and increased again from alert to stress. All changes in each of the groups are highly significant, with p values ranging from 10^{-4} to 10^{-8}, by Wilcoxon's nonparametric paired replicates test (1949). In the Reverse Spelling task ("Spell." in Figure I), words were spelled aloud in reverse order, and the subject had to mentally rearrange the letters and announce the correct word. This is a very difficult task. The heart-rate changes followed the same pattern as in mental arithmetic, with comparable significance levels (10^{-3} to 10^{-8}). In the Make-up Sentences task ("Sent." in Figure I) the subject had to think up meaningful sentences of at least five words, each of good grammatical construction, in which each of the words in the sentence began with the same letter of the alphabet (which was announced to the subject only at the beginning of the "s" period). No talking was permitted until the end of the "s" period. As can be seen, heart-rate changes again followed the same pattern of acceleration. The p values ranged from 10^{-3} to 10^{-8}.

These three tasks differed from each other in formal and detailed demands, but each required the internal manipulation of symbols and the retrieval of stored information. They all produce pronounced cardiac accelerations.

On the other hand, in two situations where the major demand on the subject was to receive environmental inputs, without strong demands for cognitive elaboration or for storage or retrieval of information, we found, as expected, cardiac decelerations. When the subject was stimulated by flashes at 10 cycles per second by a Grass Photostimulator, under instructions to note and detect the varying colors and patterns so produced ("Flash" in Figure I) the heart decelerated upon the presentation of the flashes, with p values of 10^{-8} and 10^{-3} for groups C and F respectively. (There was a minimal demand for storage of information, for the subject was told he would be asked at the end of the experiment to describe what he saw.) The stimulus situation labeled "Drama" in Figure I is a particularly noteworthy one. The subject was under instructions only to listen carefully and to empathize with the affect presented in an effective and moving tape-recorded recitation, executed by a professional actor, of the verbalized thoughts and feelings of a dying man, seriously injured by a falling beam. Despite the high "emotionality" of this stimulus situation, the heart decelerated, with confidence levels of 10^{-6} and 10^{-5} for groups C and F respectively.

To be noted is the remarkable fact that the heart-rate levels during these environmental intake situations tended to be driven *below* the resting levels. This effect was significant (10^{-3} and 10^{-2}) for the two stimulus conditions for the larger C group. For the small F group, the effect was significant for the photic stimulus at the .05 level, but failed to be significant for the recorded drama.

What has been shown so far is that cardiac acceleration was produced by three stimulus situations which demanded "mental" problem-solving activity; on the other hand, the two stimulus situations which demanded sustained attentiveness to external stimuli produced cardiac deceleration. Our hypothesis, as stated before, is that these stimulus situations represent approximate extremes of a continuum. If there is truly a continuum, intermediate effects on heart rate should be found in situations that require both "acceptance" and "rejection" of external stimuli. Two stimulus situations were designed specifically to test this deduction. They are Rules of the Game and Noise.

In Rules of the Game ("Rules" in Figure I) the subjects had to listen to a tape recording of a set of rules for a fictitious card game. These rules had to be stored in memory and held in some sensible and available form, because the subjects knew that at the end of the "s" period they would be questioned closely about the rules of the game. This was put to them as a test of their intellectual ability. Throughout, then, the subject had to pay attention to incoming stimuli, but also had to resort to those internal activities which we call cognitive elaboration, involving storage, retrieval, and recombination of information. It was our hope, of course, that the effects of this situation on heart rate would lie between those of the so-called environmental rejection stressors and those of the so-called environmental intake stressors. As can be seen in Figure I, this crucial hypothesis was clearly supported in both the C and F groups. For the large group of male college freshmen there was no change of average heart rate from the alert to the stress period. For the Fels subjects, there was a deceleration, but this deceleration was not as great as in the environmental intake situations. The data indeed do support the hypothesis that a situation simultaneously requiring attention to environmental inputs and internal cognitive work has a balanced effect on heart rate, intermediate between the cardiac deceleration of what we may call "external orientation" and the cardiac acceleration of "internal orientation."

It was hoped that white noise also would have an intermediate effect on cardiac rate, for, while the instructions to the subject were to note and detect the environmental input, the noise was definitely unpleasant. It fluctuated irregularly in loudness, reaching peak intensities in excess of 100 dbs. above threshold. The instructions were to attend, which should tend to produce deceleration; but the stimulus was unpleasant, which should tend to produce acceleration. We hoped to find, then, little or no change in heart rate from alert-to-stress. This, as the data in Figure I show, did not occur for either sample. Attention to this unpleasant stimulus produced deceleration, significant at 10^{-6} and 10^{-3} levels for the two groups. It should be mentioned, however, that in another experiment, not to be presented here, it was shown that while blood pressure decreased in the harm drama and in photic stimulation, it increased modestly in Noise and Rules of the Game, and increased markedly in the problem-solving situations. When, therefore, recourse is had to the combination of two cardiovascular variables it appears that white noise indeed resulted in balanced and intermediate effects on the cardiovascular system.

It should be noted, finally, that the data of the third sample, in which blood pressure was measured, prove that the decelerations observed in the intake stressors are not secondary to elevated blood pressure.

It can be seen that these cardiac decelerations do not signify a lack of somatic impact of the stimulus on the organism, as the results of the skin-conductance measurements show. It can be seen also, however, that in general (Noise being an exception) these skin-conductance changes are more modest for the environmental intake situations than they are for the environmental rejection situations.

We have not yet mentioned the painful cold pressor test ("Cold" in Figure I). This test was included in the battery to remind us that other variables can affect heart rate and skin conductance than those implied by our postulated environmental rejection-environmental intake continuum. It can serve, also, however, to promote the possibly useful speculation that the "reason" for cardiac acceleration in the cold pressor test is to enable "rejection" of the painful stimuli. Neurophysiological evidence on central control of sensory afferent pathways certainly gives support to the notion that the organism has resources at its command for the dampening or rerouting of sensory stimuli. Moreover, research on the inhibitory effect of increased pressure within the carotid sinus on cortical and sensorimotor functions (which we have reviewed elsewhere in the context of behavioral science; Lacey, 1959; Lacey and Lacey, 1958) suggests that elevated heart rate and blood pressure could lead to decreased sensory sensitivity.

Before proceeding to a discussion of our research concerning some relationships between these autonomic responses, on the one hand, and cognitive performance and behavioral measures, on the other, it may be useful to clarify what we think has been established so far. In truth, the only completely defensible conclusion that can be drawn from these data is that situational stereotypy does exist: patterns of heart-rate and skin-conductance responses can be shown to be dependent upon the stimuli or tasks that are used. Any statement that implies more than this is an inference. The inference that is closest to the data stems from an attempt to characterize the elements that are common to stimulus situations that produce like effects.

Clearly, the four stimulus conditions that produced cardiac deceleration (Rules of the Game, Harm Drama, White Noise, and Flash) have in common the fact that the subject was instructed to note and detect the incoming stimuli throughout the period of stimulation. They differed among themselves, however, in modality of sensory input (auditory noise and visual flash), in appeal to emotional participation (Rules of the Game vs. Harm Drama), and in semantic and symbolic complexity (Noise and Flash vs. Rules of the Game and Harm Drama). By contrast, Sentences, Mental Arithmetic, and Reverse Spelling, which produced cardiac accelerations, have in common the element of "mental" work and concentration. They differ among themselves in the novelty and routineness of the task, in whether they deal with arithmetic symbols or words, whether or not they require adherence to long-established and familiar rules, and in other less easily verbalized characteristics.

It is not too great an extrapolation to hypothesize that "mental concentration" is accompanied by cardiac acceleration, and that attention to the environment is accompanied by cardiac deceleration. That we can at least pit "mental concentration" against "intent to take in the environment" and secure balanced effects on heart rate is suggested by the results for Rules of the Game.

We do not know, of course, if these formulations hold universally. It is noteworthy, however, that Obrist (1962), after observing these results, undertook an independent replication and extension of the study, and found cardiac deceleration for still other "environmental intake" situations (looking at colored pictures of landscape scenes, listening to a short essay, and finding hidden figures in a picture), and that one of us (J. Kagan) is finding like effects in six-year-old boys.

From this point on, the extrapolations and interpretations become more remote and speculative. If we accept the common-sense notion that "mental concentration" is facilitated by ignoring external stimuli and by eliminating distractions, then it becomes easier to accept a continuum between, at one extreme, the intent to pay attention to and to accept environmental inputs and, at the other extreme, the intent to reject environmental inputs. At a still higher level of speculation, we wonder if the cardiac acceleration produced by the cold pressor test can be viewed as an example of cardiac acceleration accompanying environmental rejection (of a painful and unpleasant stimulus). At the highest level of speculation is our theory that all these phenomena may be explained, at least partially, by the demonstrated inhibitory effect on cortical and sensorimotor function of increases of pressure within the carotid sinus, and the facilitatory effects of decreased intrasinusal pressure. This speculation, at present, has only the virtue of calling attention to a small chapter in neurophysiology which has been neglected by autonomic psychophysiology. It will need much direct experimental support in intact humans.

Correlates of Autonomic Activity with Psychological Assessments

In the studies to be reported now, we explored further the question whether palmar-conductance and heart-rate responses have differential significance for behavior. Rather than the stimulus-response analysis of the just reported experiment, we embarked upon some correlational studies.

The psychological data were gathered as part of a project being conducted by the Department of Psychology (Kagan and Moss, 1962), the primary goal of which was to study the development of behavior from childhood through adulthood. In this project, a group of seventy-one adults, who had been studied from birth through adolescence, were subjected to an elaborate psychological assessment as young adults. This adult assessment included twelve hours of interview and testing. In addition, thirty of the thirty-five males in the study were the subjects in the psychophysiological experiment on situational stereotypy.

There is no contamination of the correlations to be reported. Kagan and Moss pursued their studies in ignorance of the results of the Laceys' study of situational stereotypy; the Laceys pursued the latter study in ignorance of the psychological findings. Moreover, in evaluating and summarizing the childhood behavior of these adults, Moss used only the behavior recorded in the files and records, without knowing the persons involved, and Kagan made ratings of adult behavior independently of Moss. Independent ratings of childhood and adult behavior were also made to establish interrater reliability.

Autonomic activity and tachistoscopic recognition speed. In our earlier review of the possible differential significance of palmar-conductance and heart-rate responses (Lacey, 1959), we discovered a seemingly forgotten paper by Darrow and his collaborators (1942), in which it was maintained that two "sympathetic-like" changes had different correlations with electroencephalographic changes produced by sensory stimulation. Palmar-conductance increases were termed "excitatory" because they were positively correlated with alpha blocking. Blood-pressure increases, on the other hand, were called "homeostatic," because they were negatively correlated with alpha blocking and hence could be said to result in inhibitory effects on cortical excitation. This interesting result suggested an experiment (Lacey, 1959) designed to demonstrate differential effects of heart rate and palmar conductance, not on the electroencephalogram, but on sensorimotor behavior. We found that subjects were more prone to make a response to irrelevant stimuli, although responses to these stimuli were specifically forbidden, if the stimuli were presented when the subject's heart rate was momentarily low than when his heart rate was momentarily high. We interpreted the results to mean that high heart rates were inhibitory, and low heart rates facilitatory, for sensorimotor impulsivity. Skin-conductance changes, however, seemed to have a modifying effect on this relationship. A prior increase in conductance was found to be positively related to the occurrence of an impulsive motor response when the heart rate was high; but no relations were found between conductance and impulsivity when the heart rate was low. We interpreted these results to mean that an increase in conductance was excitatory and could overcome the presumably inhibitory effect of a high heart rate, but had no detectable effect when heart rates were low, this latter state itself being excitatory. The demonstration was far from conclusive, and, in the present experiment, evidence of another kind was sought concerning differential inhibitory and excitatory effects of sudomotor and cardiac changes on perceptual behavior.

In the way already discussed for the tape-recorded drama used in the experiment on situational stereotypy, the anticipatory (base-to-alert) physiological responses of the subject were measured as he prepared to listen to tape-recorded material concerning "Aggression to Peer," "Aggression to Mother," "Sex," and other areas of potential conflict. We will deal here only with the aggression episodes, and with the anticipatory base-to-alert responses, because they alone yielded statistically significant results. The data may be selected, therefore, and must be viewed with caution. They are presented primarily for their heuristic value, and because they are the kind of result, among others, that has led us to acute dissatisfaction with traditional views of the relationship of autonomic function to behavior.

The subjects were told, at the alerting announcement, the general area to be dealt with in the subsequent tape-recorded drama. We then measured the cardiac and sudomotor activity as the subject *prepared* to listen to a recording in areas he might "like to avoid." Twenty-four hours earlier, as part of the independently conducted psychological program, each of these subjects had been required to identify line drawings of human figures engaged in activity relevant to these same conflict areas. Such figures were exposed in a tachistoscope at successively greater exposures, until the subject correctly identified the age and sex of the two figures, and the exact nature of the action shown. All exposures were supraliminal. At the shortest exposure all subjects could see something. The speed of exposure in which we were interested was the speed at which the subject clearly identified the important aspects of the action involved.

The first hypothesis of the study was that the larger the cardiac acceleration shown by the subject while he was preparing to listen to tape-recorded material in a potentially conflictful area, the longer would be the required exposure in the tachistoscope before the figures and actions were correctly identified. In terms of our speculations, we hypothesized that reluctance to attend to the tape-recorded aggressive episode would lead to cardiac acceleration, and would be paralleled by reluctance or difficulty in interpreting visual information containing similar content. The second hypothesis was that palmar conductance would act in an opposite way and, therefore, that palmar-conductance increases while preparing to listen to the recording would be correlated with readiness to receive the visually presented information.

The measure of increase in heart rate and palmar conductance was the autonomic lability score (Lacey, 1956), which is highly correlated with both percentage and absolute change, but which is freed of relationship to the base level.

There were four line drawings dealing with aggression. The intercorrelations among the recognition-speed scores suggested that they be considered in three pairs; the members of each pair were highly intercorrelated. The average of the required exposures was used for each pair as the measure of speed of recognition. For details of the technique, the recent publication by Kagan and Moss (1962) should be consulted.

In analyzing the results of this experiment, we quickly encountered an unexpected complication. The correlation between conductance and heart-rate "alerting" responses depended strikingly on the announced content of the tape recordings. When we told the subjects that they were going to listen to a recorded anger episode in which peers were involved, the product-moment correlation between heart-rate and palmar-conductance "alerting" responses was +.66, significant at below the .001 level. When, on the other hand, the subjects were told that they would listen to an episode in which a son was expressing his anger toward and to his mother, the correlation was −.06! The only finding like this with which we are familiar is that of Ax (1953) who was the first, we believe, to point out that the correlations among autonomic variables can depend upon the affect aroused by the stimulus conditions. In his study, higher correlations were found in anger states than in fear states. This phenomenon—situational determination of the correlation among autonomic variables—seemed to result in an interesting discrepancy in our results when we correlated autonomic activity with perceptual behavior.

For "Aggression to Peer," where palmar-conductance and heart-rate responses were highly correlated, both autonomic functions were positively and significantly related to delayed recognition of the tachistoscopically presented drawings. For differing combinations of pictures, we secured the results shown in the following tabulation. This lists the product-moment correlations between physiological responses, on the one hand, and the average required exposure for three different pairings of the visual stimuli in which aggressive actions were depicted, on the other hand.

Picture numbers	Heart rate	Palmar conductance
1 and 13	.32	.15
2 and 14	.36 ($p<.05$)	.38 ($p<.05$)
13 and 14	.48 ($p<.001$)	.36 ($p<.05$)

The greater the response, then, whether in heart rate or palmar conductance, while preparing to listen to an episode of "Aggression to Peer," the greater the exposure that the subject required to report accurately the details of line drawings depicting aggressive action.

In this instance, the direction of the correlation with behavior was the same for both autonomic variables, and the result is contrary to our hypothesis. But we got a very different result for the tape recording that dealt with "Aggression to Mother," for which palmar-conductance and heart-rate responses were uncorrelated. The results were:

Picture numbers	Heart rate	Palmar conductance
1 and 13	.00	–.39 ($p<.05$)
2 and 14	.29	–.35 ($p<.05$)
13 and 14	.22	–.50 ($p<.001$)

Here, palmar-conductance response was significantly *negatively* correlated with the perceptual threshold, whereas heart-rate response was still *positively* (but insignificantly) correlated. Subjects who exhibited large increases in palmar conductance when preparing to listen to an episode of "Aggression to Mother," then, were significantly faster in the tachistoscopic task. If heart-rate responses have any predictive value in this situation, the tendency is opposite to that shown by palmar conductance.

These results essentially are in accordance with the hypothesis under test. They would be completely so if the correlations of heart-rate response with perceptual behavior had been high enough to be statistically significant.

A further attempt was made to verify the notion of antagonistic and opposed relationships of sudomotor and cardiac responses to behavior. An index was formed, expressing the preponderance of palmar-conductance reaction over heart-rate reaction. The autonomic lability scores for heart rate were arranged in rank order from low to high; the same was done for palmar-conductance lability scores. Each subject was then assigned two ranks, one for palmar-conductance reaction, the other for heart-rate reaction, and a difference score between the ranks was taken: palmar-conductance rank minus heart-rate rank. A large negative score, then, would mean that the subject's relative standing within the group was much higher for heart-rate reaction than for palmar-conductance reaction, and we would expect him to have a high threshold in the recognition task. A positive score would mean that the subject's palmar-conductance reaction was greater than his heart-rate reaction, and we would expect him to have a low threshold in the recognition task. We expect, therefore, a negative correlation between threshold and the autonomic index so formed. The results for "Aggression to Mother" supported the hypothesis, and are given in the tabulation below:

Pictures 1 and 13: –.13
Pictures 2 and 14: –.48 ($p<.01$)
Pictures 13 and 14: –.43 ($p<.05$)

Even for "Aggression to Peer," where we contend with a high positive correlation between heart-rate and palmar-conductance responses and with like-signed correlations of these variables with performance in the tachistoscopic task, we again found negative correlations, one of —.07, and one of —.31. (The latter correlation just misses being significant. The correlation for picture pair 1—13 was not computed.) The direction of these correlations, of course, is again in accordance with the hypothesis.

These results, then, exhibit one instance in which palmar conductance and heart rate correlated in the same direction with behavior, and one in which they acted with opposite effect. They also suggest that the relative magnitudes of these fractions of autonomic response are of some importance for elucidating autonomic correlates of behavior.

We cannot really explain the discrepancies between the results for "Aggression to Mother" and "Aggression to Peer." We feel that one requisite to understanding and explanation is a clear understanding of differential patterns of organization of autonomic nervous system response to different stressor conditions; at present there are insufficient experimental data to enable meaningful generalizations.

The relation of autonomic responses in adulthood to childhood involvement in intellectual tasks, and to intellectual competence. For a small sample of seventeen to nineteen of the adult subjects, sufficient material had been recorded in the files at the time the subjects were ten to fourteen years old, to enable reliable ratings of the subjects' attempts at mastery of intellectual and academic subjects, and of their expectancy of failure in intellectual tasks (for details, see Kagan and Moss, 1962). Aside from the interest in studying historical and developmental determination of autonomic responses, we hoped to find again some differential significance of heart-rate and palmar-conductance responses. In particular, the experiment on situational stereotypy had shown that marked heart-rate accelerations occur during "mental" problem solving. We wondered if heart-rate response to problem-solving activities would be greater or less in individuals with a known history of application to intellectual tasks. Heart-rate responses, from base to stimulus level, were computed by means of the autonomic lability score to which we have already referred. The scores were then correlated with the ratings. The results are shown in Table I.

Those men who, at the ages of ten to fourteen years, were actively seeking gratification in intellectual and scholastic activities, consistently showed greater cardiac acceleration while they were engaged in intellectual tasks when they were adults. The correlations are substantial, ranging between +.45 and +.72. It is fascinating to note, moreover, that "failure expectancy" as a child is substantially and *negatively* related to cardiac acceleration during problem-solving activity as an adult. Apparently, those who earlier in life had developed a feeling that they were not successful in scholastic and intellectual tasks show less cardiac involvement in such tasks as adults. The correlations again are substantial, ranging from —.47 to —.71.

It is not true, however, that individuals with a history of concern with, and anticipation of success in, intellectual tasks are in general autonomically more reactive. They do not show greater cardiac response to the nonintellectual stressors, and they are not as strongly nor as consistently more reactive with respect to palmar conductance.

These findings suggested an investigation of the relationship between intelligence and autonomic response. The cor-

TABLE I

These are product-moment correlations between autonomic responses to various stimulus situations when the subjects were aged 20 to 30 and the subjects' concern with intellectual mastery and expectancy of intellectual failure when the subjects were 10 to 14 years old. The superscripts a, b, and c denote significance at below the 5%, 1%, and 0.1% levels, respectively. N is 19 for correlations with "Intellectual Mastery" ratings, and 17 for correlations with ratings of "Failure Expectancy."

Stimulus situation	*Heart-rate response correlated with*		*Palmar-conductance response correlated with*	
	Intell. Mastery	*Failure Expect.*	*Intell. Mastery*	*Failure Expect.*
Make-up sentences	+.45[a]	—.47[a]	+.24	—.44[a]
Mental arithmetic	+.65[b]	—.57[a]	+.07	—.22
Reverse spelling	+.72[c]	—.71[c]	+.39	—.37
Game rules	+.69[c]	—.54[a]	+.34	—.31
White noise	+.05	—.22	+.44[a]	—.29
Cold pressor	+.10	—.27	+.43	—.35
Photic flicker	+.16	—.19	+.40	—.28

relations are shown in Table II. Heart rate does not appear to be a more specific correlate of I.Q. than palmar conductance, as we might have expected. But it is instructive to observe two things in the table. First, six of the seven significant correlations link autonomic reactivity with verbal I.Q. rather than with performance I.Q. Secondly, the heart-rate responses that correlate significantly with I.Q. are heart-rate responses to the intellectual stressors only.

These two sets of results seem to mean that the more involved with the task at hand (early attempts at intellectual mastery), the less the history of expectation of failure, and the more competent the individual (the higher the verbal I.Q.), the greater the autonomic response to intellectual tasks. A concept linking *involvement in relevant and interesting tasks* to autonomic reactivity fits these data far better than more traditional concepts of "emotionality" or "anxiety" over failure. A recent study by Mandler and his collaborators (1961) provides support for this view. They found that subjects who avoided personal involvement in a stimulus situation showed less autonomic reactivity than those who became personally involved in the task.

Autonomic response and the use of affective labels. Another contrast between heart rate and palmar conductance was found in studies of the correlation of autonomic responses with individual differences in the manner of classifying and organizing the multitudinous stimuli in our environment. Kagan and Moss have found stability over time and over tasks in the way in which individuals approach and classify aspects of their environment. These individual differences can be called preferred modes of conceptualization (again, for details, see Kagan and Moss, 1962).

One of the tools for assaying such differences is a concept-formation task, in which cardboard representations of human figures are the materials to be sorted. In this task, the subject is presented with a total of three arrays of twenty-two figures each. The subject's task is to select out groups of fig-

Table II

These are product-moment correlations between Wechsler-Bellevue intelligence quotients and autonomic responses to various stimulus situations. Correlations with asterisks are significant at below the 5% level. N = 29.

Stimulus situation	*Heart-rate response correlated with*		*Palmar-conductance response correlated with*	
	Verbal I.Q.	*Performance I.Q.*	*Verbal I.Q.*	*Performance I.Q.*
Make-up sentences	+.07	—.06	+.39*	+.05
Mental arithmetic	+.43*	+.23	+.22	+.06
Reverse spelling	+.30	+.40*	+.39*	+.23
Game rules	+.38*	+.25	+.36*	.00
White noise	.00	—.05	+.34	+.20
Cold pressor	—.09	—.10	+.33	+.23
Photic flicker	—.03	+.05	+.36*	+.23

ures that "go together" on some basis. The basis for classification is up to the subject.

One response category—the affective-elaborative concept—is defined as a grouping of figures on the basis of similarity in affective or motivational state. The figures are said to be mean, maladjusted, mad, happy, dejected, sad, or content; or they are said to belong together because a common motive, intent, or desire appears: they want help or are asking for something, or want power. This highly inferential conceptual preference is not significantly correlated with verbal I.Q. ($r = .16$).

In Table III are shown the correlations between this affective-elaborative conceptual preference and autonomic responses to the different stimulus situations.

TABLE III

These are product-moment correlations between autonomic responses to various stimulus situations and the tendency to sort pictures of human figures on the basis of similarity in affect or motive state. The superscripts a, b, and c denote significance at below the 5%, 1% and 0.1% levels, respectively. N = 29.

Stimulus situation	*Heart rate*	*Palmar conductance*
Make-up sentences	$+.53^{b}$	$+.42^{a}$
Mental arithmetic	$+.45^{a}$	$+.41^{a}$
Reverse spelling	$+.49^{b}$	$+.60^{c}$
Game rules	$+.37^{a}$	$+.48^{b}$
White noise	$+.10$	$+.40^{a}$
Cold pressor	$+.23$	$+.58^{c}$
Photic flicker	$+.49^{b}$	$+.37^{a}$

First, it can be seen that, without exception, cardiac acceleration during intellectual problem-solving activity has substantial positive co-variation with the tendency to utilize affective-elaborative concepts. The correlation is about +.50.

Second, the two tasks involving storage and organization of input information for later retrieval and report also reveal co-variation between cardiac response and the exhibition of the affective-elaborative preference. One of these storage and retrieval tasks was Rules of the Game which, it will be remembered, involved attentive listening to elaborate input information, and simultaneous organization and storage. Cardiac response to this stressor condition was positively and significantly correlated with the production of affective-elaborative concepts, the correlation being about + .40.

Although "Flash" was primarily a simple input situation, it did have a minimal demand for organization and memory storage, since the subjects were told that they would be asked later to report what colors and patterns had been seen. Cardiac response to the photic stimulus was also correlated with the affective-elaborative preference (r = .49).

In sharp contrast, cardiac reactivity to the two stressors that did not involve internal elaboration or memory in any way (white noise, which produced deceleration, and the cold pressor test, which produced acceleration) did not correlate with the conceptual measurement. This result shows that we are not dealing with a generalized factor of cardiac reactivity or a generalized factor of affectivity. It does not seem to be true that people who use elaborate affective and motivational language tend to be cardiac accelerators in all stressor conditions. Rather it seems, as we might have expected, that elaborative conceptual classification of human figures is correlated with cardiac acceleration only in those stimulus conditions where our theory implies that cardiac acceleration facilitates problem-solving activity, "internal orientation," and the retrieval of stored information.

By contrast, palmar-conductance reaction seems to be a more general correlate of individual differences in affective-elaborative conceptualizations. Not one correlation in Table III fails to reach significance. They range from +.37 to +.60. Thus, without regard to the nature of the eliciting stimulus (within the limits of this experiment, of course) palmar-conductance hyperreactors tend to be individuals who are prone to use affective-elaborative concepts. Here we may indeed be dealing with a generalized factor of affectivity. Palmar conductance and heart rate, then, are shown again to have differential significance for behavior, palmar conductance being a generalized response, heart rate a response with more specific correlates.

Summary and Discussion

We began this paper by expressing our dissatisfaction with points of view that link autonomic function automatically and exclusively to such concepts as stress, homeostasis, emotion, and arousal. The studies reported in this paper have strengthened this dissatisfaction. Each study yielded data that called for modification and major supplementation of existing concepts.

In one of the studies, we measured changes in heart rate and palmar conductance in two different groups of subjects exposed to eight stimulus conditions. In a second investigation of a small subgroup of these subjects, we correlated the autonomic responses with some background information that had been collected some ten years earlier. The data of both these studies suggested somewhat novel principles and cast serious doubt upon the applicability of the concepts usually invoked to account for psychologically induced autonomic activity.

The first study tested a hypothesis, one part of which asserts that heart rate will decrease, other things being equal, when the subject sustains attention to the external environment—when the subject "wants to accept" environmental inputs. Four of the eight stimulus conditions required sustained attentiveness, although they differed in avenue of sensory input, in symbolic and semantic complexity, and in affectivity. All four situations produced cardiac deceleration, and in three of these stimulus situations, the heart rate actually decreased to below the level observed when the subject was sitting motionless and relaxed between tasks. The results of another study, now being prepared for publication, demonstrate that these decelerations are not secondary to induced elevations of blood pressure.

The hypothesis also required that heart-rate acceleration be observed when the subject "wants to reject" environmental inputs. This part of the hypothesis was tested indirectly. Because it is commonly observed that mental concentration is often accompanied by diminished responsiveness to irrelevant external stimuli, and sometimes by attempts to eliminate such stimuli (e.g., by closing one's eyes), three mental problem-solving tasks were used. The assumption that these stimulus conditions induced a "need to reject" irrelevant external stimuli may not be justified, of course. It can be fairly stated, however, that each of the three tasks, while differing from the others in content and in the specific nature of the required problem-solving activity, called for mental concentration and for the cognitive manipulation of symbols according to predetermined rules. In each of the tasks, moreover, attention to the external environment was limited to brief moments of time in which a problem was stated succinctly to the subject. In accordance with the hypothesis, marked cardiac acceleration occurred with each of the problem tasks.

The eighth stimulus condition was the painful cold pressor test, which required immersion of the foot in ice water maintained at 4°C. This stimulus produced marked cardiac acceleration. However, the degree of acceleration was somewhat less than that accompanying mental arithmetic, and approximately equal to that produced by the other two problem-solving activities. It may be only coincidence that the effects of the cold pressor test on heart rate are practically indistinguishable from those of problem-solving tasks. It is provocative to speculate, however, that the common effect is attributable to the fact that the cold pressor test has some behavioral similarity to a task such as mental arithmetic. The common factor might be the subject's need and ability to "reject" environmental stimuli. In support of this admittedly tenuous notion we referred briefly to neurophysiological evidence concerning central control of sensory afferent pathways, and to the suggestive fact that increases in heart rate and arterial pressure are effective stimuli to the baroceptors within the carotid sinus. Effective stimulation of these pressure-sensitive receptors has been shown to result in diminished transmission along sensorimotor pathways. The "reason" for cardiac acceleration in both the cold pressor and the problem-solving tests, then, might lie in the mechanisms involved in the organism's attempt to decrease the effectiveness of external stimuli. Similarly, the "reason" for cardiac deceleration might lie in the mechanisms facilitating sensory receptivity.

Two of these eight stimulus situations were designed specifically to test two interrelated deductions from our general hypothesis concerning the conditions that determine the occurrence of acceleration or deceleration of the heart rate. In one of these situations—Rules of the Game—the subject had to listen attentively to the rules for a fictitious card game and simultaneously had to store the rules in memory for a later quiz on the game. We hoped to find an effect on heart rate intermediate between the deceleratory effect of sustained attentiveness to external stimuli and the acceleratory effect of mental concentration. This crucial hypothesis was supported decisively in both groups of subjects. In the other of the two special stimulus conditions, the subject was required to attend to an unpleasant white noise. We hoped again to find an effect on heart rate intermediate between the acceleratory effect of an unpleasant stimulus (which the subject "wants to reject") and the deceleratory effect of sustained attentiveness to external stimuli. The data, however, clearly failed to conform to this expectation. Heart rate decreased decisively for this stimulus in both groups of subjects. It would be unfair to the hypothesis, however, to omit mention of the study in which arterial pressure was measured, even though the details of this study were not presented here. Arterial pressure increased markedly in problem-solving tasks, as did heart rate; it decreased, as did heart rate, in the two purest "environmental intake" situations. In both Rules of the Game and White Noise, however, arterial pressure increased modestly. The combination of the two related cardiovascular variables, then, yields decisive support of the hypothesis being tested.

No specific hypotheses were made in this study about differential effects of the eight stimulus situations on skin-conductance measurements. The data showed that although skin conductance increased in all the stimulus conditions, the changes were generally smaller for the "environmental intake" than for the other conditions. White noise was the exception to this generalization. The change in palmar conductance to this stimulus was as great as or greater than the change in palmar conductance to the problem-solving tasks or the cold pressor test. Thus heart rate, rather than skin conductance, consistently differentiated episodes of sustained attentiveness from the stimulus conditions not involving such an "external orientation." These results, we believe, could not have been anticipated by traditional concepts.

We took some pains, in the body of the paper, to separate demonstrable fact from interpretation. The only completely defensible conclusion to be drawn from these data is that situational stereotypy of autonomic response patterns exists. Patterns of heart-rate and skin-conductance responses are shown to be dependent upon the stimuli or tasks that are used.

The facts, however interpreted, obviously raise difficulties for the many investigators who infer states of affect, anxiety, arousal, or activation from the occurrence of sympathetic-like changes in the target organs of autonomic activity, and for those who similarly infer "tension reduction" from parasympathetic-like changes. Unpleasant white noise, for example, is "tension reducing" on the basis of its effects on heart rate, but "arousing" on the basis of its effects on skin conductance. As another example, the tape-recorded drama, which elicits associations of injury and death, would be regarded as "soothing" or "tension reducing" on the basis of its decelerative effect on heart rate. As a final example, the Make-up Sentences test would be judged more "emotional" or "arousing" than the task called Rules of the Game because of the greater cardiac acceleration to the former test. By any reasonable nonphysiological criterion, however, Rules of the Game was by far the more difficult and taxing of the two stimulus conditions.

Sizable correlations were found between the autonomic responses of our adult Fels subjects and their concern with intellectual and scholastic activities during childhood and adolescence. The greater the childhood involvement with such matters, the greater the cardiac response as adults to problem-solving tasks similar to those practiced in school. The less involved the child, the smaller the adult cardiac response to problems. These findings also raise obstacles to the easy and glib use of such concepts as "anxiety" to explain the occurrence of cardiac acceleration to potentially conflictful situations. It would be easy to say that tasks such as mental arithmetic are commonly associated with "anxiety" in our culture, and that this accounts for large cardiac accelerations during such an activity. But we would then be forced to conclude that subjects who, as children, developed feelings of successful participation in intellectual matters were more "anxious" as adults, when performing intellectual tasks, than those who had not developed confidence in their intellectual skills. A common meaning given to "anxiety" is the apprehension of dangerous, punishing, or unpleasant consequences. Without some complicated and unverifiable reasoning, it would be difficult to explain why the child who does not anticipate failure (behaviorally) becomes an adult who does (autonomically). It seems to us that our results can be viewed more simply: *Involvement in motivationally relevant tasks*—tasks that interest and engage the subject because they correspond with his own achievement needs—is accompanied by high autonomic reactivity.

This notion, however, should not be applied indiscriminately. "Involvement in a motivationally relevant task" was not clearly accompanied by increased skin-conductance responses. Only cardiac response was decisively predicted by the subjects' earlier histories, and even then only cardiac response to problem-solving tasks. This specificity of the pattern of correlations calls to mind the fact that increases in heart rate seem to be a hallmark of mental concentration, as was found in the investigation of the stimulus-bound nature of autonomic response patterns. The two sets of findings suggest a principle that is difficult to verbalize, in the present state of knowledge. However, it might be said that "involvement in a motivationally relevant task" seems to be accompanied by accentuation of that aspect of the response pattern that can be shown to be typical or characteristic of the task. Thus, for example, the hallmark of mental concentration, in contrast to environmental intake, is cardiac acceleration. Subjects who show the largest accelerations to problem tasks have histories indicating greater involvement in these tasks. Perhaps this is a reflection of the fact that the requirements of the task, as defined by the experimenter, are the requirements of the task, as perceived by the subject. The experimenter wants the subject to engage in mental problem-solving activities. If the subject does so wholeheartedly (!), his physiological responses so indicate, perhaps because they are indispensable to or facilitatory of the successful performance of the task.

The results reported also suggest the value of investigating the relationship between intelligence and autonomic responses to intellectual tasks. Wechsler-Bellevue I.Q.s (adult form) had been obtained contemporaneously with the autonomic data. The results showed that the autonomic responses were positively and moderately correlated with verbal scale I.Q. Of seven significant correlations, six involved verbal scale I.Q. Verbal scale I.Q. scores, of course, are determined by arithmetic and verbal skills to a much greater extent than are performance scale I.Q. scores. In this correlation study, additional evidence was found that heart rate increases during problem-solving activity specifically reflected involvement in such activity. Heart-rate responses to intellectual tasks tended to be greater in those individuals most competent to deal with such tasks, i.e., in those with higher verbal scale I.Q. The results were not completely uniform, however, for only two of the four correlations, which ranged between +.07 and +.43, were significant. On the other hand, heart-rate responses to nonintellectual tasks clearly were not related to verbal scale I.Q. The three correlations were .00, —.09, and —.03 for the same sample of subjects. In contrast to heart rate, palmar-conductance responses during the performance of intellectual tasks had no greater correlation with verbal scale I.Q. than did conductance responses to nonintellectual stimulus conditions. The correlations between conductance responses to varied stimulus conditions and verbal scale I.Q. were all quite comparable in magnitude. They ranged between +.22 and +.39, and four of the seven correlations were statistically significant. Palmar-conductance reactivity, then, appears to be a more diffuse and generalized correlate of verbal scale I.Q. than is heart-rate reactivity. Conductance responses to flickering light had as much in common with verbal scale I.Q. as conductance responses to Rules of the Game.

In a third study, surprisingly substantial relations were found between physiological reactivity and the tendency of subjects to group together cardboard representations of human figures by using inferential labels describing motive and affect states. In this study, too, palmar-conductance reactivity was a more diffuse and generalized correlate of behavior than was heart-rate reactivity. Whatever the stimulus condition, palmar-conductance responses were significantly correlated with the tendency to use highly inferential concepts in classifying human figures. The correlations ranged between +.40 and +.60. Heart-rate responses were significantly correlated with this mode of behavior only for those stimulus conditions in which some form of intellectual activity was required. For such stimulus conditions, the correlations between cardiac acceleration and the use of inferred affect and motive states ranged between +.37 and +.53. In the two stimulus conditions which required no intellectual activity, however, the correlations dropped to insignificant levels of +.10 and +.23.

The studies reviewed so far have shown, in different ways, that palmar-conductance and heart-rate responses have different behavioral significance, and respond differently in different stimulus conditions. In another analysis, we tested a specific hypothesis concerning differential correlations of heart rate and conductance with perceptual recognition. We expected cardiac acceleration to be correlated with difficulty in perceptual recognition, whereas we expected conductance increase to be correlated with facilitated recognition. Thus, we hypothesized that the larger the subject's cardiac acceleration while he was preparing to listen to tape-recorded material in a potentially conflictful area, the longer would be the required tachistoscopic exposure for clear identification of line drawings depicting action in the same content area. Palmar conductance, we hypothesized, would act in an opposite way; palmar-conductance increases while preparing to listen to the recording should be correlated with greater sensitivity to the visually presented stimuli. Support was found for these two hypotheses for the content area involving Aggression to Mother. For another content area, however, Aggression to Peer, we found that the greater the autonomic response while preparing to listen to the tape recording, whether in heart rate or palmar conductance, the greater the tachistoscopic exposure required for accurate report of line drawings depicting aggressive action. The difference between these sets of correlations for Aggression to Peer and Aggression to Mother seemed attributable to another aspect of situational determination of response patterns: the correlations among autonomic responses may be determined by the stimulus conditions. For Aggression to Peer, heart-rate and palmar-conductance responses were correlated +.66. For Aggression to Mother, however, the correlation dropped dramatically to −.06.

This brings us full circle to the clear realization that concepts currently invoked to relate autonomic activity to behavior are inadequate. They involve generalizations that repeatedly are found wanting when specific empirical data are uncovered in experimental investigations that deliberately widen the scope of observation beyond the traditional confines of emotion and activation. How can one explain the fact that for one content area (Aggression to Peer), palmar-conductance increase in preparing for an auditory presentation is correlated +.36 ($p < .05$) with visual recognition, whereas for another content area (Aggression to Mother), the correlation changes sign and becomes −.50 ($p < .001$)? Only detailed and specific principles, yet to be found and verified, can cope with these and kindred findings.

CHAPTER 10

Autonomic Responses and Emotions: Further Discussion

ALBERT F. AX, PH.D.

To emphasize what Dr. Lacey said, certainly the expression of emotions is differentiated. The autonomic nervous system is highly differentiated both within the sympathetic and within the parasympathetic systems. My study, to which he referred, on the differentiation between fear and anger clearly demonstrated this and convinced me that all types, qualities, and degrees of emotion probably can be described and measured through the functioning of physiological processes.

With this firm conviction in mind some years ago, I looked to see what had to be done next. Of course, I could have gone on and tried to describe all the various emotions in this way, but those of you who have not worked with polygraph records may not realize how extremely time-consuming and expensive both in time and money it is to analyze them. Actually it takes anywhere from 50 to 100 hours to analyze a ten-channel polygraph record of one hour's recording, and that is not really an exhaustive analysis. Therefore, even at that time, back in 1950, I visualized an automatic data-processing system which could do this for us. In the subsequent ten years I have been trying to acquire this, and finally have succeeded. I shall describe briefly what it involves and what its capability is.

We first start out with our transducers or electrodes that we attach to the subject, and our system is prepared to handle up to twenty-nine of these, so we could record twenty-nine separate physiological variables. At the same time that these are being recorded on a multiple-channel-strip chart recorder or polygraph, they are also being fed into an analog-to-digital converter—an electronic device which rapidly samples the variables, converts them into binary numbers, and records them on magnetic tape, in a format suitable as input to a computer. That concludes the recording phase. Then, before starting computing, we examine the polygraph record for sections of artifact or for parts that we do not want to analyze; we program the computer to skip those sections. Then we feed the magnetic tape into the computer, and the primary program is set to discover what we call "points of interest," namely, the maximum and minimum points, end of rise, end of fall, beginning rise and beginning fall—six different types of points of interest. It identifies each one of these, tells us what type it is, what the amplitude of the variable is at that point, the exact time of occurrence, and the area under the curve between this point of interest and the last one. So these four items of data for each point of interest are acquired. These are the raw data from which we proceed to do further statistical work. Of course, another computer program can obtain cross-correlation between any pair of variables, do power-spector analysis or whatever one wishes. Once the data are in digital form, any desired kind of computing can be carried out without any further degradation of the data or loss of accuracy.

I think that such data-processing equipment when in general use will be a major factor in making the psychophysiological examination practicable for diagnosis of personality and medical conditions. It has not been practical in the past except in a very limited way because of the time and cost of analyzing the data.

Our program includes three kinds of study. One seeks diagnostic patterns—physiological response patterns to various kinds of stressors to aid in the diagnosis of schizophrenia. The stressors that we use are pain stimulus, a tracking task, a psychiatric interview, and various drugs. Another kind of study concentrates on psychotherapy. I think that this is probably the most practical way of studying genuine emotion which can be legitimately aroused in a medical setting and which is at the same time well known. The psychotherapist has as accurate information about the emotional state as can be obtained.

The third type of study is the more systematic type of analysis in which we study very closely the types of curves, the nature of the response of each variable, and the responses to frequently repeated standard stimuli. By then integrating their interaction with appropriate mathematical tools the ultimate goal of describing the autonomic nervous system as a total system may be approached.

MILTON GREENBLATT, M.D.

As the discussion has developed I have observed that certain fundamental parameters have been neglected. People have spoken of expression of emotion as though it were a discrete time-limited act. Now, as a matter of introspection, it is difficult to assume that all emotion arises as discrete events; it seems rather that emotional value is attached to almost every moment of time. Certainly in the conscious waking state we find prevailing background mood, tones, or qualities of affective experience at all times; and in dreams, emotional meaning of some significance appears to be attached to every dream event. On this affective background more or less discrete emotional events take place, some rising as modest swells over the background, others appearing in sharper wave forms, and some so large and strong as to dwarf into apparent insignificance the background from which they arise. This is one problem.

A second problem concerns the socioenvironmental context in which the emotion is developed and expressed. Although apparent innate potential for emotional expression sets the basic elements of the *stage,* emotional expression seems largely to arise and take place in a psychosocial context that not only plays a role in its elicitation, but modifies and molds it, so that the individuality of each person reflects in later life these primary conditions. When we think of it there is relatively little emotion that we express that is not *somehow* in relation to an interpersonal situation. Even our feelings about *things* and abstract qualities, such as *justice, democracy, love itself,* are basically determined by a specific psychosocial matrix.

When emotional expression is investigated as a research task, it is almost necessarily studied in some interpersonal context. This basic assumption in our investigations should be made very explicit: the type of emotional expression is almost always in relation to *others*—real or imagined; furthermore, these others *determine* to a large extent, certainly *strongly influence,* the form, context, and meaning of the emotional expression. The very names we give to some of our emotions—fear, anger, love, resentment—imply an object with special qualities and reacting potentials. Therefore, the *other* or *others* must be included; less than this degree of experimental sophistication sets us back into the period in which the individual subject was the essential reactor to stimuli or stresses that were too often assumed to have neutral or indifferent significance. Later, I shall quote some of our own studies that have attempted to understand emotional expression from the psychophysiological transactional standpoint in a psychotherapeutic situation in which the *interacting diad* is considered as a whole.

Another problem concerns the *quality and purity* of emotions. We speak casually of a variety of emotions expressed by man, suggesting not only that we can identify and recognize them, but that they have a given purity and quality. In this respect we believe *love, anger, etc., are not emotions in a discrete sense but affective territories!* In any one individual, his many expressions of love or anger have qualities that are complex and highly variable—perhaps few expressions of a given "emotion" are identical within the same individual. It seems more acceptable to recognize that quality and purity vary enormously than to assume the emotion is a constant, although it is expected that some invariable qualities will also be found within a series of expressions called love, anger, etc. Depth analysis of emotional expressions in psychiatric patients reveals underlying meanings, significances, overtones, etc., to each sharp emotion experience that give it its true flavor, and like the dream, our understanding of the significance and quality of the emotion is a progressive function that seems never to end until the last therapeutic session.

Thus, each emotion is like a tone sounded on an instrument. The note, *A,* at a specific octave on the violin, for example, may be sounded in many different ways, depending on bowing techniques and vibrato, emphasis of overtones or undertones. In the moving context of the concerto, *A*'s meaning depends on the particular passage in which it is set, and the total context of the musical arrangement. If now we think of *A* sounded by several different instruments, the qualities of *A* are remarkably different, depending on whether it is piano, oboe, flute, etc. This analogy could be developed considerably more; however, it is perhaps sufficient thus to illustrate different properties possessed by a so-called "specific" emotion *within one individual* and *between different individuals.*

Now we come to the problem of the *intensity* of emotions, since this, too, is one of its fundamental aspects. Here we immediately enter the complexity that, as intensity of emotion rises, new qualities may be introduced. As the "quantity of excitation" associated with a given emotion increases, the identity of the emotion may change; thus tension may become fear; irritability, rage; warmth, aggressive love; and pleasure, pain. Research must then find a way to quantify emotion in its magnitude; otherwise communication of what we mean becomes confused.

When we come to the problem of *duration* of emotion, we are faced with the implications of the homeostatic mechanism of the organism. How long can one emotion be felt before natural mechanisms call a halt, reversing the psychophysiological events and often requiring a compensatory phase? Thus anger, depression, love, etc., especially in their acute forms, are difficult to sustain for long, and some of these emotions may pass into their opposites. After anger, love may be facilitated, and after depression, excitement. Thus, a specific stimulus situation or stress may call for anger immediately, but soon anger is at the mercy of basic neurophysiological mechanisms that change it altogether.

Although the problems are extremely complex, we are nevertheless able at this time to undertake simple experiments in this field with some hope of reaching validity.

Some of the earliest experiments in our laboratory were in 1949 when Ax, and later Schachter, tried to determine the physiological concomitants of different emotions in man. Cannon, you will remember, many years before, had stated on the basis of experiments in cats that different emotions could not be differentiated on the basis of peripheral physiology. Ax's experiments were among the first to challenge the Cannon hypothesis. Briefly, Ax showed that two emotions—fear and anger—*could be differentiated* on peripheral physiological grounds. This study and others that followed opened the door to a science of the physiology of the emotions, which has flourished since.

In Ax's study, emotions were produced in an interpersonal situation. Fear was *staged* by structuring the situation so that the subject thought he was in danger; and anger was evoked by constant badgering of the subject by a technician particularly suited to the task. We felt that the two experimental emotions could be best elicited in an interpersonal context, and that considerable attention must be paid to the details of the interactions, and particularly to the subject's interpretation of the situation. Sophisticated subjects (college students) could not easily be drawn into the laboratory drama, and some reacted blandly or mirthfully to the situation, but without the requisite "fear" or "anger." Less sophisticated subjects, drawn from the ranks of the unemployed, impressed by the laboratory and the apparatus, appeared to get involved in the situation and to produce emotions that we could classify with some conviction as "fear" and "anger."

Later, Schachter and Ax repeated many of the experiments with hypertensive subjects, again with differentiation of the two emotions. In a separate series of experiments, Funkenstein and co-workers, using a frustrating situation, were able to differentiate "anger in" from "anger out"—another demonstration of the value of the physiological approach.

I want to report here also investigations into the *interactive* nature of emotional expression in the two-person situation of the psychotherapeutic interview. Both patient and psychiatrist are attached to devices that record side-by-side their physiological changes, while observers note activity in the therapeutic chamber by looking through a one-way screen and by listening via earphones to all verbal interactions.

The relationship between the two interacting parties can be approached in several ways. For example, it is possible to ask whether, for portions of the interview judged as showing "positive" transference from patient to therapist, the physiological activity of the patient's heart is different from those in which he is in a state judged as "negative" transference. We do not yet know whether this is an invariable trait for all patients in such a situation; however, for some patients it is clear that average heart rate is statistically different in "positive" and "negative" periods.

We have asked the question whether the heart rate during "positive" utterances of patients (not "transference") is any different from that during "negative" utterances—judged by Bales's categories. Again, in some patients, this proves to be true.

In one well-studied patient, we observed that *heart-rate level and variability differed* in relation to the kind of emotional experience ("emotion" judged by an independent observer), and that these differences tended to be repeated over many interviews.

Probably we were the first to demonstrate that the psychiatrist apparently participated in the situation to the extent that he, too, showed changes in his heart rate corresponding to the patient's changes. This was true for the emotions "depression," "intrapunitive anger," "extrapunitive anger," but not for "anxiety." It was as though a "physiological rapport" asserted itself in some areas but not in others. Indeed, when the psychiatrist indicated that he was strongly involved in the interview, his "physiological rapport" manifested itself more than in those interviews in which he did not participate fully, was distracted, or, so to speak, "out of tune." We hope that these exciting results will be rechecked in our laboratory, and we hope others will also explore the many facets of this "interpersonal physiology."

Not only is it possible to correlate physiological shifts within the interview on a short-time basis with psychological transactions between two parties, but it is also possible to show patient-doctor physiological relationships on an inter-interview basis. In other words, fluctuations of over-all heart-rate level and variability, for example, from one therapeutic interview to another, of patient and psychiatrist are not random—they are correlated with each other and with the over-all tone and meaning of the interview. Simply stated, "tense" interviews are physiologically different from "relaxed" interviews for both patient and psychiatrist.

Thus, a field of "interpersonal physiology" is emerging. In the psychotherapeutic interview, patient and doctor respond to each other in lawful ways, psychophysiologically speaking. Whether this phenomenon is limited to homologous organs, or exists for heterologous organs, too, remains to be developed. Also, it is likely that the phenomenon is influenced by many other factors in the environment. For instance, it has been noted that climatic variations may affect the over-all nature of the psychophysiological functioning during the interview period.

One further, rather whimsical note may be added. Certainly the presence of a psychiatrist is not necessary to assure that the patient talk, nor is it necessary to produce physiological changes or emotional expression of the subject. In our laboratory, one patient, properly instructed, talked abundantly during six different hours, without benefit of the psychiatrist's presence. Furthermore, she appeared to gain considerable emotional relief from her soliloquy—rather more than she was able to obtain in previous interviews with a psychiatrist (in another setting). It is true that during her soliloquy she often fantasied a psychiatrist present, so that her emotional expressions were apparently in relation to a fairly conscious, although fantasied, object. However, his physical presence was not necessary to promote emotional expression and an apparent degree of catharsis.

Part III

TOWARD A SYNTHESIS

Introductory Comments

The task of the contributors to this section is a difficult one, comparable to that posed by Humpty-Dumpty. "Emotion," fragmented by psychoanalyst, linguist, kinesicist, and autonomic physiologist alike, is now to be put together again. The task, however, is not impossible. Closer examination shows that some of the fragments of the corpse, strewn across the battleground, are made of straw. Old concepts have been exposed as limited. The phenomena are still real and important. Furthermore, certain unifying themes have already been stated, which will be amplified in these chapters.

Pribram, in a near tour de force, shows the depth of Freud's genius and the strength of Freud's original neuropsychological model. Some limitations of this model may also indicate that progress is possible even after Freud. In particular, I refer to the lack of a concept of positive pleasure. The Olds-Miller experiments on self-stimulation may be more than a minor stumbling block to the more traditional theories of emotion and motivation which hinge upon relief from tension.

The theme of "polyphony," mentioned in the introduction and expanded upon by Greenblatt in his closing remarks in the previous section, is developed by Engel. He points out than "an" emotion is an abstraction, albeit a useful, even necessary one. Emotion occurs always in a complex field. On a phenomenologic basis, Engel makes a compelling effort to isolate nodal points within that field. Whether or not his efforts can be successful without more fundamental isolation of the building blocks which underlie the phenomena is for the reader to decide. At least the effort defines the problem clearly and proposes a solution.

The communicative importance of emotions and their ontogenetic emergence from psychobiologically unified origins is also stressed by Engel. The need to consider context and meaning, which has already made itself manifest, is further elaborated by Bateson and Colby. They point out in different ways that the total characteristics of the emotional field are important in assessing and understanding its different components at any moment and during the course of time. Finally we come full circle. The explicit statements of the evolutionary point of view in Hamburg's paper and in Margaret Mead's concluding remarks speak for themselves. I hope that the lexical transcript which follows will express some of the emotion stirred by the confluence of thinking and feeling at this Symposium.

CHAPTER 11

A Neuropsychological Model: Some Observations on the Structure of Psychological Processes

KARL H. PRIBRAM, M.D.

My argument in this paper will be to the effect that a multi-level analysis of the psychological process can add fruitfully to our understanding of emotion in man. Indeed, such an analysis is one powerful tool for unraveling the complexities of the problem. Emotion, studied from these several levels, encompasses shades of phenomena from a primary process disruptive of the organism's equilibrium to a complexly patterned state that influences both the results of sensory inputs and of thoughtful activities.

Let me begin where Dr. Knapp in his introductory chapter left off: with Freud's "Project for a Scientific Psychology" written in 1895. My reason for beginning here is that as I read the Project, I find in it a neurological model of things psychological which is more sophisticated than any of the more current popular models. This came as a surprise to me. I originally read the Project for historical reasons, but found it to be an up-to-date useful research tool. To summarize this usefulness, I will use modern neurological and behavioral language, often derived directly from the German, rather than abide by the more usual psychoanalytic English translations to which we have become accustomed.

Some Primary Definitions

First and briefly, some primary definitions. Reference can be made to the accompanying diagram for further clarification. A more comprehensive treatment of the neurological model presented in the Project is available (Pribram, 1962a).

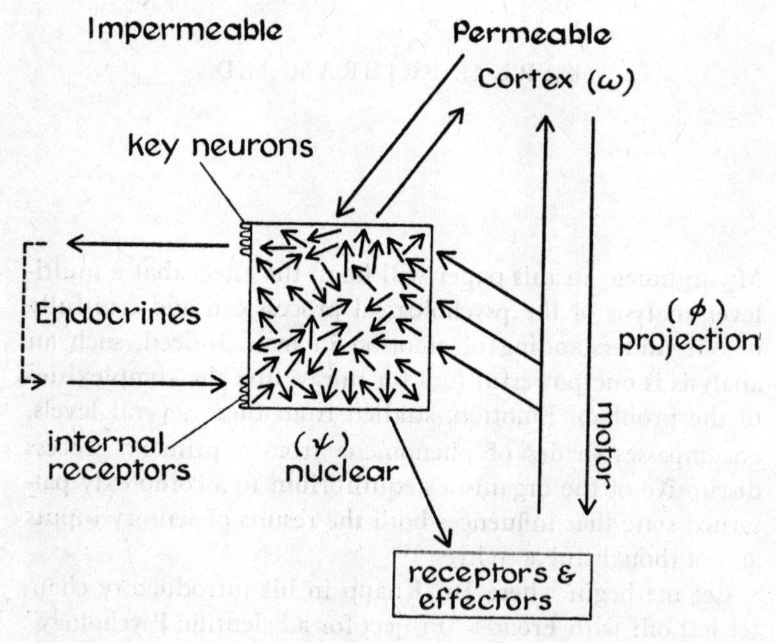

Figure I

A simplified diagram of the major system relationships of the neurological model proposed by Freud in the "Project for a Scientific Psychology." See text for amplification.

Excitation: Organisms are alive; they therefore make transformations on systems of energy. Metabolic processes are one example of such transformations. Behavioral interactions with chemical and physical stimuli (i.e., psychological processes) are another. These interactions must be quantifiable. The problem is, what to measure. The nervous system is intimately involved in regulating behavior—why not use indices of neural excitation as measures of the transformations of energy involved in the psychological process? And so, the nerve impulse, recorded electrically, is used as a measure of propagated neural activity. That leaves local, nontransmitted excitation. Electrotonic potential changes (and in today's language, other graded response mechanisms of neural tissue such as dendritic and synaptic potential changes) serve as indices of this type of neural activity. Freud uses the term *cathexis* to denote this localized neural excitation. The transformations of energy involved in the psychological process are therefore to be understood as changes in the neural processing of the interactions between the organism and its physical and chemical environment.

Cathexis: The excitation of neural tissue is measured as change in electrical activity recorded from the tissue. Abrupt potential change—the nerve impulse—is a measure of propagated excitation. Recently the attention of neurophysiologists has again focused (as it did in the latter half of the nineteenth century) on the nontransmitted electrical activities of neural tissue: the graded, spontaneously waxing and waning mechanisms characteristically found where synaptic and dendritic fields predominate. These electrotonic manifestations of local neural excitability are measures of the cathexis of the tissue. Cathexis, therefore, refers to the amount of local, nonpropagated, neural excitation which leads to impulsive, transmitted excitation only under certain special circumstances.

Resistance: The property of synapses that counters the propagation of quantity of excitation in a neural net. The transmission of frequency patterns of nerve impulses is not altered by resistance. Synapses have no other property. Current neurophysiological knowledge has not been looked at from this viewpoint—the techniques to study the transmission of patterns of frequency are in their infancy.

Memory: Synapses have only one property—they resist the transmission of quantity of excitation through the neural net. (They do not distort the propagation of frequency patterns, however.) Synaptic resistance is usually overcome only when the quantity of excitation on *both* sides of the synaptic junction builds up above some threshold. Resistance can also be overridden by excessive excitation. Repeated lowering of resistance at a particular synapse leads to a permanent conduction path through that synapse. Such permanent facilitation is the basis of memory. In the projection and cortical systems synaptic facilitation is relatively complete due to fairly direct contact with an ever exciting environment—their local patterns of excitation are therefore determined for the most part by the inputs to these systems. The nuclear systems, on the other hand, somewhat more isolated from external stimulation, provide the locus where synaptic facilitation can be selective. Here, therefore, patterns of excitation are dependent as much or more on traces left by previous synaptic facilitations as on those produced by current stimulation. The structure of memory at any moment is thus a function of these nuclear system traces as they are currently activated.

Motive: Each cell within the nuclear system is in multiple contact with its neighbors. If resistance were overcome with equal ease at all these contacts, transmission would be random. The organism does not behave randomly—its behavior is directed, i.e., motivated. To account for this the assumption is made that the resistances of the various synaptic contacts of a cell are differentially affected in the nuclear system. All parts of a neuron must therefore not necessarily behave in the same way at any moment. That this is so has been demonstrated conclusively, at least in the invertebrate nervous system. Neurons therefore are the selectors of the paths of conduction that build up the memory trace. The function of this selection is to give direction to behavior—i.e., to motivate. The pattern of pathways of lowered resistance that are based on the selection form the memory trace.

Notes on the Structure of Awareness

Now for the secondary definitions. These are all predicated on the notion that awareness is a function of certain neural processes—that awareness results when the cortical mechanism is excited not only by input from peripheral receptors but also by Freud's memory-motive mechanism.

Pain: A sudden, dramatic increase in cortical cathexis follows noxious stimulation of somatic receptors. The psychological concomitant of this increase is pain. Not only are the usual frequency patterns of neural impulses transmitted to the cortex through the projection systems, but a large quantity of excitation erupts from the nuclear systems because synaptic resistances are overwhelmed. With removal of the stimulus there is a sudden drop in cortical cathexis and thus a relief from pain.

Strain: All noxious excitation cannot be escaped: e.g., stimulation of the neuroreceptors in the core of nuclear systems. Such excitation must be held at a minimum by actions on the part of the individual and his environment—e.g., actions designed to reduce the amount of the chemical substances that stimulate the neuroreceptors. The gradually increasing cathexes produced by such stimulations, when transmitted to the cortical systems, are experienced as strain (i.e., as unpleasure).

The Affects: The excitations that initiate and relieve pain and strain intimately involve the nuclear system; traces of these excitations are left in this system; these traces facilitate conduction paths so that on future occasions they will be selectively activated. As already noted, these selectively activated neural networks are the basis of memory and motive. Cathexis of the cortical system derived from the excitations in these networks of the nuclear system is the neural concomitant of the affects.

Under what conditions, asks Freud, do affects occur and what are their components? Negative affects cannot be differentiated on the basis of whether the irritant was external or internal, for there is in the nuclear system considerable convergence of the pathways initiated by the somatic and by the internal neuroreceptors. In fact, Freud points out that the nuclear system is endowed in its midline portion with secretory mechanisms and these are activated whenever the quantities of excitation in the system reach a certain level. This is one reason why strain cannot be simply relieved: stimulation of the internal neuroreceptors activates the nuclear system; when a certain level of excitation has been reached, the neurosecretory cells are discharged; this in turn results in the production of more of the chemical substances that stimulate the internal receptors. The cycle can be interrupted only through external intervention designed to diminish abruptly the chemical stimulation, e.g., by feeding or by sexual release. So also, when a noxious external stimulus results in marked increase in the quantity of excitation in the nuclear system, chances are that this will activate the neurosecretory elements to pour out the chemical substances that stimulate the internal neuroreceptors. As an example, should one burn one's hand and withdraw it ever so quickly, there is nonetheless a temporary increase in the adrenalin circulation in the blood. Freud postulates a neurosecretory, i.e., a neurochemical stimulation of the adrenal rather than (or in addition to) the direct neural stimulation of this gland.

Thus, the neural traces left by stimulations initiated either externally or internally come to include the effects of internal excitation. Negative affects therefore are based on more than a one-to-one reproduction of the initiating experience. The neural concomitants of the negative affects, i.e., increases in cortical cathexis, are the results of the interactions of the affects of the initiating experience with those of the organism's internal reactions to the experience.

Positive affects are based on an additional complication. Whenever stimuli excite the nuclear system, they activate not only the paths associated with an increase, but also those that on prior occasions had led to a decrease in excitation. The effects from these trace excitations are to activate efferent motor discharge and so to diminish cathexis in the cortical system; thus the organism experiences a positive affect. Should circumstances be similar to those that relieved the strain on prior occasions, positive affect accompanies actions that lead to pleasure. Should circumstances have changed significantly, however, then strain will not be relieved by these actions.

What recent support is there for this conception of affect? There is one well-controlled experiment done by Schachter and Singer which is of extreme interest to us in this context. Schachter and Singer (1962) injected people with adrenalin (and controls with saline) just prior to making them take verbal tests—very difficult tests. The person who had been injected was not alone, however. In one situation the group taking the test made light of the whole affair. Another group griped and made nasty remarks about the tester and the whole experiment. The affect experienced by the adrenalin injected subjects was entirely different in these two situations. In one case, elation, stimulation, and excitement were expressed; and in the other, hostility and depression. The same amount of the same physiological substance, adrenalin, produced opposite effects that depended on the *social* context in which the subject was tested. Only the complexly structured memory traces activated by the social context can account for these differences in affect.

All recent experimental results do not so easily fit Freud's framework, however. You all know of the Olds (1956) experiments on self-stimulation. In their simplest aspect these data seem, superficially at least, at odds with the model presented in the Project. Yet, Olds is now using self-stimulation to condition isolated neural units in the cortex—so Freud's model may be found to fit even this exciting experimental result.

Suggestions Concerning the Structure of Adaptive Processes

Defenses and Satisfactions: These mechanisms invoke yet a third level of complexity: this level is predicated on the adaptive mechanisms to which Dr. Spitz referred earlier in this Symposium. Prolonged and intense excitation can be initiated by an affect, i.e., by awareness of a memory of pain and strain and the situations that led to their alleviation. Such remembrances can stimulate the neurosecretory cells of the nuclear system—and thus start the accruing strain spiral anew. The normal organism is not continually strained—Freud postulates, therefore, that the individual develops a *defense* against this release of neurosecretions. The defense mechanism is conceived as a lateral distribution of excitation in the neural network of the nuclear system, i.e., a distribution in a direction other than the transmission of excitation to the neurosecretory and cortical cells. The defense consists therefore of a diffusion of excitation that brings into functional contact an increasingly larger pool of neurons in the nuclear system and so delays and often prevents the transmission of excitation to the neurosecretory and cortical cells. Defense mechanisms so conceived prevent the build-up and maintenance of excessive strain.

The emphasis throughout the Project is on the interpersonal as well as on the neurological bases of the intrapsychic process. Freud therefore takes this opportunity to define as hostile those people whose actions could induce affects that would lead to strain. Defense in this context deals with hostilities. More of this in a moment.

Just as defenses develop to prevent affect from producing prolonged or overly intense strain, so satisfactions develop when affects result in pleasurable actions. The characteristics of satisfactions are rather different from those of defenses. The neural mechanisms of satisfactions involve primarily the cortical system. When the organism repeatedly experiences pleasure—i.e., the relief of strain—memory traces of the experience are built up in the nuclear system. When these traces are activated for whatever reason and the excitations are transmitted to the cortical system, the person becomes aware of positive affects. When the actions he undertakes on the basis of these positive affects are in concordance with the current situation, they lead to an experience of satisfaction. "As we showed in the beginning of the discussion, no discharge can bring about any permanent relief of tension as long as endogenous stimulations continue to be initiated and, in the nuclear system, excitation continues to be reestablished. The removal of these stimulations can only be effected by actions which will more or less stop the release of chemical substances in the interior of the body."

Again the emphasis is on the interpersonal: "The excitation of the cortical system thus acquires an extremely important secondary function—that of bringing about an understanding with other people. The infant is so constituted that an extraneous helper must carry out specific actions in the external world on its behalf. Only when these are accomplished is the infant in a position by means of reflex contrivances to perform what is necessary in the interior of his body in order to remove the endogenous stimulus. This total series of events constitutes the basis of an experience of satisfaction: persons become a prime source of satisfactory (and unsatisfactory) experience; further, the actions undertaken to obtain satisfaction usually involve other persons—thus moral motives are built up. But these are only some of the momentous consequences in the functional development of the individual" (Freud, 1895).

Before we go on to other momentous consequences a *brief review* is in order: At the simplest level Freud differentially defines pain and strain. Pain is consequent upon somatic receptor excitation and strain ensues from excitation of the neuroreceptors in the center of the brain. Pain can usually be escaped by removing the receptor from the excitant. Strain cannot be so easily done away with, especially since the neural mechanism into which the excitation feeds (the nuclear system) contains neurosecretory elements whose secretions directly regulate the chemical substances that presumably excited the neuroreceptors in the first place. The vicious spiral of accruing excitation that results in prolonged and excessive strain can be prevented only by the intervention of a complex series of actions undertaken by the organism or by others on his behalf.

The excitations that accompany experiences of pain and strain and their alleviation leave traces in the nuclear system. These traces, when they minimally change cathexis in the cortical system, are the basis of the affects. Affects may be set off by the current situation or they may be internally triggered. Affects are based on experience and they motivate (i.e., give direction to behavior).

Accruing excitation that could accompany affects has to be defended against. Neural defense mechanisms are conceived in terms of the development of lateral pathways in the nuclear system which act to diffuse excitation and so prevent, or at least delay, its transmission to neurosecretory and to cortical cells. Thus the organism is relatively protected against the prolonged unremitting strain that would otherwise be initiated by hostility, pain, and the stimulations of neuroreceptors that recur in the ordinary course of events.

Satisfactions are obtained when positive affects are congruent with reality, i.e., when the inputs to the cortical system from the projection and the nuclear systems are comparable, so that actions undertaken on the basis of positive affects lead to the relief from current strain. Pleasure can occur by happenstance; satisfaction depends always on achieving a match between the record of experience and stimulations produced in the current situation.

Learning: Freud contends that learning results through the experience of satisfaction. When learning takes place, interconnections must be facilitated between trace and new neuronal excitations in the nuclear system; thus the initial network is functionally extended so that subsequent excitation will cathect this larger network. Freud notes that this conception of the learning process assumes a fundamental "law of association by simultaneity." His mechanism of learning is also a physiological-drive-reduction theory of reinforcement.

There is a difference, however, between Freud's conception and that which characterizes current drive-reduction theories. In much of current learning theory, drive reduction is assumed invariably to initiate the association of an environmental stimulus with the organism's response to this stimulus. For Freud, drive reduction is achieved as a *consequence* of an association by contiguity between the input from an environmental stimulus and memory traces left by prior drive-reducing experiences. Only when these associations lead to adaptive actions that reduce internal excitation for a fairly prolonged period can learning be said to have taken place. When, on the other hand, the situation has changed, and the actions taken are incongruous to the situation, no learning results. Nonetheless, reinforcement continues to occur by virtue of a temporarily effective discharge of the cathexis of the nuclear system. But this is accomplished only at the price of a rebound of even greater strain: the initially exciting stimulation is not removed; on each subsequent occasion it cathects a larger network of nuclear neurons. Thus there is an increasing likelihood that the defense mechanism will be overrun—unless it is simultaneously strengthened—and the accruing neurosecretory-neuroreceptor spiral of excitation established. In Freud's scheme, therefore, a nonadaptive neural process can be reinforced. Again Freud has anticipated struggles that learning theorists have had with a problem.

Thinking: Freud now has the basis for making a distinction between two types of thinking, productive (cognitive) and reproductive (wishful). When an affect is modified (because a disparity between a memory and the reality situation is recognized), or when a new affect replaces the old, productive thinking is taking place. When, on the other hand, such a change in affect does not take place, thinking is purely reproductive.

Reproductive thinking results when the cathexis of the neural networks involved in the positive affect overrides that produced by the current input. Such reproductive or *wishful* thinking carried to the point of hallucination involves a complete expenditure of the lateral cathexis (defense) in the nuclear system and is noted by Freud to be a *primary process,* since excitation is thus completely though temporarily escaped. Moderations of the total escape from excitation—i.e., the maintenance of some cathexis in the nuclear system—is the *secondary process.* Correct exploitations of the indications of reality are possible only when there is sufficient lateral cathexis (i.e., defense) in the nuclear system to delay or prevent the accruing of excitation through the vicious spiral of neurosecretory-neuroreceptor stimulation. This defense against excessive discharge by dispersal of excitation within the nuclear system Freud calls the organism's *ego function.*

The case of cognitive thinking is the more puzzling one for Freud from the neurological standpoint. When the thought about a possible external object is initiated by a positive affect, i.e., when a *wish* has been initiated and this wish and an external object are perceived to be similar but not identical, a "judgment" is made. There must be some mechanism to compare the similarities and differences between the excitation set up by the memory trace and that initiated by the current input. What that mechanism might be was far beyond the scope of nineteenth-century neurology and Freud could not even hazard a guess as to its nature.

But recent work on the habituation of orienting reactions has begun to fill gaps in Freud's model of cognitive thinking: We have heard Dr. Lacey present his model of the opening and closing of organisms to sensory input. Taken together with the work of the Russians and some of our own neurophysiologists on habituation of the orienting reaction, a story emerges that may be summarized as follows. Again, these observations have been spelled out in greater detail elsewhere (Pribram, 1962b). For our purpose, however, a summary suffices.

1. When exposed to a novel event an organism "takes this in"—and this stage is accompanied by desynchronization of the electrical activity of both the isocortical and basal allocortical formations of the endbrain. The only behavioral concomitants of this stage are "reflex" orientation movements that focus the stimulating event. Lacey has noted that this stage corresponds pretty much to "primary attention" as this was defined in introspective psychology.

2. Should this novel event recur repeatedly, remain unchanged, or change relatively slowly, another process supervenes. This is characterized by continued desynchronization in the electrical activity recorded from the isocortex, but a change in the activity recorded from allocortical structures (especially of Ammon's formation). From this neural location slow waves (i.e., hypersynchrony) can now be recorded. Behaviorally, searching characterizes the activity of the organism. This is the orienting reaction—the organism follows the stimulating event; searches when changes occur, especially once habituation is underway. In many respects this is similar to the secondary attention described by the "introspectionists."

3. After repeated exposure to the unchanging or recurrent event, habituation has resulted. The desynchronous electrical activity recorded from isocortex has become restricted to relevant input channels and slow activity has disappeared from allocortical structures. Here, electrical phase has shifted from precedence of brainstem input to precedence of input from isocortex. And any noted change in the situation is immediately and specifically accompanied by recrudescence of the electrical activities in both the iso- and allocortex characteristic of stage 2 (the orienting stage).

Thus when an organism is repeatedly exposed to a stimulus which on the first occasion was a novel one, electrical activity is concomitantly recorded from the brain; gradually, the electrical patterns that are characteristically recorded only during the organism's exposure to novelty drop out. That this "habituation" to the novel stimulus is not due to fatigue of nerve cells has been shown. For instance, dishabituation (reorientation) occurs immediately when, after habituation to a tone of a certain frequency and intensity has been in effect, the intensity of that tone is suddenly diminished. Dishabituation also occurs when the duration of the tone is shortened; the electrical patterns characteristic of orientation begin only at the moment the tone is turned *off* and persist for the duration of the "expected" length of the tone: traces representative of the stimuli aroused by the situation must be built up in the nervous system during habituation so that the input of the moment can be matched against these traces. Response depends on this match or "judgment."

Electrical patterns have also been demonstrated to be characteristic of various phases of problem solution (Adey, 1962; Freeman, 1960). Certain electrical patterns recorded from limbic areas of cats during the early stages of training recur during later stages of training only when the animal makes an error. And two very sophisticated analyses of these electrical records have been interpreted to show that a "comparator" must be located in the regions from which the recordings are made!

Summary: For Freud, learning takes place only when the memory traces of initially pleasurable, i.e., strain-relieving, experiences are modified by the current situation. On the other hand, reinforcement occurs whenever excitation in the nuclear system is discharged. A rebound from the discharge results when the actions on the basis of the memory trace are inappropriate to the situation—i.e., when affect is inadequately modified or unmodified by the input of the moment. In such instances, the thinking that accompanies the discharge is termed wishful or reproductive. Satisfaction results only when the affect is modified sufficiently to take into account the current situation; so that the actions undertaken change the situation until it becomes conducive to lasting relief from strain. The thinking that accompanies this type of discharge is productive—i.e., cognitive—and entails a judgment of comparison between a wish and the reality of the moment. This comparison leads to the modification of the memory traces that initiated the wish—the modification necessary for learning to take place.

Beginnings of a Structural Analysis of the Antecedents of Action

Apperception: I want to turn now to the final point in the discussion which bears upon what we heard earlier in this Symposium. So far we have been concerned with the structure of awareness, the structure of our image of the personal, physical, and social world. But there is, of course, much more to the interpersonal process. This has to do with the ordered sequences of behavior, Freud's "complex series of actions undertaken by the organism or by others on his behalf," to which Prof. Bateson has addressed his remarks and which were so beautifully illustrated by Dr. Birdwhistell. Dr. Spitz dealt with this problem under the label apperception. Certain events are reinforced and other things drop out. Dr. Spitz showed that the structure of the apperceptive mass is dependent on the anticipation of ordered behavior sequences. We have called these antecedents to ordered action "Plans" (Miller, Galanter, and Pribram, 1960). Computer scientists call them programs. The Plan is based on a Test-Operate-Test-Exit sequence: this unit is derived from recent neurophysiological evidence that necessitates the replacement of the reflex-arc concept with one that takes into account the universal presence of feedback.

The TOTE: Livingston (1958) and Granit (1955a) have thoroughly reviewed the large body of evidence that receptor activities are under efferent control from the central nervous system. With respect to muscle spindles, one third of the efferents in the ventral spinal root serve this function

(Kuffler and Gerard, 1947; Kuffler and Hunt, 1952). In the optic and otic systems (Galambos, 1956; Granit, 1955b), experiment has shown that the afferent activity originating in the receptors can be directly modified by central nervous system excitation. These facts make it difficult to maintain any longer the uncomplicated view of the functions of the central nervous system in behavior that are based on the simple S-R reflex arc. Bruner (1957) has suggested some of the ways that psychology could be enriched by taking into account these new data. It is worth while, therefore, to re-examine for a moment the concept of the reflex arc and to see whether a useful alternative to this war horse can be found.

Sherrington, more than anyone else, is responsible for the popular conception of the reflex arc. Yet Sherrington (1906), more than anyone else, cautions again and again against oversimplification: "The simple reflex-arc is a useful fiction"—used by Sherrington to explain the behavior of the spinal preparation. The most quoted example of the "simple" reflex is, of course, the stretch reflex, e.g., the knee jerk. Sherrington expressly states that he does not conceive this reflex to be an example of his "simple" reflex. Indeed, he questions whether the stretch mechanism is a reflex at all. The reflex arc was invented by him to explain the difference between the observed properties of nerve trunks and the properties that had to be inferred to describe the neural tissue that intervenes between receptor stimulation and effector response. Nerve trunks transmit in either direction; characteristically, signals are of the all-or-none type. Reflex action, on the other hand, is unidirectional and is characterized by graded response. Sherrington explained the differences by espousing the neuron doctrine. This doctrine proposes that the nervous system is made up of discrete neural units (cells) which have the properties of nerve trunks; intercalated between these units are discontinuities which he christened synapses, and these have the properties unique to reflexes. In Sherrington's discussion of the interaction of reflexes, these synaptic properties become complicated indeed. Central excitatory and inhibitory states, simultaneous and successive spinal induction, and convergence and divergence of pathways are only a few of the most important intervening variables he postulated to explain reflex action of the spinal preparation. These properties are a far cry from the ubiquitous S-R reflex-arc diagrams that grace (more appropriately, one wants to say "disgrace") today's texts.

The evidence that receptors are under efferent control from the central nervous system makes possible a revision of the reflex-arc concept that is at the same time more in keeping with the data and is definitely in keeping with the richly flexible nervous system that the psychologist needs if he is to have any useful conception of what goes on in the central nervous system during behavior. Since World War II, communications and control engineers have publicized the utility of a device that "feeds back" to a sensing mechanism the results of the actions of the machine of which the sensing mechanism is a part. This device is called the simple servomechanism, and neurophysiologists were quick to see that many of the processes that they had been studying in the central nervous system have the properties of simple servos (von Foerster, 1951). In fact, the central regulation of receptor activities makes it necessary to conceive of even the simplest reflex mechanisms in these terms.

What are the essential differences for psychology between the S-R reflex-arc concept and the simple servomechanism concept? Most important is a shift in emphasis. The shift is from the notion that an organism is a relatively passive protoplasmic mass whose responses are controlled by the arrangement of environmental stimuli to a conception of an organism that has considerable control over what will constitute stimulation. This control is exercised both through regulation by central processes and through a double feedback to receptors from response through environment and through the nervous system. Anyone who has spent any effort on the intricacies of "shaping" an animal or human preparatory to an operant conditioning experiment should sympathize with the validity of this shift in emphasis.

In detail, then, the alternative to the simple S-R notion of the reflex arc is a double mechanism that is constituted of one neuronal aggregate that is sensitive to a variety of inputs and another aggregate that is reciprocally connected to the first and effects the changes initiated by the first. Peripherally, the sensing mechanism includes the receptor; the effecting mechanism, the muscles, and the glands. Miller, Galanter, and Pribram (1960), among others, have developed in detail the idea that the essential characteristic of the sensing mechanism is to test for incongruities and that the essential characteristic of the effecting mechanism is to operate on other units (that may include the environment) so as to decrease incongruity in the sensing mechanism. They speak of this sequence as Test-Operate-Test-Exit (TOTE) and suggest that this, rather than the S-R reflex arc, is the basic unit that controls action. A diagram of the simple feedback unit is given in Figure II.

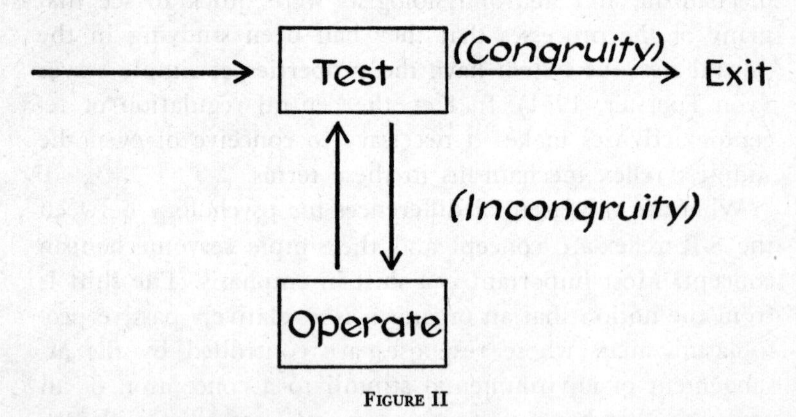

FIGURE II

The TOTE (Test-Operate-Test-Exit) unit, a feedback alternative to the reflex arc. Note that exit occurs when matching or congruity is achieved in the test phase, and *not* as a consequence of the operation or action per se.

The Plan: This TOTE unit includes characteristics which go beyond the simple notion of feedback. Test-Operate-Test-

Exit units are organized into larger aggregates both sequentially and hierarchically. Dr. Birdwhistell speaks about the

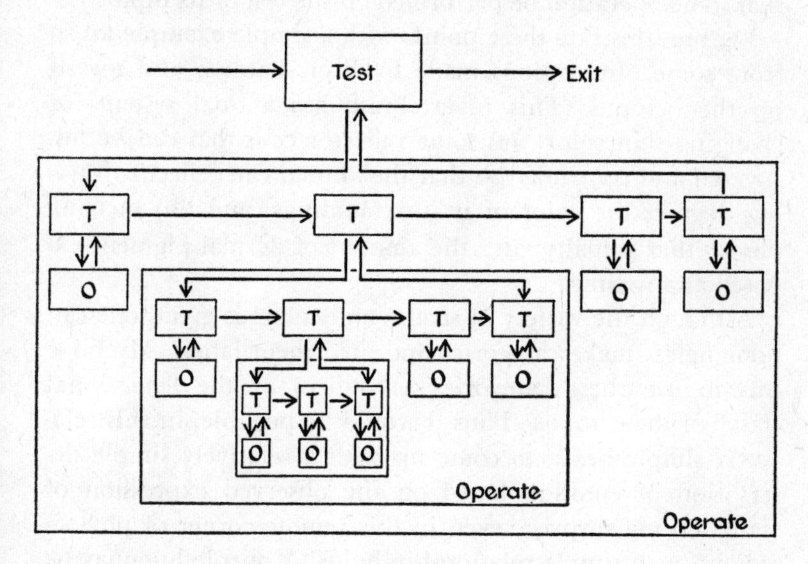

FIGURE III

The hierarchical arrangement of TOTES within TOTES: ordered behavior sequences always occur with contexts. Alternate notations that denote the same relationships are the "trees" used in set theoretical mathematics, the "lists" used in writing computer programs, and the outlines made as preparations for manuscripts.

structure of interpersonal interaction in terms of action and context. Action isn't just a string or chain of behavior. Action occurs always against context—action always influences the congruity or incongruity of the image against which the action occurs. And what is context for one organism is, of course, the behavior of the other and vice versa: this is the burden of Prof. Bateson's remarks.

CONCLUSION

So we are returned to the Image as context against which an expressive activity must be tested. But, interestingly, this image, this context itself occurs *within the operate portion* of the plan of next higher order. Context arises only when the results of tests for incongruity (at another level) demand that some operation be performed on the test or its input.

Let me illustrate these points with a simple example taken from some observations made by Prof. Bateson and myself on the octopus. This invertebrate has a dual system for changing skin color: (a) some reflector cells that can be uncovered and protruded so that the animal can reflect to varying degrees the color of its surroundings; and (b) melanophores that actually alter the amount of dermal pigment exposed at any time.

Although the variety of shades and colors is great, one can nonetheless make categories and give them labels. My hope was to use these categories as indices of the "emotional state" of the octopus. Thus it would be possible, in this relatively simple beast, to come up with a relatively simple description of emotion based on the observed expression of state. To my surprise, even in this remote corner of phylogeny, no such simple relationship holds. A purple hue may be expressive of some process elicited by the observer jabbing the arms of the octopus; it may be equally expressive of some process elicited by putting live snails within the view of the beast. Blanching may occur in response to prodding that leads to retreat; blanching also indicates that a hearty meal has just been completed. So, the beloved octopus turned out to be as difficult to fathom as the fair sex of our own species—blushing or flushing of her face may indicate embarassment, love, or the fact that she has been in the sun all day and the burn is just beginning to show, aided by the preprandial ingestion of a bit of alcohol. Taken by themselves, the skin-color changes of the octopus or of the girl are meaningless. Taken in a context created by the activities in which each is engaged, these same changes are interpretable. The single-level approach, even when only behavioral observations are under consideration, is found wanting. One is pushed by the data to a multilevel approach when one examines the problem of emotional expression, even in the octopus. When interest encompasses the neural mechanisms of emotion, and/or emotion in man (and woman), one seems to have no choice but to have recourse to this most powerful tool of analysis.

These are the rambling impressions brought forth by the preceding papers. I have not excluded neurophysiological data when they are relevant—just because this is primarily a group of psychiatrists. Nor have I shunned data derived from an experiment on social context just because my own competence lies primarily in the neurological sciences. I have even discussed observations on the octopus and admitted analogy to computers when I deemed this to be appropriate. I have made such extensive use of all of these because I believe that by detailing structure at several adjacent levels of discourse, body is given to the psychological process. This method is certainly not the only one—neither is it to be belittled, however. From my reading of the Project I suspect that a not inconsiderable part of Freud's strength as the pioneer psychoanalyst derives from his firm foundation in and significant contributions to such a multilevel structural analysis. After all, he was brought up in the sophisticated neuropsychological tradition that is clinical and experimental neurology and neuropsychiatry.

So too, I have not deleted references to verbal descriptions of introspections. All science, not only psychological science, begins with such verbal descriptions. And this level of discourse cannot be excluded without impoverishing psychology and excising analytic psychiatry from the scientific universe. Such exclusion is unnecessary when inclusion is guarded by certain constraints which are spelled out elsewhere (Pribram, 1962b; Miller, Galanter, and Pribram, 1960). So profitable has this approach proved that it has been given a name: "subjective behaviorism." Thus as a neuropsychologist and subjective behaviorist, I rest my argument: the untapped power of observation and experiment at adjacent levels of discourse.

CHAPTER 12

A Social Scientist Views the Emotions

GREGORY BATESON, M.A.

The central point which I want to make is that we have at the present time two scientific languages for the discussion of affect and, further, that these two languages are mutually translatable. The first is the beginnings of a scientific language for describing the psychology of an individual. The second is the beginnings of a language for describing relationships between individuals.

Dr. Pribram has used the term "signals of state" and this I believe is a perfectly appropriate term in discussion of individual psychology, but when we begin to talk about relationship between individuals the event which Pribram calls a signal of state takes on a different aspect. The wag of the dog's tail which for individual psychology signifies an inner state of the dog becomes something more than this when we ask about the functions of this signal in the relationship between the dog and his master. I want to suggest to you that it becomes an affirmation or a proposal about what shall be the contingencies in that relationship. I think it was Warren

McCulloch who pointed out that every message has a report aspect and a command aspect. The firing of neuron B in the chain A B C is, on the one hand, a report that A fired immediately previously and, on the other hand, it is a command that C shall fire immediately after. Matters become more complex when we deal with circular relationships between learning organisms instead of relationships between neurons, but what I am trying to say is related to this paradigm of McCulloch's.

Let me explain what I mean by the contingencies of relationship. Any context of learning can be defined in formal terms according to the contingencies which govern (or make predictable) reinforcement. In a Pavlovian experiment the occurrence of the so-called unconditioned stimulus—the meat powder—is contingent upon the conditioned stimulus, and upon the lapse of time. It is not contingent upon the subject's behavior. In other types of learning context the reinforcement may be variously contingent upon time, probability, the subject's behavior, peculiar combinations and characteristics of the stimulus, and so on. It is in this sense that I use the word "contingency."

Let us suppose that the relationship between organisms A and B can be represented by . . . *abababab* . . . where the lower case letters stand for behaviors or signals emitted by A and B. In such a sequence we can see every lower case letter as having not two aspects as McCulloch proposed but three. In any triad of signals, *aba* or *bab,* the first item is a stimulus, the second is a response, and the third is a reinforcement. But every single item of the total sequence is a member of three such triads. In one it is the stimulus, in another it is the response, and in a third it is the reinforcement.[1]

[1] I have here focused attention upon the triad partly in order to simplify presentation and partly because this unit of interchange has figured so conspicuously in experimental studies of learning. A more complete formal presentation would indicate that any item in the sequence of interchange may be a "response" or "reinforcement" for *any* earlier item and that it may be "stimulus" for any later item. It is also possible for any group of items to function as

If I do not respond as you expect to the stimulus which you give me, I am punishing or frustrating you either for that behavior which you thought would stimulate me in a certain way, or for your incorrect assessment of the rules of contingency in our relationship.

Now we should notice that in any such sequence the signals of state stand out conspicuously as having preponderantly the reinforcing function. Of course these signals are also stimuli for the other person and responses to the other person, but they are outstandingly either reinforcements of what the other has just done or are statements about how future behavior of the other will be received with reward or punishment.

Signals of state in the language of psychology thus become either reinforcements or signals about the contingencies of reinforcement in the language which would describe relationship.

Notice that the occurrence of an expected punishment may be a positive reinforcement of the subject's view of the contingencies of the situation and, conversely, an unexpected reward may be painfully confusing.

Next, I think I should underline the fact which is familiar to all of us: these signals of state which function to define the contingencies of relationship are usually nonverbal, often unconsciously emitted, and often unconsciously received. We do not stop to analyze the structure and grammar of our relationships while we are participating in them. Indeed, to do so would be to change this grammar. Instead, we trust to the fact that we are all members of a culture and have therefore been trained in expectations regarding the contingencies of relationships. This training, of course, involves a more abstract order of learning—learning of a higher logical type—than that which I was talking about in discussing the triads of stimulus, response, and reinforcement. I call it a "higher"

---

a unit of this sort. The problem of describing such series becomes methodologically similar to the problem of describing orders of redundancy in such stochastic series as codes and ciphers.

type of learning because the Gestalten with which it deals are larger, but this learning about the contingencies of relationship is in general more archaic and more unconscious than the learning of the single adaptive act.

Here again we encounter an important parallel between the "signals of state" and the signals which define the contingencies of relationship. It is not too much to say that the language of nonhuman mammals is limited to signals of this higher order. It is a commonplace to say that cats and dogs cannot talk about things or ideas, they can only express emotions. Clearly, however, they manage to get across, even to human beings, a number of ideas and even to communicate demands for things. What is interesting in the present connection is that these relatively concrete communications are achieved by signals which have a relatively high order of abstraction. These are the signals which a psychologist would call signals of state, but which I am here calling definitions of the contingencies of relationship. When I open the refrigerator door, the cat comes and rubs against my leg stating some variant of the proposition "meow." To say that she is asking for milk may be correct, but it is not a literal translation from her language into ours. I suggest that more literally we should translate her message as "be mamma." She is trying to define the contingencies of relationship. She is inviting me to accept those contingencies and to act in accordance with them. She may step down somewhat from this high abstract level by indicating urgency—"be mamma *now*"; or she may achieve a certain concreteness by ostensive communication "be mamma now in regard to that jug"; but, in its primary structure, her communication is archaic and highly abstract in the sense that its prime subject matter is always relationship.

In passing, it is interesting to note that the metaphoric language of dreams is intermediate between the relational language of the cat and the objective language which human beings think they would be able to use if only it were possible to stop dreaming. In dream, we define relationships with an utter disregard for the relata. I perceive the contingencies of relationship between myself and my mother as being comparable to the contingencies which would obtain between a little man in a desert and a spring on top of a granite mountain. The mountain appears in a dream and the "interpretation" of the dream becomes possible when we see that the mountain is the analogue of one of the relata in the original perception.

Let me now discuss very briefly what happens when communicational pathology is introduced at the level of those signals which define the contingencies of relationship. As you might suppose, it is precisely at this level that "feelings" get hurt.

Notice first of all that in the language describing relationship many words which are commonly used to describe individuals now become technical terms for systems of contingency in the interchange. Such words as *dependency, hostility, trust,* and even the names of feelings or emotions such as *fear* and *anger,* can be translated by the formal characteristics of the sequences in which they occur.

It follows necessarily that misunderstandings and inconsistencies (either deliberate or accidental) regarding the contingencies of interchange are likely to be profoundly traumatic. These misunderstandings have been the subject of the research into the experiential base of schizophrenia which we have been conducting at Palo Alto for the past eight years. What has come to be called a "double bind" is in fact a sequence in which A and B punish each other for discrepancies in how each sees and acts upon the contingencies of the interchange. This also has been the subject of extensive experimentation with mammalian subjects.

In the classical experiments, the animal is educated by the experimenter to believe that reinforcement is contingent upon his (the subject's) discriminating between two stimuli, e.g., an ellipse and a circle. When this premise of the relationship between subject and experimenter has been intensely communicated, the experimenter starts to fatten the ellipse and flatten the circle without warning the animal that this process will result in a formal change in the contingencies of the relationship. When finally the stimuli become indistinguishable, the animal gets punished or finds himself put in the wrong when he acts according to the contingency pattern which the experimenter had taught him. This is grossly unfair and the animal starts to exhibit symptoms of profound disturbance. These phenomena are conventionally called experimental neuroses, but since the procedures which induce these symptoms are formally comparable with the sequences which seem to induce schizophrenic behavior in man, the term *psychosis* would perhaps be more appropriate.

At the human level, let me very briefly illustrate what happens by an extract from a work of fiction by Travers (1934). Mary Poppins, the English nanny, has taken the two Banks children to get gingerbread. In the little old gingerbread shop, there are two large sad young women, Miss Annie and Miss Fannie. Mrs. Corry, a tremulous, whispy little old lady, the mother of Annie and Fannie, comes out from the back of the shop:

> "I suppose you've all come for some gingerbread?"
>
> "That's right, Mrs. Corry," said Mary Poppins politely.
>
> "Good. Have Fannie and Annie given you any?" She looked at Jane and Michael as she said this.
>
> Jane shook her head. Two hushed voices came from behind the counter.
>
> "No, Mother," said Miss Fannie meekly.
>
> "We were just going to, Mother—" began Miss Annie in a frightened whisper.
>
> At that Mrs. Corry drew herself up to her full height and regarded her gigantic daughters furiously. Then she said in a soft, fierce, terrifying voice:
>
> "Just going to? Oh, indeed! That is very interesting. And who, may I ask, Annie, gave you permission to give away my gingerbread—?"
>
> "Nobody, Mother. And I didn't give it away. I only thought—"
>
> "You only thought! That is very kind of you. But I will thank you not to think. I can do all the thinking that is nec-

essary here!" said Mrs. Corry in her soft, terrible voice. Then she burst into a harsh cackle of laughter.

"Look at her! Just look at her! Cowardy-custard! Cry-baby!" she shrieked, pointing her knotty finger at her daughter.

Jane and Michael turned and saw a large tear coursing down Miss Annie's huge, sad face, but they did not like to say anything, for, in spite of her tininess, Mrs. Corry made them feel rather small and frightened.

In this sequence Mrs. Corry sets up the rules of contingency in such a way that Annie and Fannie would naturally suppose that this is a context in which to have given gingerbread would be approved. The two young women have been caught in similar traps before, but even so they get caught again.

Annie is even further penalized for the pain which she feels.

CHAPTER 13

A Psychoanalyst's View of Methods for Studying Emotions

KENNETH MARK COLBY, M.D.

It is fitting, I think, that the psychoanalyst is listed on our program between the social scientist and the experimentalist. Because in his daily clinical work with patients, this is where a psychoanalyst stands (or sits), in part a resigned naturalistic observer and in part an active experimental interferer in processes to some degree under his control.

At the start I would like to make something which is obvious even more so by stating that I am speaking as *a* psychoanalyst, not as *the* psychoanalyst. Psychoanalysts, as you all know, are highly individualistic members of several classes—*clinician, scientist, artisan,* and *magician.* To speak as a representative of all of them would be asking for trouble from too many directions. I can speak only as *a* psychoanalyst who sees himself as clinician-scientist working in the domain of persons.

Although I have been designated the task of synthesizing and criticizing methods of studying emotions, I do not feel very comfortable in this reverse role of telling other investigators what they should do. In psychiatry and psychoanalysis we have been on the receiving end of this sort of advice for a long time. Natural scientists and philosophers of science seem confident that if we would correctly apply traditional scientific methods in the domain of persons, we would solve our problems. They say, "If you would *just* describe, classify, measure, experiment, find regularities, and develop explanatory theories, you would solve the problems of human behavior." But these global prescriptions are misleading since they really refer to aims rather than to methods, and they are so nonspecific as to be valuable only to undergraduates or the Boy Scouts of methodology. We all try to do these things, but discerning and hard-working scientists realize one must go far beyond these vague recipes to achieve useful results. So having listened many times to those who wish to save *us* with *their* constructs and *their* methods generously offered, I have sympathy for anyone who is told what he should be doing by someone with little understanding of the nature of the problems being approached.

Before applying methods one must first *find* appropriate methods for a *problem,* and to understand a problem is to know *what it is* and *what it is not* in terms of the properties of a subject matter.

I shall try to discuss the methods we have heard about in the first part of this Symposium solely, and perhaps selfishly, from the standpoint of psychoanalytic problems. As a clinician-scientist, a psychoanalyst is interested in the questions: how do emotions work in pathological states, and how can these states be modified? In clinical work a psychoanalyst finds himself several times a day, and day after day, exposed to expressive situations of great range and intensity. The range includes positively valued affects of hilarity and relish, but it is in the negatively valued distress of chronic or momentary anxiety, rage, guilt, and despair that his work is cut out for him. His concern with the patient's states is ultimately a pragmatic one since his aim is to relieve mental suffering.

Before he can evaluate the contribution of a method toward *that* end, he has to have a clear idea of what are and what are not problems in his field. If you insult a man and he becomes angry, this is no problem. If you ask why is that baseball player jumping and shouting and laughing as he runs around the base paths, the explanation is simple—because Mazerowski has just hit a home run to win the World Series against the Yankees. These behaviors are expectable, the explanations obvious at the level of persons, and they are not really problems to analysts.

But I would grant they might be problems to someone else. To a physiologist or a biochemist the insulted man or the happy ballplayer might contain a problem. Human beings can be viewed as having the properties of things, of organisms and of persons. A physiologist, interested in the organism properties of the insulted man, might want to measure his heart rate to solve some problem of cardiac function during anger. What is chosen as a problem by one investigator is not a problem at all to another.

To me as an analyst there are all sorts of emotional expressions in man which are not problems. A problem arises only when there exists a *lapse from the expected.* If the insulted man became elated or if the ballplayer trudged around the base paths in gloom, these are genuine problems since the behavior is unexpected and we are at a loss for an explanation.

Here I am using the term *problem* to indicate something more than simply stating a fact and asking *why* about it. By problem I mean *worth-while* problem about which one can formulate a decidable question asking for a *useful* answer. My terms *worth while* and *useful* stress the value judgments involved. In contrast to some philosophers of science, it seems to me that all scientific research, not just applied, attempts to construct valued itineraries, i.e., charts rather than maps.

The patient in Dr. Deutsch's film presents a genuine problem to us not merely because of his distressing head symptoms but because, as even he recognizes, some of his emotional reactions are not congruent with his realistic situation.

The cause of this incongruence is not obvious. He feels he has no reason to be jealous, yet he becomes enraged at the thought of his wife being laid by another man. At the same time he needs and is deeply attached to this woman who is a source of such painful feelings and the object of repeated and intense hatred. These are the sorts of problems a psychoanalyst deals with constantly. They are psychological problems in persons viewed as persons.

The film gives an example of one type of clinical procedure in approaching such a problem. It represents an experimental variation of the usual psychotherapeutic interview in which a new variable, the odor, has been introduced. It contrasts somewhat with the free-association method used by a psychoanalyst, since an interview method relies heavily on question and answer discourse. In the free-association procedure an analyst is silent for long stretches of time to allow a patient to describe his self-observation at great length—to let the system declare itself, as it were, before trying to interfere with it. An analyst occasionally uses questions as an input but much less so than in this interview method.

In any clinical discourse a question from the doctor serves as an instruction to the patient to reply with relevant information. An instruction, as I will define it in computer terms, consists of an operation telling the patient to do something, e.g., to find a memory—and an operand, the object of the operation, e.g., the data inquired about. An instruction represents a type of control flowing from doctor to patient.

In a given field it often takes us a long time to discover what the field is really about. Initially in the history of psychotherapy we thought we were treating a psychoneurosis in the medical sense; then we realized we were dealing with transference-resistance and countertransference phenomena in persons; and only lately have we begun to realize we are also engaged in the processing of certain kinds of information and control. Here I am using the term *control* not in the crude sense of a curb or restraint but to mean the serial *order* in which a sequence of instructions is carried out. So, an interview or a psychoanalytic session is not simply a doctor submitting a patient to treatment, as in a surgical procedure, but such a session represents a dyad, a single system with two components in which the flow of information and control is two-way. Doctor and patient are collaborators in a discourse in which two persons study and influence and program one another. We well know that control flows from doctor to patient. As an illustration of control flowing from patient to doctor, notice twice in the interview how the patient makes an appeal for help and the doctor responds. The patient says, "I've got to get over this, and if that is bothering me, how am I going to get over this? I can't see where to start." The doctor immediately tries to help by changing the topic and directing the patient's attention to what he feels is a relevant area, "But you said you had two little kids at home?"

Somewhat later the patient is expressing his lack of understanding of psychiatry, his inability to see what he is looking for in himself—"but some string to get a hold of, to start me on my way out of this. I don't know what I've got to do when I find it. I don't know nothing. Maybe when you've got no start you can't do nothing about it, but as far as I'm concerned, I can't help myself." Dr. Mahl pointed out that such negative utterances should evoke nurturing behavior on the part of the listener who hears them. They *do* in this interview.

Dr. Deutsch again takes a jump away from the preceding context and, I believe, responds to the patient's appeal for a string by again raising what in his mind is a relevant topic of concern: "But when you smelled the beer from her mouth you were jealous?" Although interrogative in its grammatical form, this utterance consists of an instruction having a specific operation on a specific operand. It says to the patient: "Attend to the topic of smelling beer on your wife and your concern of jealousy about her because this may be a string you are looking for." These are examples of how the *order* in which a doctor's utterances occur are programmed by instructions from the patient.

All this is merely descriptive of what we think goes on in

interviews and probably digressive for this Symposium. Our question is how to evaluate this clinical method as a means of understanding and overcoming the patient's emotional problem. As a way of getting to and eliciting the relevant concerns of the patient, this clinical interview certainly is effective. Whether using manure and ammonia as adjuncts is any quicker than the usual clinical interview would require a comparative study of two groups to come to a decision. To say that it is more effective in reducing the patient's distress would also take comparative studies. It seems to me that while this particular interview was effective in acquiring relevant information as far as the doctor was concerned, it did not appear effective in relieving the patient as far as the patient was concerned.

The chief technical problem in psychotherapy is resistance or (to use a more general term) impedance, and the chief problem of impedance is how to get by it, to reduce it. Parenthetically, notice how psychoanalysts still use many electrodynamic metaphors from the domain of things in describing persons. All patients show this property of impedance. The challenge to a clinician as practical artisan is to find the right adjustable inputs for a particular patient. A psychotherapeutic or psychoanalytic session is the one place in life where the ordinary man still can have his scientific moment which other sciences now must deny him since they are so far removed from the experience of everyday life. In this scientific moment a patient has a chance to work directly with a collaborator-expert in subjecting the patient's descriptions of self-observation to rational inquiry, i.e., to repeated observation and plausible inference. An analyst has to find out what sorts of utterances reach a patient. What topics will the patient's impedances tolerate long enough for him to subject them to rational inquiry: what ways to present relevant topics to the patient so as not to arouse too many painful feelings connected with the defenses in his conflicts? How can the programs utilized by the analyst become adopted by the patient in his self-programing? In the film not much progress is made along *these* lines, but we should not expect it to. It is the first meeting between doctor and patient, and they do not yet click. Notice how often the patient simply does not understand what the doctor is alluding to. And at the end the patient says: "Thanks a million for coming in *anyway.*" In that utterance of "anyway" I think we can all sense what affect is being expressed.

This term "anyway" serves as an introduction to what I would like to say about lexical, linguistic methods of study. The import of *anyway* in this context lies not in its dictionary translation but in what a clinical psychoanalyst would call its "meaning." Language, vocalizations, and body movements are interesting to the analyst only as vehicles of meaning. They offer problems in their own right for particular fields of study such as linguistics and kinesics, but what the analyst hopes to gain from them is some contribution to this hard problem of meaning. Meaning, to him, is the most important property of utterances. Yet this property seems to have been shunned by almost everyone dealing with language and communication. It has been avoided not because we have been ignorant of it, but because we have chosen to ignore it. It has been considered just too hard a problem. Titchener even demanded that descriptions of consciousness exclude statements of meaning.

Semanticists are concerned with the relation between signs and their referents, mathematical information theorists are interested only in the frequency of signs or symbols regardless of what they stand for—but few empirical workers tackle the problem of pragmatics, or, in Shannon and Weaver's terms, the effectiveness problem, the effects o*f meanin*gs of signs on persons. This, it seems to me, is the central problem of clinical discourse. It is not just that doctor and patient communicate but what the communication means that is important.

In the programing that takes place, it is not only the operation part of an instruction but the operand which counts. We analysts attach much weight to those utterances whose concerns and topics of concern refer to significant persons in one's life from childhood to present. Previously I mentioned that there is reason to think that programs control the serial order of processes in clinical discourse. These programs are mediated by the meanings contained in the utterances exchanging information—meaning as intended by the speaker and meaning as decoded by a listener. There is not a wholly imperfect correspondence between a speaker's meaning and a receiver's decoded meaning, since the two persons manage most of the time to progress in a nonchaotic way. Psychoanalytic information theory, in contrast to mathematical or statistical information theory, is concerned with meaning, with the flow of control. It is the precise effect of speakers on receivers that the psychoanalyst wants to know more about. How a speaker's utterances program a receiver and what are the probabilities of altering his self-programing—these are important questions to an analyst.

Knowledge that the patient's speech becomes flustered in an interview or that body movements are used for communication does not help me very much as an analyst. I thought I knew this already. Nor do exact measurements of these aspects help me in my work. I hope you will not feel that I am against measurement or basic science. The other panelists have happily shown no reluctance in asserting what their problems and methods are. I would like to follow their precedents and show no hesitation in asserting whether or not their methods help *me* in improving my operations with psychoanalytic problems. There should be nothing dishonorable about expressing a thoughtful self-interest.

While I believe linguistic methods have a good chance to contribute to the meaning or effectiveness problem in clinical discourse, I wonder if visceral or physiologic methods of study have any useful answers for psychoanalysts. This is not to say that they have no appeal to us, since most psychoanalysts have been trained in biology, physiology, and other disciplines. However, the psychoanalyst is primarily concerned with humans as persons. There is more than a double-language difficulty between physiologists and psychoanalysts. We may have stimulating things to say to one another as Freud did for MacLean and for Pribram. We should meet, talk, and exchange information and hunches with one another. But I do not believe we have *answers* for one another's problems. We should not expect physiologists to solve psychoanalytic problems any more than vice versa.

Also involved is the traditional monist-dualist-neutralist scuffle which has raised so much dust over the mind-body puzzle for so long. Regardless of his philosophical or other nonrational beliefs on this question, a psychoanalyst is methodologically an unashamed dualist in his everyday operations. To be sure, persons have bodies, but that is only a necessary and not sufficient condition for the mental properties of persons. By *mental* I mean simply everything which in principle can appear in descriptions of self-observation. Mental properties are observed, conceived, and programed in terms of serial descriptions of wishes, feelings, thoughts, conflicts, and aversions. What can physiology say about a program of descriptions? Nothing except pointing out physiological concomitants correlated in time, e.g., when a person is describing his feeling of anger his heart rate is up or down or sometimes up and sometimes down. Such temporal, but not necessarily causal, correlations are certainly striking and intrinsically interesting and may tell us how an organ or the body as a system reacts when a person is angry, but they do not contribute anything to our knowledge of humans as persons. Perhaps I am being excessive in stressing this dualist position. But it seems to me that physiology contributes to physiology and its methods are selected in accordance with their suitability in solving physiological problems. We should not sit back and expect physiologists with their methods to solve psychoanalytic problems which involve quite different properties of subject matter, quite different methods of operation, and a logically different type of constructs. As Dr. Lacey said so succinctly and emphatically, "You can't use physiology to measure a concept."

That mental properties will eventually be talked about only in the single language of physiological terms seems a wildly metaphysical belief to me. There is good justification for the double languages we have. Mind concerns programs which control information. Information and control are basic irreducible constructs, like the basic undefined notions of space and time in classical mechanics or energy in thermodynamics. Science as an activity of persons represents a way of ordering human experience. One can order his experience with *things* using constructs of space, time, matter, and energy. But to order one's experience with *persons,* or with things made by persons, new constructs such as information and control must be added.

Information is not matter and it is not energy. It cannot be discussed in terms of particles obeying laws of motion. Control, as serial ordering, cannot be reduced to energic states obeying the laws of thermodynamics. Knowledge of physiological conditions is valuable in itself for physiological problems. It is asking too much to expect it to tell us anything useful about the nature of information concomitantly being processed in the form of descriptions of self-observation. An electrical engineer with a galvanometer can tell us about variations in voltage or frequency of electrical pulses along the wires and cables of a computer, but this says nothing about what messages the pulses stand for. I was happy with Dr. MacLean's careful statement that the limbic system or mammillothalamic tract are "concerned with," "involved in," "play a part in." Finding a storage area or pathway in the brain is quite different from asserting what is the nature of the information stored or what is the program of messages being transmitted.

So once again I return to my theme regarding problems and methods—that studies should be problem-clarified before they can become method-evaluated. Our current over-preoccupation with methodology in behavioral science misleads us to think that if we sharpen our definitions, apply Scientific Methods, and use a little probability theory, out will pop the answer. But an answer to what problem? And is this really the way we solve problems in science?

A psychoanalyst is committed to a method in which clinical discourse is used to gather information about patients' problems. He further uses the method in attempts to relieve patients' distress in a nonharmful and reasonably time-enduring way. Having a personal commitment to the clinical method, I feel it to be the best method for *our* problems. I welcome the use of other methods to study what is going on in clinical procedure if I can get something out of them which would improve what I already know and am already doing. The honest working analyst knows better than anyone else that his clinical methods are too slow, too inefficient, not always safe, too costly and demanding, and too draining as a personal commitment on the part of the analyst.

The great mystery for the clinical method remains: what are the essential conditions in clinical discourse, and how does it come about that patients are benefited when they are? Benefit is neither predictable nor retrodictable in any expected way in clinical methods. What are the necessary and sufficient conditions for psychotherapeutic benefit? A psychoanalyst would be very satisfied to understand only this. He would like to lessen the degree of empiricism in the practical art of therapy by finding a testable explanatory model of this special and unique situation. It is much too ambitious and even grandiose to search for a single law, a single explanation, and a single formula which serves as a panchreston trying to explain all human emotions in all situations in life. It is an old story in science that today's law is tomorrow's limiting case. We should be satisfied with limited explanations of emotional expressions in limited circumstances which are relevant to a worth-while problem.

To sum up my part of this synthesis and critique: I have no criticism of methods themselves, only of problemless methods. Any method which can add something *new* to our knowledge, for example, of what is going on in the discourse of the clinical method, I would consider useful. As for a grand synthesis of all these methods we have considered, it is not a lack of time which prevents me from offering one—it is a lack of assurance that it can be done, at least by me.

Discussion

Lewis L. Robbins, M.D.

I would like to stress, like Dr. Colby, that I am another psychoanalyst rather than another example of *the* psychoanalyst. However, although we can be subclassified, I find myself in agreement with most of Dr. Colby's remarks, so that my comments will largely pick up some of the areas covered by Dr. Colby that I think warrant underlining.

It is obvious that in the study of the emotions we are constantly dealing with the fact that emotions are expressed physiologically and behaviorally, and these various forms of expression of emotions become the data with which all of us, regardless of our specific disciplines, are concerned. As Dr. Colby has pointed out, each of these fields focuses its attention on the various signs appropriate to itself, and uses those methods which are appropriate to its particular point of view. As psychoanalysts, we are much more concerned with the meaning of what we have seen, and we are furthermore concerned with the fact that the manifest data often fail to reveal the deeper meaning. Therefore, we have to deal with latent emotional states as well as manifest material. Thus we have a need to obtain data which will reveal the unconscious meanings of that which we hope to understand. We are not likely, as has also been said, to concern ourselves with what we consider to be the physiological concomitants of affective states, since our search is for an understanding of meaning, and the underlying emotional states which may be quite different from the manifest data that are available to us. Unfortunately, the language of science with respect to emotions is still very imperfect, leading us to use the language of literature. This, in turn, causes considerable confusion, because we are apt to interpret the descriptive terms derived from literature in a variety of ways. Therefore, some more precise use of language in respect to describing emotions is very much needed.

Dr. Colby has stated that the position of the psychoanalyst is somewhere between those of the sociologist and the basic scientist and between the clinician and the experimenter. We are constantly making experiments as was illustrated by Dr. Colby in his previous remarks. Every diagnosis, no matter how it is derived and which in turn carries with it a treatment recommendation and a prognosis, is a prediction. And it is a prediction that is usually put to some kind of test. Every doctor, when he institutes a therapeutic measure, has made an assumption and a prediction, and then applies a therapeutic test as it were, determining whether or not the outcome that was anticipated by the intervention of the chemical, physical, or psychological device that he has chosen to employ actually eventuates. In psychoanalysis we are constantly doing the same thing. We are constantly sifting data. We are constantly utilizing assumptions. We are constantly erecting hypotheses. We are constantly offering interventions of one sort (the input concept that Dr. Colby mentioned) and then trying to assess the reliability of these in terms of the responses they elicit in the patients.

Unfortunately the data necessary for scientific study are often not available because in our clinical practice we are not called upon to record. If one were to record everything that occurs in treatment sessions, including comments regarding one's own mental processes and interventions, significant interference in the therapeutic process would undoubtedly occur. Nevertheless, I think a great deal of value can be achieved in our work if we could and did, as I think we can, make as explicit as possible the inferential processes whereby we evaluate data. We apply certain assumptions to our data; we derive from them certain ideas on the basis of which future actions are determined; and the evidence for and the accuracy of the outcome of the predictions can be explicated in advance.

All the predictions that we make in our daily work, whether in a consultation, in a psychoanalytic session, or a psychotherapeutic interview, are probability predictions. None of them are absolute; therefore in these predictions we have to state not only the degree of probability but also the circumstances upon which the outcome is contingent, etc.; namely, if so and so happens, then thus and so is likely to happen. And the degree of probability has to be stated in advance.

Predictions are usually made on four bases: inductively, deductively, actuarially, and finally by fortune telling: the hunch. We should consciously label what kind of data, what kind of assumptions, what kind of inferences were drawn, and what kind of intellectual methods are being used, so that we can further pin down the probability as well as the kind of information we need to determine the outcome of these predictions. Clinically, we look for changes in the symptoms and behavior of patients.

It should be remembered that the psychoanalyst is not entirely dependent on free-association data to test his hypotheses. The interview that Dr. Deutsch presented was an example. That is, the analyst can, using his hypotheses, apply his clinical methods to other behavioral data, for the purpose of investigation.

However, it should be stated that in the current stage of psychoanalytic development, thinking, and research, we should recognize and accept the fact that today we are in the stage of hypothesis finding and hypothesis refining. This is akin to what Dr. Colby referred to as the selection of the problems to be studied, and the relevance of these problems to our particular field of investigation. The nature of our hypotheses as we elaborate and refine them will in turn determine the methods with which to study and test these hypotheses. Accompanying this effort at finding and refining hypotheses, which I think is our current major task, is our need for the forging of methodological tools for testing our hypotheses. Here I am in complete agreement with Dr. Colby that the tools generally available and offered so generously, shall we say, by other researchers from other fields are not entirely useful, and for this reason we have to do a lot of work on our own. There is a great need at this point for the application of a degree of scientific rigor in our development of methodological devices. In these respects we can share the appropriate methods from other fields of scientific research, but, as I have already stated, we must as scientists in a unique field (just as every other scientific field has its own unique approaches) develop new methods. We are helped, for example, by the development of statistical methods which can be used on small-sample studies. We are helped by other statistical methods such as the analysis of variance and parametric devices that give us an opportunity to wade through tremendous amounts of data and tremendous amounts of inferential material with which we have to deal. One of our biggest problems is that of data reduction because the data gathered in the clinical situation are so vast that one can readily be overwhelmed by them. In this regard new devices have appeared and become very popular. One is the tape recorder which gives us the opportunity at least to repeat and repeat and repeat certain sessions for analysis and study. However, I am inclined to feel, as Dr. Merton Gill once said, that all of the problems of humanity might be solved if someone would invent a way to convert tape into spaghetti.

In addition to tape recorders with which we can replicate sessions, we have other devices such as computing machines for handling vast amounts of data, and the tremendous number of variables with which we are concerned. These will not help us in determining the meaning of human behavior, but they will help us in determining whether or not the hypotheses that we have generated from clinical studies can be used scientifically for the prediction of human behavior and ultimately for the refinement of techniques to influence pathological behavior, which is the psychoanalyst's primary function as a clinician.

In closing, I would like to comment by way of a story. As Gertrude Stein lay dying and was intermittently in coma, she aroused periodically in an agitated state and asked, "What is the answer, what is the answer, what is the answer?" Her friends wanted to help her but could not. Finally, she opened her eyes, and looking very serene she asked, "What is the question?" and died comfortably.

Karl H. Pribram, M.D.

For shame! For shame! I strongly disagree with the preceding argument that we have little to learn from adjacent disciplines. I am a subjective behaviorist, as some of you know; and by that I mean we start out with introspections, we try to externalize those introspections into instrumental behavior which is easily communicable and even quantifiable. Ideas derived from this instrumental level of discourse will never completely match those that come from the introspective level, but some kind of partial match must be found. And the same argument is to be applied to matching the behavioral and physiological levels.

To me, the arguments just advanced by Dr. Colby sound very much like the arguments that the biologists gave 100 years ago when they were strict vitalists. This is not the way science is going to proceed. We must have a common language which goes all the way from literature down through physical sciences. I do not mean this in a reductive sense, asserting that everything is reducible from the social and biological to the physiological and biochemical and physical. Rather I mean that there must be translation terms from the poetic all the way to the physical.

Mathematics may be such a universal language if mathematics is taken in the larger sense, the logic of computers and information-processing systems. This kind of approximation of reductive levels is necessary. It does not say that there are no emergent properties, whether this be in the physical sciences or elsewhere. We do not try to explain the wetness of water in terms of its molecular structure as H_2O. We do not deny water this property, which is a very unique property, nor that of turning solid at temperatures below 4 degrees Centigrade and floating. Very few other substances do this, and we have not explained it by the precision of the term H_2O. Nevertheless we have translation terms that tell us what water is made up of, and we gain something from this knowledge.

So often we expect too much of psychology. We expect it to explain things that we should not expect to have explained. For instance, for your hi-fi set at home, have you ever worried about explaining completely in physical terms why a piece of corrugated paper rolled into a cone emits a Beethoven symphony? You don't try to explain this in the reductive sense. Nor do we state that the paper cone wrote the symphony. What we can adduce is the structure of the symphony and the structure of the reproducing apparatus, and by translation terms begin to understand the match between these two structures.

CHAPTER 14

An Experimentalist Views the Emotions

HARRY F. HARLOW, PH.D.

I would first like to spend a moment on definition and clarification. I do not think that we should categorize viewpoints as those of the social scientist, the psychoanalyst, and the experimentalist, since the experimental method is used extensively by social scientists and is a part of the scientific armamentarium of many psychoanalysts. Furthermore, I believe that the implied isolation of psychoanalysts from the other clinically oriented investigators is unfortunate. In terms of problems and methodology, the tripartite classification of viewpoints which I will discuss is: (1) that of the viewpoint of the social scientist, which includes sociologists, social psychologists, and anthropologists; (2) the viewpoint of the clinician, which includes psychoanalysts, psychiatrists, and clinical psychologists; and (3) the viewpoint of the biosocial scientist, which includes the experimental psychologists and the ethologists. All three of these groups should be classified as behavioral scientists, and I wish to emphasize the fact that there is no particular method which is the exclusive property of any one group. All scientific techniques and methods are the common property of all disciplines and all scientists, to be used as best they see fit in attacking the problems of their choice. I would agree with Dr. Colby that there is no exclusive or fundamental difference in methodology among any of the behavioral scientific disciplines.

The particular method that any scientist chooses is determined primarily by the specific problems he attacks. Since this Symposium is oriented to techniques of measurement of the expression of emotion in man, it is important to classify emotion briefly in terms of the way expression can be measured. There are four fundamental techniques of measurement: analysis of emotions through verbal report or introspection; analysis of emotions through visceral responses; analysis of emotions through direct measurement of skeletal-muscle responses; and analysis of emotions by indirect measurements of skeletal-muscle responses.

The Method of Introspection or Verbal Report

From the point of view of introspection or verbal report, emotion implies behavior associated with strong or relatively strong feeling tones, pleasant or unpleasant; and the clinician, regardless of his special field, is likely to give particular emphasis to these behaviors because of a proper concern for the kind of information which can be obtained through the use of verbal techniques. Indeed, the complexities and subtleties of human behavior probably defy analysis if techniques of verbal report are not fully utilized.

Although the social scientist may not place as much emphasis upon the introspection or verbal technique as the clinician, these techniques are utilized in many social science investigations either through the medium of informants in the analysis and development of emotional patterns within primitive cultures or indirectly by the sociologist and social psychologist through the use of questionnaire techniques.

Although many of the early experimental psychologists,

including Wundt and Titchener, made primary use of such methods in the analysis of emotions, introspection as an exclusive method is not commonly used by experimental psychologists at the present time. Many experimental psychologists use techniques of verbal report, but these are frequently employed to obtain data which are correlated with various physiological measures.

Method of Visceral-Response Measurement

As I have already indicated, one criterion of emotion or measure of emotion is that of the visceral changes activated through the autonomic nervous system. Although this is not the primary tool of the clinician, many investigations have been carried out by clinicians, too numerous to name, including psychoanalysts, in which the verbal reports of patients are being correlated with autonomic changes. However, in these studies, or most of these studies, we may presume that the physiological measures are secondary and that the verbal reports are primary.

I do not believe that the use of the visceral measures of emotion is within the primary areas of interest of most social scientists. However, anthropologists sometimes aided by friendly physiologists have used such techniques in conducting field studies. Indeed, no member of any primitive society is now free from the threat of physiological gadgetry, particularly if he tries to survive under conditions of extreme environments, such as the Bolivian and Peruvian Indians, the Australian Bushmen, the Eskimoes, and the Ona Indians.

Many human experimental psychologists are primarily interested in using visceral measures of emotional responses, as exemplified by the researches of Lacey, Wenger, Davis, Malmo, and others whose researches have already been described in this symposium. Even the comparative psychologists are fascinated with these problems. Visceral measures of the affective processes of cats, dogs, sheep, and rats have been made for many years, and recently McLeary (1960) tapped the heart throbs of the goldfish under conditions of emotional stress. With the advent of miniaturization, it now seems that no insect is free from having its innermost emotional life recorded for posterity on photographic film, and such studies are actually in progress.

Furthermore, with the advent and development of telemetering equipment, there will be no place to hide from visceral measurement of emotional states, even in the sanctity of the bedroom, or the gloomy confines of a capsule in outer space.

Direct Measurement of Skeletal-Muscle Responses

A third kind of measurement of emotion is that of direct measurement of responses mediated by the skeletal muscles, such as movements of approach, avoidance, hesitation, vocalization, and facial expression. In view of the magnificent researches and demonstrations by Dr. Birdwhistell in this area, it is quite certain that human nonverbal expressions are interpretable as having definite emotional communication value. Not only can human beings respond differentially to emotional pictures and facial expressions but so can subhuman animals. Mason (1962) has recently shown that monkeys respond differentially and appropriately to pictures depicting various emotional responses by other monkeys. Furthermore, monkeys will respond differentially to various assumed facial emotional expressions on the part of humans.

Emotions as indicated by skeletal-muscle movements have been both recorded and measured by use of photographic or cinematographic techniques, and, again, these are methods common to any and all disciplines, even though they have probably been used more frequently by the social scientist, particularly the anthropologist, than by clinicians or biosocial scientists.

Many clinicians have, however, used cinematographic techniques by photographing subjects during analytic sessions for experimental purposes. Indeed, this is an expanding and also expensive process, particularly in the biosocial area where it should be noted that no self-respecting ethologist is ever seen in the field without a camera. Some of the finest ethological researches such as those by von Frisch (1950) on the language of bees would seem almost unbelievable if not supported by motion-picture records.

The skeletal-muscle expression of emotions can be measured by the use of rating scales, and this is a time-honored practice on the part of comparative psychologists and child psychologists. Thus, Yerkes used such techniques in measuring aggression and timidity in rats in his classical studies in the early 1910's on inheritance of emotions. As I have stressed before, I stress again, all methods are available for use in all behavior areas. Methodological differences in their utilization are differences more in degree than in type.

Indirect Measurement of Skeletal-Muscle Responses

Emotional responses, like all other kinds of response, may be measured indirectly as some end product or consequence of behavior, such as stepping on a treadle, moving a physical object, or pressing a lever at some differential rate. Thus, here the skeletal-muscle responses are not measured and recorded directly as on photographic plates or film but in terms of some end result which the emotion accomplishes.

There can be little question that experimental psychologists have utilized this method more frequently and have put more faith upon it than any other of the behavioral sciences. A classical example of the indirect measurement of emotions by the end product of behavior rather than by the direct measurement of behavior is the conditioned-emotional-response technique devised by Brady and Hunt (1955). Brady demonstrated that lever-pressing rate would slow down or cease altogether when a stimulus initially conditioned to electric shock in a different situation was presented subsequently while an operant response was being emitted at a steady rate. This method has proved to be a very effective and very useful technique in many test situations.

Miller (1948) has measured anxiety by the rotation of a wheel interposed between the two chambers of a shock-avoidance apparatus, and Brown (1948) has quantified this emotion by measuring tension on harnesses attached to rats in a straight-alley situation. In our own studies we have measured affection or attachment by objectively and automatically recorded activity records showing differential times spent by neonatal and infantile baby monkeys on various mother surrogates or dummy mothers (Harlow, 1958, 1962).

The clinicians, for obvious reasons, have given far less emphasis to indirect measures of emotional behaviors since the technique of verbal report serves their needs more directly and more effectively. However, at least one psychoanalyst has supplemented clinical interviews with the indirect objective data obtained from Chapple's interaction chronograph. Furthermore, there are today schizophrenic adults and autistic children pressing levers on fixed and variable interval schedules for food, candy, cigarettes, mechanical horseback rides, and autoerotic stimulation.

I know of no case in which social scientists have utilized indirect measures to assess emotional behaviors, but this probably reflects my limited acquaintance with the literature. In a rather indirect way anthropologists, in tracing cultural development by human manufactured products, chipped flints, stone knives and axes, bows and arrow, habitations and countless other cultural byproducts make indirect measures of skeletal-muscle responses.

Longitudinal and Cross-sectional Methods

Clinical studies tend to differ from social science investigations and biosocial science researches in that clinical investigations are usually longitudinal and deal with long-term phenomena, whereas social scientists and biosocial scientists are more prone to conduct cross-sectional researches. Clinical investigations here must be taken to refer broadly to the therapeutic process.

However, long-term researches are becoming increasingly prevalent in the social sciences and the biosocial sciences as indicated by the California and Minnesota growth research programs, by Terman's (1947) follow-up investigations on his gifted children and their descendants, and by Kelly's (1955) pursuit of marital happiness or unhappiness in his subjects almost through their silver wedding anniversaries. Many of the longitudinal studies conducted by the social and biosocial scientists are anterospective, with objective data obtained early in life and at subsequent periods. Most of the longitudinal data obtained by the clinicians are retrospective, but fortunately this limited and perilous procedure is now being supplemented by anterospective clinical research.

The laboratory experimental psychologists are more prone to do cross-sectional researches and less to do longitudinal investigations than either the clinicians or the social scientists. Nevertheless, there now exists a wealth of longitudinal studies conducted by biosocial scientists, such as the inheritance of maze-learning investigations by Tryon (1929), the life-span study of the chimpanzee at the Yerkes Laboratory, and our own researches on the effects of various kinds of early experience on adolescent and adult heterosexual and maternal behavior by monkeys (Harlow, 1958, 1962).

Formal Experimental Design

The biosocial scientists are far more prone than the social scientists to use formal experimental methods, and the social scientists are far more prone to utilize such methods than are the clinicians. By experimental methods we refer to researches in which some specific dependent variable, usually a response variable, is measured in terms of systematic changes of an independent variable or variables. Thus, the experimental psychologist measures the speed and efficiency of typewriting by subjects given graded doses of ethyl alcohol, and some experimental psychologists measure the speed with which rats will run down a straight alley when deprived for various periods of time of food. Actually the experimental psychologists are more comfortable in formal laboratory researches than are the ethologists, who remain enchanted by animals in their natural environments. But even here we find in Holland that there are terns that are sitting on artificially produced and artificially warmed eggs, and there are Swedish ducks that are being imprinted on rubber balloons. We can only hope for their sake that the bauble does not burst.

Although formal experimental method does not lend itself usually to ethnological investigations, theoretically oriented ethnologists have manipulated various cultures as independent variables, and attempted to assay differential cultural practices as independent variables. One of these attempts was the evaluation of the effect of infant toilet training on adult personality, and even though these efforts may represent little more than quick and dirty researches, they do establish a model for the use of the experimental method in the ethnological effort.

There now exists a number of experimental studies by various clinicians, including psychoanalysts, in which the effect of various illnesses and child-raising practices, particularly institutionalization, are utilized as independent variables to determine their influences on subsequent personality development. Although the precision with which these studies have been carried out varies, many important investigations along these lines have been conducted by Spitz, Levy, Goldfarb, Bowlby, and a great many others, and a number of these have been surveyed at this meeting.

At the cost of redundance I will again assert the viewpoint of the experimentalist, at least my personal viewpoint as an experimentalist. The methods of the clinicians, social scientists, and biosocial scientists are fundamentally the same even though utilized in different degrees because of natural and necessary interest and biases. Differences in methods reflect differences in points of view, differences in the problems attacked, the kinds of subjects used, and the test situations employed.

Discussion

John Paul Scott, Ph.D.

One basic function of emotion often emphasized in this Symposium is that of communication, but there are many others. Another important function, which Dr. Pribram has developed in more detail, is that of the prolongation and magnification of reactions to external stimuli. In our laboratory we often have metaphysical arguments about what behavior is —how do you distinguish behavior from the activity of an inanimate object? On one occasion we had a very illuminating argument. We had defined behavior as the adaptive, coordinated activity of the entire organism, in response to stimulation, and someone said, "How can you distinguish that from what a brick does when you place it on an inclined board and let it slide down to the bottom? It is responding to a stimulus, that of gravity, it makes an adaptation, and it is an activity of the whole brick." Then one of us pointed out that one thing that the brick never does is to go back up to the top of the board and slide down again. But this is the kind of thing animals often do. Otters, for instance, do this kind of thing all the time. Presumably the reason why the otter does this is that he has an emotional reaction which prolongs and extends his behavior to the original stimulus.

This kind of prolongation may last for minutes, for days, for weeks, or even for years. In other words, people may react emotionally to stimuli which have long since passed, and on the positive side this leads to the great prolongation of effort which is needed in true creative work. Without emotion most creative work, whether artistic or scientific, would be impossible. On the other hand, prolongation of stimulation may quite well be involved in the problems which the clinician encounters. This brings up another basic problem connected with emotional behavior: its relationship to abnormal behavior and the consequent problem of the control of emotion.

My own work with emotion has been concerned with its development. This is related to what Dr. Harlow called longitudinal studies, but we ought to think about these as more than just long-term studies; emotions are not static but are phenomena that develop and change. We can learn a great deal about emotions from watching their development.

One of the obvious emotional reactions of young puppies is their tendency to vocalize in reaction to pain or discomfort. Unlike human infants, their cries are short in duration, and it is easy to obtain a quantitative measure of emotion by counting the number of yelps or whines. We did this for a large number of very young puppies while they were being weighed and discovered that the maximum amount of vocalization on the scales occurred at birth or one week of age. Thereafter the amount declined rapidly, so that there was almost no vocalization at four weeks. We interpreted this early vocalization as the effect of contact with the cold scale platform. As the puppies grew older they developed longer fur and also were able to stand up and thus avoid uncomfortable contact with the cold metal.

A neonatal puppy is quiet as long as he is well fed, warm, and comfortable, no matter where he is, but beginning at about three weeks he begins to vocalize if he is left alone, either in his home pen or in strange surroundings. The amount of yelping in the strange situation becomes progressively greater in subsequent weeks, reaching a peak between six and seven weeks of age, and thereafter declining rapidly, so that by twelve weeks of age there is relatively little vocalization.

This reaction of the puppy is related to the formation of its primary social relationships, and the point where maximum distress vocalization is elicited is also the point in development where contact with a person produces the most rapid and complete formation of a social bond.

This brings up another function of emotion which I have not mentioned before, its relationship to the formation of social bonds. In the example I have just given, the emotional reaction of distress vocalization is an indication that such social bonds have been formed. If puppies are isolated before the age of three weeks (Fisher, 1955; Fuller, 1961), isolation does not produce vocalization and the puppies continue to live apart without giving signs of distress.

We have here a curious sort of emotional reaction, dependent on previous experience, but produced by the absence of certain individuals and familiar objects rather than by positive stimulation.

As Dr. Harlow has shown in his work with developing rhesus monkeys, the attachment of a young animal to a mother model can take place in the absence of food rewards, and he has concluded that the attachment cannot be explained as an acquired drive based on hunger. Fisher (1955) reared puppies in a situation in which they were never fed in the presence of the experimenter but were given different sorts of social contact with him. In one case he punished all positive behavior exhibited by the puppies toward him for a period of several weeks. When he discontinued the punishment the puppies almost immediately began to come toward him. Subsequently they paid much more attention to him than the control puppies which he had treated with uniform kindness. It looks as if the formation of the social bond is largely independent of conventional rewards and punishments. Fuller (1961) has subsequently shown that puppies will develop reasonably normal social attachments with people if they are exposed to them as little as two twenty-minute periods per week during the critical period.

As I have indicated above, the formation of this bond is not necessarily dependent upon conventional rewards and punishments. At the proper stage in development, the young puppy has a tendency to become attached to the individuals and objects in its environment irrespective of what they do. This is obviously an internal process, and it appears to be an emotional one. We have other evidence that induced emotional states, either that of hunger or that produced by isolating the animal, result in speeding up the process of the formation of the social bond.

The data which we now have thus lead to the conclusion that the process of becoming attached to places and individuals requires nothing more than extended contact at the critical period in development. It is not even contact comfort, as Harlow (1958) has suggested, but contact alone; and as Gray (1960) has shown in chicks, such contact need only be visual. Furthermore, it seems likely that in mammals like the dog, at least, this capacity is never completely lost but becomes reduced by various sorts of interfering behavior which is later developed or learned. External rewards and punishments may encourage or discourage prolonged contact but have little effect on the basic process.

In short, science has led us to the absurdly simple conclusion that the formation of a primary social bond (which Dr. Harlow has not hesitated to call love) is something which just happens. This, however, fits with a number of clinical observations, such as the fact that it is possible both to love and to hate the same individual. Further scientific progress along these lines, in my opinion, will depend upon the success of neurological research. There should be a center somewhere in the brain for the genesis of the kind of emotion which I have described. The person who finds it will have a fundamental and very important discovery to his credit.

CHAPTER 15

Toward a Classification of Affects

GEORGE L. ENGEL, M.D.

For some years our research has concerned the transitions between states of health and disease (Engel, 1960b). Regardless of whether the disease state ultimately is manifest in somatic processes or in psychological or behavioral terms, it is a consistent finding that such transitions are regularly accompanied, if not heralded, by affect changes. The physician's opening inquiry to ascertain his patient's state of health or disease, "How are you feeling?" and our everyday greeting, "How are you?" are tacit acknowledgments of this fact. This has imposed upon us the need to systematize and conceptualize affects in terms which are both operationally useful and theoretically sound. The present paper represents

This is a revision of a paper entitled "Affects in Terms of Drive, Ego, and Self-Object: A Developmental Perspective," presented to the Canadian Psychoanalytic Association (October 16, 1959), The Society for Psychoanalytic Medicine of Southern California (November 23, 1959), and the Western New York Psychoanalytic Society (April 2, 1960).

Supported in part by grants from the Ford Foundation and the National Institute of Mental Health (M-750).

an effort to achieve within the framework of psychoanalytic theory an adequate classification of the phenomenology of affects. In so doing we still recognize not only that in nature affects do not exist in pure, unalloyed forms but also that to deal with affects in written, verbal, or conceptual terms is fundamentally inconsistent with their nature and can succeed only at the expense of their oversimplification and impoverishment. Yet the practical task of identifying and differentiating affects, especially in research endeavors, demands that such an effort be carried out. In this paper no attempt will be made fully to review the literature, which has been adequately covered by others (Rapaport, 1953).[1]

Ontogenetically, the problem of affects is first of all a biological and not a psychological one, a point already made by Freud (1926). Before affects come to have an existence as psychological phenomena, there already exist in the central nervous system neural organizations for their expression. What is the function of these neural organizations and how are they related to what eventually evolves as affect? Whether we examine animals or the human infant, it is obvious that the behavior expressive of affect serves as a means of communication to and with others to indicate needs, distress, or degree of comfort, as the case may be. Further, the more helpless the young, the more does such expressive behavior constitute the communicative aspect of drive activity, especially the appetitive aspect of the drive (to borrow a term from the ethologists). Helplessness requires the infant to depend on the adult for fulfillment of needs and therefore for such behavior also to be a communication. As the organism matures, some of these communicative manifestations of drive become more subtle, some drop out, and some new ones develop. In the human there is a unique change in the means of communication, namely, the development of verbal speech, which Spitz (1959) refers to as the "third or-

[1] I am indebted to Franz Alexander, who, in his discussion of the earlier version of this paper, called my attention to Spinoza's descriptions of certain affects and their close similarity to some found in this paper.

ganizer of the psyche." Once speech, with its secondary-process characteristics, is established, not only is affect expression no longer the only medium of communication of need, distress, desire, or reassurance of the other, but also these two modes of communication, nonverbal and verbal, may at times be dissociated.

But this is only part of the story. What about the systems of internal communication and regulation and the neural organizations underlying them? Clearly, survival and development require not only that the needs of the body be anticipated long before depletion takes place, but also that the signaling internally of these needs provokes both internal regulatory mechanisms as well as the externally (object-) directed communicative activities. Thus, this system of internal communication may be regarded as including both signals or messages indicative of impending needs as well as those indicative of satiety and satisfaction.

And, finally, reference must be made to the communicative "fit" between the infant and adult. Suffice it to say that under ordinary circumstances the mother is so organized psychologically and biologically as to be in tune and responsive to the affective communications of her infant, thereby constituting an external regulatory system as well as the basis for the eventual development of object relations for the infant. Whatever the modes of communication between mother and child, what is of importance in respect to the role of affects in the mother-child relationship is the learning and synthesis which take place between the systems of internal and external communication of each. What is experienced by or takes place internally in the infant is communicated in body terms to the mother, who with varying degrees of success and through her own affective, felt experience responds to the infant's situation, thereby constituting and defining the biologic unit, mother-infant (Benedek, 1949, 1956). This is the prototype of a characteristic property of affects, namely, that the manifest expression of affect by one person typically evokes an affective response in others.

In brief, then, I am proposing that affects, as psychic experience, evolve from communicative processes within the organism and between organisms, processes that are intimately concerned with the regulation of those basic life activities which for their success require the presence or participation of an outside organism (object). Affects do not simply reflect crises, but are present at all times, even during sleep (see also Novey, 1959). At the more primitive biological, prepsychological level, we have no difficulty in recognizing how such primitive affect behavior operates as a communication to assure the gratification of needs and the maintenance of an optimal steady state. Obviously, this is mediated by the central nervous system, presumably by the old brain. From this alone it should be clear that the transition from the biological to the psychological, whereby affective behavior becomes psychic process and experience, must parallel and reflect the maturation of drive systems, the development of ego, and the delineation within mental apparatus of self and object concepts.[2]

The earliest affect experiences are relatively undifferentiated and reflect basic biological tendencies which are more likely to be identifiable by their impact on the observer than by any data obtainable from the infant organism. Accordingly we speak of these as the *primal undifferentiated affects*. The primal undifferentiated affects indicate only satiety or need, pleasure or unpleasure, as communicated to the environment and within the organism. With the development of the mental apparatus, the progressive internalization of the environment, and the delineation of self and object representations, distinctive affect qualities evolve, differently ex-

[2] This development is properly a consideration for metapsychology and is beyond the scope of this paper. My emphasis on the biological or prepsychological organization underlying affect and its formulation in terms of internal and external communication process obviously does not do justice to the full range of affect activity characteristic of the developed mental apparatus. But as will be evident from the presentation to follow, attention will be given to the discharge aspects, the motivational aspects, and to the signal functions of affects, though without strict regard for structural and economic relationships as elaborated by metapsychology.

perienced and variably reportable. These we refer to as the *differentiated affects.* While agreeing with Freud (1926) that the ego is the seat of all affects, it is worth noting that these distinctive qualities of the differentiated affects reflect differing aspects of drive, ego, and self-object activities, as Schmale (1958) first emphasized.[3] Furthermore, the differentiated affects may be contrasted in that some are more prominently characterized by signal or scanning properties, while others are more characterized by drive-discharge properties, though both properties are found in all. I have therefore subdivided the differentiated affects according to the relative prominence of these characteristics, namely, as the *signal-scanning* affects and the *drive-discharge* affects. Before considering the primal, undifferentiated affects, a further elaboration of this differentiation, which is more phenomenological than strictly metapsychological, is called for.

The *signal-scanning* affects have as their distinguishing characteristics a warning or signal function and a "how am I doing?" or scanning function, yielding information to self and to the environment of good or bad, success or failure, pleasure or unpleasure. They serve as signals and means of reality testing for orientation to both external reality and internal reality "in a continuum extending in all shadings from massive affect experience to mere signals and even signals of signals" (Rapaport, 1953). They have both regulatory and motivational properties. When some satisfactory defense or behavior is immediately available in response to a change in the internal or the external environment, the signal evoking such presumably operates instantaneously and silently and no affect is consciously felt. But if such a simple, economical signal is ineffective, some unpleasant quality of affect is felt, this, too, functioning to provoke further ego mechanisms or behavior to assure need gratification or to end conflict. On the other hand, when needs are assured in an acceptable fashion, the signal serves to foster psychic

[3] Novey, in a paper which appeared after this was written, also emphasizes the self- and object-related functions of affects.

processes or behavior to maintain that state and what is felt is pleasurable. Thus, the signal-scanning affects reflect the operation of reality principle, warning against that which is dangerous and sustaining that which assures adjustment and is acceptable. What is felt, ideationally and as a reflection of body sensations and physiological changes, may include discharge, not in terms of consummation of drive activity in relation to objects, but rather in terms of the bodily processes which implement the communication or prepare for some type of activity. These bodily changes may in themselves serve as signals, consciously or unconsciously, as they are perceived by mental apparatus. But in contrast to the drive-discharge affects, such discharge qualities do not follow the characteristic biological sequence of rising tension followed by consummation and relief.[4] Instead, the signal-scanning affects operate to provide information which is then used by the self-inspection part of ego as a guide for subsequent ego activities in the service of the reality principle. Success and failure are indicated in the modalities of comfort and discomfort, pleasure and unpleasure. Accordingly, we subdivide the signal-scanning affects into those indicating unpleasure, as anxiety, shame, guilt, disgust, sadness, helplessness, and hopelessness, and those indicating pleasure, as contentment, confidence, joy, pride, and hope.

The *drive-discharge* affects, relatively speaking, show more discharge quality and less signal quality. The feeling state experienced and the ideational content are more directly the expression of drive seeking discharge. The felt affect achieves a climax and is then dissipated as this goal is achieved; or it is blocked if the underlying drive is incapable of fulfillment. In either case, the drive-discharge affect is then replaced by or fused with a signal-scanning affect, pleasurable or unpleasurable, depending upon the ego's evaluation of the consequences of the drive seeking discharge.

[4] A similar contrast may be made between pain on the one hand and hunger or thirst on the other, psychobiological processes which may also be productively considered in relationship to affects.

Thus, the drive-discharge affects cannot be classified as either pleasant or unpleasant, this being an ego judgment which is reflected by the appropriate signal-scanning affects, as when an angry feeling or an expression of anger is followed in one case by anxiety or guilt and in another by joy or pride. I classify the drive-discharge affects in relation to the main drive tendencies, anger and rage being the affects of aggression, and love, affection, tenderness, and sexual feelings being the affects of the libidinal drive. In addition, I may note the affects of partial or fused drives, such as envy, greed, impatience, stubbornness, sympathy, pity, etc.[5]

[5] Rapaport, in his recently published *The Structure of Psychoanalytic Theory* (1960), uses the terms "discharge affects" and "signal affects" but in a different sense. Thus he says, "In the course of ontogeny affects change from discharge phenomena into signals, from safety valves for drive tension into anticipations of the means of preventing drive discharge. Under 'normal' circumstances, as bereavement or danger (but also when exposed to wit and drama), as well as under pathological conditions, the *signal affects* may yield their place to *discharge affects* (see Fenichel, 1941). Also, the segregated affect charge, like all cathectic amounts, may manifest itself as a motivating force. According to the secondary model, affects may serve as discharge processes, as anticipatory ego signals for mounting drive tension and as motivations" (p. 32; my italics).

This metapsychological formulation serves to underscore some of the difficulties inherent in a phenomenological consideration of affects (as represented by the present paper) which also attempts to remain within the framework of psychoanalytic theory. Rapaport is speaking of affects in a generic sense, without specific attention to qualitative differences among affects, though he obviously refers to the fact of such differentiation taking place. The terms "discharge" and "signal" are economic concepts, referring to the disposition of affect charges. According to psychoanalytic theory, the affect charge is not segregated from the drive cathexis in the early phase of ontogenesis and when the drive object is not available, affect discharge takes place automatically through pre-existing affect-discharge channels. With the development of the motivational and structural hierarchy specific affects and affect-discharge channels differentiate, and affect charges become structurally segregated from drive cathexis. "The segregated affect charges are therefore under the control of the ego; when rising drive tension impinges on the ego defense structures, the ego uses the segregated affect charge to give an anticipatory affect signal, which—though of small intensity in comparison to affect discharges—mobilizes (by virtue of the pleasure principle) countercathexes to reinforce the defenses, and thus prevents drive discharge" (p. 32). Thus, in Rapaport's usage "signal affects" and "discharge affects" do not refer to different kinds of affects but to different economic aspects of affects at different points in ontogenetic development. In this paper I do not attempt to deal explicitly with these economic considerations, though they are included in a general sense for each affect under the heading, "the ego aspect." While this may clarify the differences in use of these terms by Rapaport and myself, I must confess to reservations as to the suitability of the terms *"signal-*

With this general introduction, I shall now return to a consideration of the primal undifferentiated affects in relation to the basic biological tendencies which they reflect and their earliest development in terms of ego, drive, and self-object concepts.

The Primal Affects

We can identify patterns of behavior indicative of pleasure and unpleasure in the very young infant and properly designate them as the manifestations of the primal affects. In infancy the unpleasure states are more closely associated with the urgencies of biological needs and of survival, the pleasure states more with satisfaction of needs and phases of growth and development. The former are more manifest and disturbing to the observer. They seem more intense and urgent, not surprising since the demand for satisfaction is upon the environment and when achieved the demand can be relinquished. Pleasure in early infancy is quieter and less apparent, yet it also evokes pleasure in the observer. We begin to identify states of contentment and joy, in place simply of quiescence and repose, when the infant comes to associate the

---

scanning affects" and "*drive-discharge affects.*" In earlier versions of this paper I used instead the terms "*ego affects*" and "*drive affects.*" Several discussants convincingly questioned the wisdom of using such derivative and explicit terms as "ego" and "drive" in this manner. Accordingly, I searched about for a more descriptive terminology, settling uneasily on "signal-scanning" and "discharge." I felt reasonably comfortable with "signal-scanning," which I believe does satisfactorily indicate the predominant qualities of this group of affects. "Discharge" was a less happy choice, chiefly because the term already has been used in a metapsychological sense as well as in a quasi-physiological sense, neither of which being explicitly implied in the present usage. In preparing this paper for final publication, it became clearer to me that drive discharge, even in a descriptive sense, comes closer to indicating what aspect of discharge is important in differentiating these two categories. I have therefore adopted the term *drive discharge* for the published paper and have modified the definitions accordingly. In any event, it cannot be emphasized too often that these two categories of affects are not mutually exclusive. As shall be evident in the text, "signal-scanning" affects can and do have drive discharge qualities and the "drive-discharge" affects can and do have signal-scanning characteristics. The differentiation is based mainly on the relative prominence of these respective features.

external object with the satisfaction of needs. Thereafter smiling, gurgling, cooing, reaching, etc., signify recognition of the object as associated with fulfillment of needs and later with anticipation of fulfillment. We can then observe the transformation of the unpleasant, even joyful, anticipation of its eventual fulfillment, a process which evolves out of the repetition of successes, and the establishment of confidence or trust that needs will be fulfilled (Benedek, 1949).

The Primal Affects of "Unpleasure"

We identify the primal unpleasure affects as *primal anxiety* and *primal depression-withdrawal* and relate them to the biological processes of irritability and biological depression, respectively (Engel and Reichsman, 1956; Engel, 1962). Irritability refers to the tendency of living organisms or cells to respond to changes in the internal or external environments by activity, and it is dependent upon the availability of energy supplies within the organism. It promotes the re-establishment of a dynamic steady state through internal rearrangements or through alterations in relation to the environment. Biological depression is similarly a basic biological response taking place when energy sources are depleted, threatened with depletion, or unavailable. It involves a reduction of activity, a husbanding of energy, and may include metabolic rearrangements or structural changes which serve to insulate against the environment (e.g., spore formation) or reduce metabolic requirements (e.g., hibernation). For the neonate, dependent as it is upon activity by persons in the environment for survival, the theoretical sequence when no supplies from the environment are forthcoming would be recurring cycles of crying fits followed by fatigue-inactivity until exhaustion and death eventually supervene. Clinical observations indicate significant differences among babies in the intensity and duration of crying fits and in their readiness for and degree of withdrawal when supplies are not forthcoming. Some infants withdraw after remarkably little frustration, while others may cry vigorously for long periods

(Fries, 1944). The evidence suggests that the mechanisms necessary for both modes of response are present in the form of pre-existing neural organizations (Hess, 1957). Since this was written, we have suggested "The Fight-Flight Patterns" and "The Conversation-Withdrawal Patterns" as more appropriate terms for these two basic biologic systems. We presume these to be represented in central nervous system organizations already present at birth. (Engel, G. L., "Psychological Development in Health and Disease, W. B. Saunders Co., Philadelphia, 1962.)

Primal Anxiety

How the undifferentiated crying fit evolves into the affect of anxiety is unknown. This requires the transition from simply being awake or conscious to knowing *that* one feels and eventually *what* one feels, a function of developing ego. We presume that primal anxiety, first evident as the crying fit with no identification of anything but unpleasure, a state of massive painful excitation, evolves gradually into more differentiated anxiety. This development requires:

1. A beginning awareness of the distinction between the "self" and the "not-self," and between the "self" and the "other," necessary for some degree of self-awareness and self-evaluation.

2. The capacity to deal with pleasure and unpleasure ("good" and "bad") by projection of the feelings of unpleasure to the outside.

3. A recognition of outer sources of gratification and the internalization of associated memory traces as the basis for the "hallucinatory gratification of the wish," permitting some delay of gratification and avoidance of unpleasure. Thereby sources of gratification can be anticipated and their absence recognized. This includes the recognition of cues or signals meaning "no gratification" and implies the capacity to anticipate stress.

Behavioral observations suggest that much of this has been accomplished by nine months of age (Spitz, 1945, 1946,

1950; Spitz and Wolf, 1946; Schaffer, 1958; Piaget, 1937). In the course of such developments we see the crying fit occurring more specifically in response to actual separation, the absence of the familiar face configuration, darkness, strange places, and then in response to the strange face (Spitz and Wolf, 1946). All of these may be experienced as danger situations, located in the outside world, and become stimuli for anxiety, an emergency response, the relief of which requires reunion with the object who is the source of gratification and protection. Central to our understanding of how anxiety evolves as a specific affect quality, a true ego state, is that it involves not only the concept of a danger but also of relief through the activity of an object.

Let us now examine anxiety in terms of ego, self-object, and drive aspects as it finally achieves the specific affectual quality that differentiates it from other affects.

The ego aspect is represented by the development of a signal alerting to danger. At the most economical level, the signal of danger is responded to rapidly and we presume no affect is felt. This may be accomplished through the available repertoire of ego defenses; through symptomatic behavior to alter the environment to reduce the threat; or through effective resolution of the problem by mental processes and behavior. To the observer only the defensive or behavioral response may be apparent or revealed, from which may be inferred the operation of the signal. When only the defenses or symptomatic behavior are used, no anxiety is felt, but the consequences may or may not be appropriate and indeed may constitute a psychopathological process, as with a hysterical conversion symptom. But if the ego response to the danger signal is not effective, anxiety is felt and the physiological concomitants as well as the manifest behavior of anxiety become overt. The less effective these devices or the less available help from or solution in the environment, the more intense will be the experienced anxiety.

The self-object aspect: Intrapsychically as well as behaviorally, anxiety includes a feeling of danger to the self, psychically and bodily, evoking a felt need to re-establish an effective object relationship and thereby strengthen the self. This is experienced by feelings of relative loss of self-confidence on the one hand, and the need for help on the other, both of which may be communicated to others verbally and nonverbally. As anxiety grows more intense, the ability to distinguish between self and object may deteriorate, and a regression to the characteristics of the undifferentiated affect takes place.

The drive aspect appears in the ideational content as well as in the behavior and the physiological processes, many of which reflect the effort to assure satisfaction of needs, often regressively through an external object or an intrapsychic object representation. This is not a discharge in the sense of a means of dissipating tension; it is a regressive activation of more primitive psychic and neuroendocrine systems concerned in the preparation for defense and flight. These physiological changes not only provide no relief but may even be accentuated through the mechanism of a positive feedback, meaning that the perception of the physiological changes reinforces the signal of danger. Only when help in the form of an object or a solution arrives, or exhaustion supervenes, will the anxiety diminish or cease.

Depression-Withdrawal

As an identifiable affect state appearing early in life, this is much less well defined than anxiety. Evolving from the primitive organization to guard against exhaustion, the main evidence for its primal existence is possibly to be found in the normal diurnal rhythms and sleep and certainly in the varieties of depressive phenomena of infancy. Grief and withdrawal reactions before the end of the first year (Spitz, 1945, 1946; Schaffer, 1958) and the instant depressive responses of Monica, the infant with a gastric fistula whom we studied (Engel and Reichsman, 1956), suggest that the psychic elaboration of depression-withdrawal as affect may develop around the same time in infancy as does that for anxiety.

However, there are fewer circumstances in infancy in which the pathognomonic traumatic situation occurs, and hence the affect ideation may not evolve as early or as consistently as does that of anxiety. By its nature, it is less likely to be verbally expressed than anxiety and much has to be inferred from the manifest behavior of the suffering child.

Depression-withdrawal, then, may be seen as the less differentiated affect warning of loss of supplies *and* as indicating the need for conservation of energy. Other more complex affects, notably helplessness and hopelessness, may evolve from this, as I shall discuss later.

The ego aspect involves a signal warning of actual or threatened loss of supplies. This is evocative of psychic mechanisms and behavior to insure the supply, to retain the object, to enhance self-esteem, and to maintain the illusion that the loss is not significant. It may lead to behavior to hold, to cling, to ingratiate, to reward, to force, or to seduce an external object to these ends. With the failure of such changes to provide a solution, the defenses shift more to withdrawal and heightening of the stimulus barrier in the course of which we assume the painful affect is felt with increasing intensity.

The self-object aspect: In its more primal aspect, depression involves a regression toward a pre-object stage, and includes extreme withdrawal, even sleep or coma (Burton and Derbyshire, 1958). From the psychobiological perspective, this may finally include withdrawal from all external sources of supply, giving up nursing and clinging, and raising the barrier against stimuli from the outside. With subsequent stages of development of self and object differentiation, other affects, especially shame, guilt, helplessness, and hopelessness, become differentiated.

The drive aspect: This is self-preservative but in a primitive, "last ditch" sense. It is essentially conserving of energy, and includes a heightening of the stimulus barrier to reduce incoming stimuli and a reduction of activity to save energy.

Clearly, however, unless the environment responds appropriately, such a state is not compatible with life for long.

The Differentiated Affects

I have so far considered primal affects in ontogenetic terms and have emphasized those aspects which become manifest early in life and which continue as a red thread throughout life. With subsequent development of the mental apparatus, affective experience becomes richer and more differentiated, and a number of distinctive affect qualities can be identified. I shall now consider these differentiated affects as they evolve and are identifiable beyond the period of infancy and early childhood. I have already proposed their classification into signal-scanning affects and drive-discharge affects, and I shall now consider each in terms of ego, self-object, and drive. As already noted, the *signal-scanning affects* are more concerned in the regulation of the psychic economy as signal systems for the initiation of defensive and integrative processes within ego, indicating the state of psychic economy in terms of pleasure and unpleasure. The *drive-discharge affects* include the affect qualities of the primary libidinal and aggressive drives and as such they press for discharge (fulfillment).

The Signal-Scanning Affects

I subdivide the signal-scanning affects into those indicating unpleasure and those indicating pleasure, referring to the subjective quality at the time experienced.

1. *The Signal-Scanning Affects Indicating Unpleasure* include anxiety, shame, guilt, disgust, sadness, helplessness, and hopelessness.

A. *Anxiety* has already been discussed, both in terms of its primal nature and its more differentiated qualities.

B. *Shame* is experienced chiefly in terms of feelings of inadequacy, inferiority, failure, and worthlessness. It comes into being as the child becomes capable of internalizing the admired standards and expectations of his important objects. The development of such internal standards (the ego ideal) involves identifications with the loving, reassuring parent, the parent who gives permission to be like him, and the parent who imposes his own ideals (sometimes unachieved) on him. It also may include the child's projection onto the admired object of qualities that he wishes that object to possess (beauty, wisdom, strength, etc.).

Shame, then, is the affect felt when the ego makes the self-judgment of a failure to live up to the performance required by the self-imposed standards (Alexander, 1938; Piers and Singer, 1953).

The ego aspect of shame includes the signal or warning that some impulse, thought, fantasy, or act will fail or has failed to satisfy the standards of the ego ideal. If the signal leads to psychic processes or behavior which insure that standards are maintained, the feeling of shame is averted. If not, shame is felt with increasing intensity and various secondary psychic and behavioral processes appear, e.g., to hide, to cover up, to blame oneself, to depreciate oneself, etc.

The self-object aspect involves, first of all, a discrepancy between the idealized self (ego ideal) and the self as actually perceived. This invokes a fear of *abandonment* by the internalized love object, expressed in terms, "I am unworthy." Shame, then, involves various aspects of the feeling that one is unlovable, so that attentive or loving behavior from persons in the environment cannot be accepted or expected. A feeling of utter worthlessness and of being held in contempt or finally abandoned expresses the most extreme of the unfavorable judgments of self in comparison to the ideal.

The drive aspect is two-layered. At one level we see restitutive or compensatory activities in the direction of accomplishment and achievement, the attempt to attain the goals and re-establish the object relation as represented intrapsychically. I would relate this tendency to correct a disturbed dynamic steady state and re-establish the conditions for growth to the drive activity of primal anxiety. The other drive quality relates to more conservative self-containing aspects as characterize primal depression-withdrawal, and appears especially in relation to the idea of prospective abandonment. The judgment that one is unlovable and unloved is then responded to by withdrawal and insulation.

C. *Guilt:* Guilt feelings come into being with the development of the superego, the internalization of the punishing and prohibiting standards of the early objects and their culture, and stem both from the actual demands and standards of early objects and from the projections of the child's magical and destructive impulses onto the objects. Guilt appears when the requirements imposed by the superego are transgressed. The feeling is of having committed a wrongdoing or a crime, and the fear is of annihilation or mutilation, the avoidance of which may be accomplished by atonement or self-inflicted punishment.

The ego aspect involves the perception of the disparity between the impulse or deed on the one hand, and the internalized prohibiting standards as represented in the superego on the other. The ego signals the danger that a transgression has occurred or might occur, leading to ego mechanisms which serve to keep out of consciousness or to deflect or inhibit the disapproved impulses or processes, resulting in atonement or punishment instead of the acting out of the impulse. Thus, signal guilt may operate silently without a felt affect as long as ego mechanisms are successful either in dealing with what would be guilt-provoking before it happens, or in effecting punishment after it happens. The operation of signal guilt often can be correctly inferred when the psychic processes or behavior involve self-punishment, atonement, and aggression turned on the self. When the response to the signal is inadequate, then the feeling of guilt is increasingly felt, and further efforts at restitution and atonement are stimulated.

The self-object aspect includes a harsh, disapproving, destructive attitude toward the self, originating from the earlier disapproval of the child by the angry parent. It is experienced, however, as a self-judgment, and often includes a turning on the self of hatred intended for an object. In this process we see some loss of boundaries between self and object, since the person feeling guilt may not be aware of the origin of the disapproval or of the presence of his own feelings of hate.

The drive aspect of guilt most prominently includes the aggressive drives turned on the self. The original drive activity to destroy the object which frustrates is now to be found in the harsh attitude toward and the cruel, merciless judgment of the self. The aggressive drive activity designed to force the unsatisfying object to supply needs may remain unconscious, although it often continues to be expressed behaviorally in disguised form. The restitutive drive components are found in the expectation that sufficient atonement and self-punishment will eventually re-estabish serenity and permit a satisfying object relationship.

D. *Disgust* is the affect quality developing from the primitive physiological organization to expel from or not to accept into the mouth that which is bad, and includes nausea and vomiting. It is closely linked to gustatory and olfactory functions and the early oral organization in the sense of "badness" being experienced in terms of smelling or tasting bad. Disgust is the characteristic affect quality developing in response to infantile coprophilic and coprophagic impulses, and thus has anal components as well. Disgust thus contributes to the development of the standards which go into the make-up of ego ideal and superego and is a special case of shame and guilt, as indicated by the expression, "I am disgusted with myself."

The ego aspect involves first the signal warning against the eruption of such primitive wishes as well as against exposure to bad-smelling or bad-tasting stimuli originating in the environment. Further, it mobilizes specific defenses, notably reaction formation, and various patterns of cleanliness, fastidiousness, and neatness. When defenses fail or are not available, the more primitive reaction pattern is evoked and disgust is felt.

The self-object aspect: Disgust involves a judgment of the self or of an object as dirty and malodorous, and therefore untouchable, to be pushed away, segregated, isolated. When a self-judgment, it may in actuality be the opinion that the person holds of the object (now ascribed to the self) or it may refer to an aggressive soiling wish intended for an object but turned instead on the self.

The drive aspect has two sides. One is the wish to taste, smell, or indulge in that which has fallen under a taboo as dirty. The other is the reaction to rid oneself by spitting out or vomiting something felt to be bad. This first expresses persistence of certain early body-pleasure wishes; the second is more in the service of survival and reality, to expel what is bad.

E. *Sadness* is a more differentiated affect indicative of object loss, real, threatened, or fantasied. It is the part of the response reflecting the absence of the source of gratification but not yet a giving up. It is a transitional affect since it includes some elements of pleasurable recollection of the lost gratifications, as noted in the expression "sweet sadness" and the associated feelings of nostalgia and longing, all of which still include the capacity to enjoy the missing object in fantasy and the hope and expectation of an eventual reunion.

The ego aspect includes the warning of the possibility of loss of the source of gratification and the mobilization of psychic mechanisms to avert such loss before it occurs or to deny or to compensate for it after it occurs. When unsuccessful, sadness is felt and now includes the ego processes concerned with memories of past gratifications and expectations of reunion.

The self-object concept involves primarily the discrepancy between the wish and longing for the missing object and the actuality of its real or impending unavailability. Commonly this includes an exaggeration in fantasy of the gratifications obtainable from the missing object, whose psychic image as a supplier of needs is aggrandized. Correspondingly, the image of the self is to varying degrees felt as impoverished, deprived, empty, weakened, or in some way lacking. As compared to helplessness or hopelessness, however, the relative identity and intactness of self and object are fairly well retained. The self is still deemed worthy and deserving of love.

The drive aspect combines both the more active tendency to re-establish the lost or threatened object relationship, especially through the use of fantasy when the object is unavailable, and the more conserving tendency, to withdraw and save energy until the object again becomes available.

F. *Helplessness and Hopelessness* are affects indicating the greatest degree of disorganization in response to stress and reflect giving up. For their elucidation we are indebted to the work of Schmale (1958, 1962). What is felt as both helplessness and hopelessness is variously expressed as despair, left out, too much, discouraged, nothing left, the end, overwhelmed, empty, etc. With helplessness, such feelings include an object-directed desire to be helped, taken care of, protected, but a feeling of impotence to bring this about by oneself. With hopelessness, there is no desire to do anything, no expectation that anything can be done, and a feeling of no capacity to relate or to accept help when proffered. As Schmale points out, helplessness has earlier developmental origins, dating back to the period when the object was not clearly delineated from the self and was seen only as a source of supply with no needs of its own, the primary object of Balint (1939). Hopelessness, on the other hand, becomes possible only when a distinction between self and object has been achieved and the judgments and the support of the external objects become internalized. Thus helplessness is more likely to be experienced by the person more manifestly dependent on external objects, while hopelessness is more likely to occur in the individual whose superego and ego ideal impose rigid requirements as to the conditions under which gratifications can be achieved.

The ego aspects are related mainly to signals warning of object loss and leading to the gamut of psychological and behavioral devices which will serve to retain the object and the source of supply and thereby the intactness of self. If successful, the feelings of helplessness or hopelessness will be avoided, although any or all of the other affects and responses to affects, including anxiety, sadness, anger, guilt, and shame, may be mobilized. If unsuccessful, then helplessness or hopelessness are felt as painful feelings which may still be responded to by denial or projection, or withdrawal and inactivity. The responses to the felt affects are indicative of the ego's attempt to deal with the painful state itself (through denial or projection) or to avoid further drain (through withdrawal and inactivity).

The self-object aspect: Helplessness and hopelessness are the affects most expressive of intrapsychic object loss and of damage to the psychic self. Helplessness refers to the helplessness of the self both to function or to survive in the absence of supplies ordinarily afforded by the lost (in fact or fantasy) object and the helplessness to initiate activity that would regain the lost object and supplies, but the capacity to respond to activity of an object is retained. Hopelessness, on the other hand, includes the feeling that help is neither possible nor acceptable. In both instances, the self is conceived of as inadequate, incomplete, weak, and impotent.

The drive aspects: With helplessness, the drive activities include features seen in both the primal-anxiety and depression-withdrawal patterns. There is a readiness to respond to an external object or source of supply in an anaclitic fashion, but such sources are enlisted mainly with signals of despair or "cries for help" rather than with activity; and until an object is available, the self-preservative activities are manifest mainly in the energy-conservative withdrawal response. With hopelessness, the drive processes involve predominantly withdrawal and insulation, a "last ditch" conservative effort which, however, is not compatible with life for long.

2. *The Signal-Scanning Affects Indicating Pleasure* indicate self-judgments of intactness, success, and gratification. For the most part they are less urgent and less intense, except when the achievement or success is of unusual degree or has involved great effort. In contrast to the unpleasure affects, the ego processes involved tend to facilitate the continuation or repetition of the conditions responsible for the feelings of pleasure.[6]

In general, these differentiated affects are felt diffusely as a general sense of comfort and well-being. They may also be considered in relation to the qualities of self, objects, and drive satisfactions, but for reasons of space, these will not be spelled out.

A. *Contentment* is a general feeling that needs are being or have been fulfilled and goals achieved. Unpleasant tension is absent. It is quiet and restful and includes satisfying bodily as well as psychic experience. One is at ease with oneself and with one's objects.

B. *Confidence* here refers to feelings of confidence in one's own strength, capacity, and potential to achieve goals, satisfy needs, avert or overcome dangers (i.e., "self-confidence"), as well as to confidence in one's objects as reliable sources of gratification ("trust") (Benedek, 1956; Erikson, 1950). It includes also confidence in one's capacity to establish new and to maintain old relationships, to love and to be loved. Confidence looks to the future on the basis of past satisfactions and successes.

C. *Joy* is expressive of a more climactic fulfillment of needs and achievement of goals. At its peak there is a sense of fusion of self and object which is felt as greatly enhancing the strength, capacity, and invulnerability of the self without at the same time damaging the object.

D. *Pride* is the affect specifically indicating success in living up to the standards of the ego ideal. It pronounces satisfac-

[6] The demonstration by Olds (1958) of sustained self-stimulation by animals of certain "pleasure" areas in the brain is an illustration in behavioral-neurophysiological terms of the same phenomenon.

tion with the self, which feels correspondingly strengthened, loved, admired, and invulnerable. The person feeling pride is eager to display himself and to be seen, in contrast to the behavior in shame. Pride, therefore, is particularly related to all varieties of achievement, the various ways in which mastery is achieved in relation to the environment and to objects.

E. *Hope,* as an affect, is a derivative of confidence with an ambiguous quality. Actually, hope may replace confidence when there is uncertainty concerning one's capacities. This implies a decrement in the concept of self as competent and a shift to objects and the environment as the expected source of support or qualification. It means that the control is less felt to be in one's own hands, so to speak, but somewhere else. Past experience may justify the confidence and trust in the object so that one can feel hope. Or there may be a return to more magical thinking to justify the hope. Thus, while confidence is based more on past reality and on the judgment of the self as able, hope, a mixed affect, is less reality based and includes a faint awareness of uncertainty. When one feels sure, one does not experience it as hope.

The Drive-Discharge Affects

The drive-discharge affects, relatively speaking, show less signal quality and more discharge quality. The feeling state experienced and the ideational content are more directly the expression of the drive seeking discharge, and the feeling dissipates as this goal is achieved, to be replaced by a signal-scanning affect, pleasurable or unpleasurable. I classify these affects in relation to the main instinct expressions, aggression and libido, as well as in terms of partial or fused drives.

A. *Anger and Rage* are relative degrees of the affective expression of aggression directed toward an external object. When aggression is turned inward or altered by virtue of an unfavorable judgment of the superego, anger is not felt but rather a signal-scanning affect, e.g., guilt, shame, anxiety, etc.[7] Thus, anger and rage are not the same as the aggressive drive but only that aspect of the drive which can penetrate into consciousness as something felt. Developmentally, it originates in the primitive, undifferentiated crying fit which includes not only the expressions of unpleasure (later to become anxiety) but also the primitive drive activity to be rid of whatever is associated with unpleasure and to secure what is necessary to re-achieve comfort and to satisfy needs. As eventually differentiated, it may be felt as manifest anger or rage with or without a conscious object; or it may be felt in terms of the physiological and bodily concomitants which any observer can recognize as those of rage, the preparation to fight or attack, but whose meaning or content may be denied.

The ego aspect: Anger does not involve a warning quality in the same sense of anticipation of danger as characterizes the signal-scanning affects, this being a function of the signal-scanning affects as part of the ego system regulating whether or not anger evolves, is felt, and is discharged. If anger is permitted to evolve, the ego aspects are to be found in the psychic mechanisms concerned with the preparation for and the organized expression of anger or rage. Controlled modes of psychic expression of anger, such as sarcasm, wit, argumentative capacities, fantasy, etc., are examples of anger coming partly under the aegis of ego and no longer requiring full discharge. Hate is a more structured, deliberate, sustained handling of aggression in which the affect remains under ego control.

The self-object aspect: The affect of anger is always object-directed, whether this is recognized consciously or not. As Schmale (1958) points out, its intent is either to destroy the object who threatens, damages, frustrates, etc., or to force the object through pain, punishment, or threat to provide

[7] The person who says, "I am angry with myself," and even hits himself may still be experiencing anger, actually intended for an external object, which he at the last moment deflects onto his own person as a substitute, but even this already involves a melding with guilt or shame.

gratification, to satisfy needs. When either is achieved, there is some measure of discharge, and the felt affect diminishes or ceases.

The drive aspect is, of course, the most prominent. Biologically, aggression begins with the overcoming of obstacles in the environment for the assurance of need gratification, its destructive aim as psychic meaning evolving later. Anger, as affect, reflects the drive activity both in the bodily changes serving as preparation for or execution of the physical act of aggression and in the unconscious and conscious fantasies reflecting the need to gain control, to master, or to overcome opposition. The feeling is relieved (or discharged) when something external is dealt with, destroyed, or in some way brought under control, in fact or in fantasy. If for any reason this goal cannot be achieved and the drive affect cannot be discharged, signal-scanning affects such as anxiety, guilt, shame, etc., may then be felt, often mixed with the continuing feelings of anger or rage, now impotent.

B. *Love, Tenderness, Affection, Sexual Excitement* represent various ways of designating the affects associated with libidinal drives. These terms are neither sharply defined nor well delineated from each other. Like their aggressive counterparts, as affects they are directed toward external objects (which may include one's own body or parts thereof).

The ego aspects include the various ego activities in the service of satisfaction of the drive wish. Such ego processes contribute particular color and tone to the affect experiences, rendering them more distinctive and individual in each case. The ego aspect also includes various alerting and preparatory signals indicating rising or falling drive activity, internally derived or externally provoked, and facilitating in an anticipatory manner the fulfillment of the drive need.

The self-object aspects are central since these are the affects experienced in relation to the drives directed toward some level or type of communion, transaction, contact, union, or consummation with objects. Object-directed strivings are also the origin of and nutriment for the concepts of self.

Hence, although the affect, as felt consciously, is object-directed, unconsciously the libidinal drive may be directed to self as well as to object.

The drive aspects appear in the form of the various bodily as well as psychic activities in the service of contact and union with the object, many of which are experienced in the form of body sensations or varieties of ideational or fantasy expression thereof. For the most part they are experienced in the form of longing for or discharge through modalities of mutually shared sensations, as hearing, seeing, touching, tasting, smelling, etc., and all the nuances thereof, ranging from the sensual to the spiritual.

The Affects of Partial Drives and Fused Drives

The vicissitudes of drive development determine that there will be multitudinous affect tones which reflect not only specific modes of drive expression or discharge characteristic of different developmental phases (e.g., oral, anal, etc.), but also gradations of fusion of the two main qualities of instinct, libidinal and aggressive. Such affects are more structured and more involved in total character structure. From the developmental point of view, they reflect responses to more or less specific psychodynamic situations of childhood, which when later reactivated are associated with a re-experiencing of the corresponding affect. Fixations in these early states promote a readiness to feel the corresponding affect and to develop character traits in keeping with the drive underlying the affect.

Because such affects reflect drive tendencies connected with infantile unresolved needs, they are not as easily discharged (i.e., the drive is not readily satisfied). This contributes to their chronicity and accounts for the development of corresponding character traits. Further, because the drive is conflict-ridden, we find these affects readily contaminated by signal-scanning affect responses (e.g., anxiety, guilt, shame, etc.) or even converted to the opposite behavior (e.g., greed to generosity). Thus, while I am including these among the discharge affects, their lesser capacity for discharge brings them into a closer relationship dynamically with the signal-scanning affects.

A. *Greed* is an orally derived affect reflecting the need to receive, to be given, and its frustration, namely, the feeling that one has not received enough, that one is unfulfilled. It has an aggressive tone in that it includes the wish to take, to get, to fill oneself. It has an anxious quality as well, relating to the discomfort of not getting enough. In object-relating terms, it involves holding onto or forcing the object to supply and a readiness for anger toward the object who does not comply.

B. *Envy* also involves an intensification of the wish to receive but includes hostility toward the person who has what one wants. In envy we see the perpetuation of the infant's lack of confidence that hunger or the need to be held and cuddled will be satisfied. This may be compounded by hostility toward a rival whose needs are being or are believed to be fulfilled. In object-relating terms, it includes both the aggressive wish to force the object to give as well as the wish to take from the rival. The self is felt as deprived but deserving. *Jealousy* is very similar except that it usually refers more specifically to sexual wishes, affection, and love. The person who feels jealousy wishes to exact exclusive devotion and is intolerant and suspicious of rivals.

C. *Impatience* is another orally derived affect, originating in the infant's anxious waiting to be fed, and includes a strong component of impulsive devouring and seizing. "I can't wait" is the characteristic expression of impatience. It, too, fuses libidinal and aggressive tendencies toward getting what is wanted without regard for the object's needs or wishes.

D. *Stubbornness or Obstinacy* (as affect) reflects the wish to hold on, retain, maintain control, which derives from childhood anal-retentive or body-mastery drive activity. In object-relating terms, it indicates a lack of confidence in the object's capacity or inclination to satisfy needs and a necessity to retain strict control over objects through control over oneself and one's body.

E. *Sympathy* is a feeling involving identification with a person who is suffering in some way from pain, a loss, a defeat, etc. The suffering person is taken as a love object, but in a special sense, namely, through a psychic sharing of the suffering and a wish to help. But by virtue of the identification with the suffering person, the psychic self also gains love. The capacity to feel sympathy requires maturation to the phase of psychic delineation of self and object as individuals, but at the same time involves some loss of this capacity to maintain separateness in the sense that the person feeling sympathy may suffer as much as the object. A low threshold for sympathy is often the means of dealing with guilt, while the seeking of sympathy is often the means whereby an unconsciously guilty person solicits and establishes relationships (Hollender, 1958).

Empathy, on the other hand, involves the capacity to know how and what an object feels and yet to maintain identity and separateness.

F. *Pity* is a more ambivalent feeling toward an object in which there is an element of hostility and contempt toward the suffering person. The receiver is humiliated and the donor is placed in a superior position. The aggression toward the object remains unconscious, hidden behind the façade of pity. The identification with the suffering person is less intense, so that the person feeling pity experiences only a modicum of suffering.

The Concept of Conscious and Unconscious as Applied to Affects

By considering affects in terms of their ego, self-object, and drive aspects, the question of conscious and unconscious is clarified. Since affects are not entities but a complex of dynamic processes, the designations "conscious" or "unconscious" have relevance only in relation to the particular aspect of affect under consideration. Obviously, the *subjective* aspect by definition refers to what is conscious, in terms of something felt. But what is felt is not necessarily translatable into words or concepts by the person experiencing the feeling and hence cannot be easily communicated in such terms. We know that affects can be communicated nonverbally, actually, a more primitive means of communication. Hence, there is possible a greater measure of "knowing" what we feel and even what others feel than can be put in terms of words and so-called secondary process. On the other hand, the drive, ego, and self-object components follow all the rules that regulate the disposition of mental activity as unconscious, preconscious, and conscious. All three aspects have the capacity to be represented in ideational terms, as fantasies, and as such may undergo all the vicissitudes of change of which the mental apparatus is capable. Thus, what is felt may be stripped of all ideational content, in which case it still will be strongly felt but not be identifiable. A man may even commit murder without being aware at the time that the intense feeling he experienced was rage. The drive components may be completely or only partially kept from consciousness, as may the signal (ego) component which may operate silently, or may be preconscious but easily available (e.g., the calm, "that's dangerous"), or it may be conscious and intensely felt, or it may be felt and denied ("I'm not afraid"). The object may be disguised, displaced, omitted, or replaced by the self. Or only the defensive response to the affect may become conscious. Or there may be awareness only of the physiological changes, which sometimes are reported as symptoms. In brief, the concepts conscious and unconscious cannot be applied to affects as such, but only to specifically designated aspects of affect.

In closing, I wish to emphasize that any attempt to classify affects in terms which take into account the relationship of affects to other mental phenomena and at the same time do not deal with affects in substantive terms will inevitably do violence to the facts. The strictures of speech not only prevent us from speaking of more than one process at a time, but also make it impossible to annotate what we are saying while we are saying it. Because the subject is affects, we have in speaking given affects the central position and discussed other mental constructs or processes, as ego, self-object, drives, in relation to affects. Obviously, this is the privilege of the investigator, but it does not necessarily correspond to nature. Nor is it necessary that it do so. But the reader (or listener) must realize that when speaking of ego, self-object, and drives, I do so in relation to affects and not in any sense with the implication that all processes considered under these headings are affects. Indeed, strictly speaking, affects are not only virtually inaccessible to direct observation but can only be communicated and received in nonverbal terms, and indeed may not always be communicated at all. In investigating affects, we have only derivatives to work with.

Discussion

Samuel Novey, M.D.

In considering the classification of affects, a consensus is necessary as to whether we are seeking a "natural" or an "artificial" classification. For most utilitarian purposes—and the present consideration of affects falls in that category—we resort to artificial classifications. To borrow an analogy, herbs may be classified according to their medicinal properties. This stands in opposition to a "natural" classification which attempts to set up classes in terms of the over-all common properties of the members of the group. In the present context Dr. Engel chooses a particularly relevant frame of reference in classifying affects primarily as communicative devices. This takes nothing away, nor should it, from classifications of affects as modes of experiencing in general, or affects as by-products of physiological states, as more or less specific expressions of the sexual processes, or any other of a number of "artificial" classifications which one may choose for particular needs.

Since my orientation is that of the psychotherapist, the expression of the emotions in man interests me particularly in so far as they are relevant to the clinical task. Experimental finding and the theoretical hypothesis no doubt influence one's mode of thinking and functioning in the clinical situation, but I am among those who feel that the clinical situation itself offers clues which are, in turn, influential in indicating fruitful directions for further research. I have myself struggled with the problem which Dr. Engel has attacked in this paper (Novey, 1958, 1959, 1961), and perhaps can spell out some of the problems involved in adapting a classification of affect to existing psychoanalytic theory.

In choosing drive, ego, and self-object as basic categories within which to view affects, Dr. Engel has attempted to incorporate a classification of affects into the existing structural theory of psychoanalysis. As I have suggested elsewhere, the theoretical model in psychoanalysis has become increasingly divorced from the question of affects as such. At the same time, as opposed to the older model of id-ego-superego, the self-object equation has become an increasingly important structural consideration in psychoanalytic theory. While these developments in psychoanalytic theory have been useful ones in other contexts, I must confess that they do not seem to me to be a frame of reference with which we can profitably fit a classification of affect. The very structural models we employ in our considerations of personality and its development expose us to the potential for a peculiar aberration of thinking. For example, we are apt to conceive of the ego as something having a psychic structure which "experiences" emotion, rather than conceiving of emotion as being of the essence of what we speak of as ego. The error of such reification is common enough, but it is essential that it be identified in any science of human personality.

I have, in the same terms, serious question as to whether the psychoanalytic model of signal-scanning and discharge emotions, paralleling the model established by Freud, will prove to be sufficiently broad in scope to be useful for classificatory purposes.

One of the major problems in the consideration of emotions has been our traditional separation of cognition, conation, and affect as definitive spheres of mental operation. Dr. Engel and his group have given due emphasis to the self-object aspects of emotions, and I should like to say a few words about an earlier attempt to deal with this problem which, perhaps unfortunately, failed to attain popularity. In 1914 Alexander Shand suggested that our emotional dispositions tend to become organized in systems about the various objects and classes of objects which excite them. He used the term "sentiments" to define a complex, basically affective state with admixtures of ideational and potential behavioral and expressional components. The sentiments are thus directed toward objects and have the tendency toward action or behavior. Whitehorn later emphasized the tendency of the sentiment to *inhibit* as well as to facilitate modes of overt behavior. Thus, foregoing our usual consideration of affects as discrete entities opens up modes of viewing human experience which are otherwise unavailable.

Along the same line, the presence of an isolated emotion is something of an artifact. In so far as we would look upon the emotions as being distinct from thinking and behavioral patterns, we have always to do with complexes of various emotions. Therapeutically or for investigative purposes we may single out one or another emotion for emphasis, but to do so is to oversimplify. A recent survey of depressive states (Mendelson, 1960) brought sharply to my attention the variety of things which have been described under the name of depression. In therapy the emotions are never observed in the pure state; and in the therapeutic process of attempting to alter disordered states, we do not in fact attempt to dissect all of the emotional components of a given state even if this were conceivable. We rather attempt to alter the state by centering our attention on one or another aspect of the emotional state which we feel to be especially crucial in the hope that this will therapeutically mobilize the entire state.

While certain of the data obtained by extrapolation from the behavior of infants as to their mental state is without question valuable, there are severe limits as to the usefulness of such models in connection with the problem of exploring the mental state of the adult. The impact of cultural stereotypes, to choose a single sphere, upon the character of and even the experience of emotional states could hardly have been anticipated from the raw material of infantile experience.

Perhaps a model of the communicative behavior and reported feelings of adult man in two-person situations might develop the basis for a more useful classification. As you know, the study of the affective aspects of the two-person child-mother situation has been of considerable value in extending our knowledge and our possibilities for fruitful classification of basic affective interaction.

The clinical situation as a two-person situation exposes the clinician to the reported introspective data of the patient, to the opportunity of observing the patient's behavioral responses as well as one's own introspective feelings and behavioral responses. While the described complex of factors falls far short of an ideal setting for usual scientific conclusions to be drawn, it offers an opportunity to explore, and to establish useful hypotheses as to the nature and functions of emotional states in man.

One must recall that the dilemma of reporting emotion through the eyes of the observer and, moreover, in verbal terms is a very great one indeed. Even where I am to be the reporter of my own state of feelings to myself or another, I do so as the observer and make such limited attempts as I can to translate a feeling I am experiencing into a rather poverty-stricken, verbal language form. In fact, the more intense my emotional state becomes, the less am I capable of maintaining the necessary distance of the observer and the less capable am I of describing it in verbal terms. Mild states of anxiety allow one to maintain the role of "I am the one who is experiencing anxiety," while panic states are, by their nature, such that one is so fully involved in living and experiencing them that they do not lend themselves to the luxuries of observing and verbal reporting.

While as clinician one is compelled to extrapolate from the observation of behavioral patterns to the assumption of certain emotional states, it would be well if we would spell out what we are talking about. The same may be said about the laboratory findings in relation to animals and humans where one cannot validate, from the subject himself, what his actual felt experience is. Clinically, one occasionally observes behavioral patterns which one has reason to believe are related to certain emotional states. It is a tantalizing problem, indeed, when the actual feeling state as experienced and reported by the patient seems incongruous with the accompanying behavioral pattern. I should suppose that based upon the observational data, this is about all one would be entitled to say. In practice, however, we are in the habit of making logical, perhaps dangerous, assumptions about linkages, presumed to be present and as yet unrevealed between the behavioral pattern, for instance, and some emotional experience not within the realm of specific awareness—and we do this despite the paradox of talking of a feeling which is not felt! As indefensible as this position may be on many grounds, it has the virtue of clinical usefulness, and a classificatory system of affects must, at least if it is to be useful to the clinician, take cognizance of such observations.

To touch upon one further point, this type of thinking in clinical psychiatry has tended to place the emphasis on the reorganizational rather than the disorganizational aspects of human experience. Various and sundry ostensibly pathological modes of feeling, thinking, and behaving are viewed, in Dr. Engel's classification, as attempts to re-establish stable states and maintain a psychic equilibrium in the Darwinian tradition. I am inclined to feel that this stems out of a present bias toward therapeutic optimism and an attitude of expectation of being of help in modifying such states. The concepts of disorganization and of being sick have seemed to be of less value in this direction. Actually whether we are to look upon the emotional state of depression as a biological response to energy depletion and hence conservative in nature or as a disorganizing nonintegrative state depends substantially upon the attitudes elicited in the therapist who would attempt to modify such a state.

In conclusion, I believe, and this Symposium has emphasized, that we are constantly faced with the interrelation of the physiologic and psychologic view of affects. Sherrington (1940) felt that, although this division made for unanswerable questions, to ask them nonetheless may sharpen one's thinking. In his words, "Witness the training of the psychiatrist and the physiologist. Only *after* the question has been discussed can they go in their respective ways, as perforce they ultimately must, disappointed it may be, but wiser, if sadder, practitioners and men."

CHAPTER 16

Emotions in the Perspective of Human Evolution

DAVID A. HAMBURG, M.D.

"The most general principle of all in biology is evolution" (Simpson et al., 1957). In spite of this fundamental fact, and the demonstrated power of an evolutionary view in relation to a wide variety of biological problems, students of human behavior have so far paid little attention to the evolution of living organisms or of man himself. Anthropology alone among the behavioral sciences has taken evolution seriously and made it a major focus of research. This neglect applies as much to the emotional aspects of behavior as to any other, and is remarkable in this context since Darwin was so strongly interested in emotions and pointed the way for future investigators. It is therefore quite appropriate that this Symposium, through its title and some of its papers, should again establish a link between human emotions and evolutionary processes.

I wish to express my deep appreciation to Professor S. L. Washburn, University of California, Berkeley, for a series of stimulating and informative discussions of human evolution, beginning at the Center for Advanced Study in the Behavioral Sciences in 1957 and continuing to the present time.

In recent years, there have been very important advances in research on the evolution of living organisms. The most basic of these has been the modern synthesis of evolution, a powerful theory which has led to a variety of significant new observations and experiments, and has been able to integrate effectively an extraordinary variety of data from all fields of biology. Moreover, the heretofore sketchy record of human evolution has been substantially filled in, although it is by no means complete. The evidence bearing on human evolution is much more abundant and penetrating than it was even ten years ago, and the implications of this evidence are now being carefully worked out.

Within the past few years, biologists in various fields have shown increasing appreciation of behavior in relation to natural selection and, in keeping with the development of population genetics, have drawn attention not only to individual behavior but to the organization and function of groups.

At this point, I believe it will be helpful to sketch very briefly a few central concepts of the modern evolutionary synthesis and indicate their linkage to behavior. In order to do this, I have chosen excerpts from recent publications of three distinguished biologists: a geneticist, a paleontologist, and a zoologist.

Dobzhansky (1956) delineates the concept of natural selection as follows:

> Modern versions of the theory of natural selection are in a way simpler than the classical. *In any one generation, the carriers of different genotypes make, on the average, unequal contributions to the hereditary endowment of succeeding* generations. The fit genotypes, and, by extension, the fit phenotypes, are those which transmit efficiently their genes to future generations. The less fit genotypes transmit their genes less effectively; the unfit ones leave little or no surviving, reproductively competent progeny. . . . Countless *genotypes with different reaction patterns* are formed in every species by *mutation* and *sexual reproduction. Natural selection perpetuates the genotypes which react to promote survival and reproduction in the environments which the*

> *species encounters more or less regularly in the territory which it inhabits* [my italics].

George Gaylord Simpson (1958) presents a penetrating statement on reproductive success and its relation to behavior:

> *Reproductive success* may be comparatively simple in asexual organisms . . . in biparental populations the matter becomes highly intricate. (1) Male and female must occur in proximity or must find each other. (2) In many, especially the more complex, animals they must be sexually acceptable to each other and must mate. (3) Fertilization must occur. (4) The gametes must be genetically compatible. (5) Normal embryological development must occur. (6) Offspring must survive to breeding age and become successful reproducers in their turn. Relatively greater or less success may occur at any one of these stages and at substages within them, and selection depends on the total outcome. . . .
>
> A central problem of evolutionary theory has always been the explanation of adaptation, and the synthetic theory maintains . . . that *adaptation is a result of natural selection.* But it also demonstrates that *natural selection always favors reproductive success of a population,* and nothing else. It might be suitable to redefine adaptation as such reproductive success, but some confusion might arise from the fact that *reproductive success of the population involves all phases of individual life cycles and will incomparably more often than not be favored by individual adaptation to the environment.* Such adaptation will therefore almost always be favored by natural selection. Nevertheless the possibility remains that selection, as here defined, could favor population reproduction at the expense of individual adaptation. . . .
>
> An aspect of the synthetic theory especially pertinent here is that it again brings in behavior as a central element. It not only points the way to *evolutionary, historical explanations of existing behavior patterns* but also involves *behavior as one of the factors that produce or guide evolution. Some phases of selection, as in zygote and embryo, are not*

> *directly behavioral, but aspects of breeding, care of young, and subsequent survival are pre-eminently so and are obviously crucial elements in selection* [my italics].

Scott (1958) emphasizes social behavior in adaptation:

> The evolution of any species, and particularly of a highly *social* species, cannot be understood without studying its behavior and social organization. *Evolution is one of the fundamental theories of biology. Its basis is adaptation, and one of the important kinds of adaptation is behavior* [my italics].

Where does emotion come into this? Interestingly, basic reference works on evolution rarely mention emotion, and similar works on emotion rarely mention evolution.

Why are emotional phenomena so universal in man and so important in behavior if they have not served some adaptative functions in evolution? I believe that emotional processes have served motivational purposes in getting crucial jobs done. What crucial jobs? Finding food and water, avoiding predators, achieving fertile copulation, caring for the young, training the young to cope effectively with the specific requirements of a given environment. In the case of man, we may go further and emphasize, as Julian Huxley (1943) has done, his increasing independence of and control over the environment, his growing ability to exploit a wide range of environmental opportunities.

Selection favors those populations whose members, on the whole, are organized effectively to accomplish these tasks. This is where emotion comes in. Let us consider for a moment the sexually aroused mature adult. We say readily enough he is quite emotional. By this, we usually mean that he feels strongly a particular kind of inner experience. From an observer's view, we can also say that in this state the likelihood of his achieving fertile copulation is greater than when he is not in this state. From an evolutionary viewpoint, we can further say that he now *wants* to do what the species needs to have done, whether he is aware of it or not. His emotion reflects a state of heightened motivation for a behavior pattern that is critical in species survival.[1]

Thus, the emotion has several components: a subjective component, an action component, and a physiological component appropriate to the action. Emotion as usually considered emphasizes the subjective component—but this is in fact the subjective aspect of a motivational pattern. On the whole, these are motivational patterns that have had selective advantage over a very long time span. There is substantial genetic variability in every aspect of structure and behavior. Selection has operated on this variability, preserving those motivational-emotional patterns that have been effective in getting the tasks of survival done.

I want to add an important qualification here. I am *not* saying that emotional responses occur *only* in connection with behavior that facilitates reproductive success of *contemporary* human populations. For one thing, contribution of an individual to reproductive success of his species may be difficult to tease out in the very large and complex human societies of recent times. Some nonreproducers may contribute much to the reproductive success of the *species*; e.g., the many bachelors who have made contributions in disease prevention. Moreover, as every clinician knows, the human is quite capable of learning motivational-emotional patterns that are maladaptive by any reasonable standard.

Any mechanism—structure, function, or behavior—that is adaptive *on the average* for populations over *long time spans* has many exceptions, may be "fooled" by extraordinary environmental circumstances, and may even become largely maladaptive when there are radical changes in environmental conditions. When we consider the profound changes in human environmental conditions within *very recent* evolutionary times, it becomes entirely conceivable that some of the mechanisms which evolved over the millions of years of

[1] I am here deliberately ignoring other aspects of such behavior which may become exceedingly complex from the viewpoint of individual psychology in modern society. What I am here emphasizing is long-run functions in evolution.

mammalian, primate, and human evolution may now be less useful than they once were. Since cultural change has moved much more rapidly than genetic change, the *emotional response tendencies* that have been built into us through their suitability for a long succession of past environments may be less suitable for the very different *present* environment. In this sense, there may be some respects in which modern man is obsolete; and this seems to me an important area for research in human biology.

In the remainder of this paper, I would like to illustrate this evolutionary concept by returning to the theme mentioned by MacLean early in this Symposium, i.e., the emotional experiences associated with interpersonal bonds—the feelings and actions referred to by terms such as attachment, affection, respect, and love. I believe this to be an important area for such illustration because these experiences were crucial in human evolution, are seriously neglected in behavioral and biological sciences, and have recently been clarified to a significant extent by research in several fields. The principal points I want to make are as follows: primates are group-living forms; the primate group is a powerful adaptive mechanism; emotional processes that facilitate interindividual bonds (participation in group living) have selective advantage; the formation of such bonds is pleasurable for primates; they are easy to learn and hard to forget; their disruption is unpleasant and precipitates profound psychophysiological changes that tend to restore close relations with others of the same species.

Since behavior, unlike physical structure, does not leave fossils, the behavior of early man must be reconstructed inferentially from a variety of sources. Some inferences regarding behavior can be drawn from the fossil record; as the richness of that record increases, which is in fact currently happening, such inferences will become increasingly dependable. Some inferences regarding behavior of early man, in its most general features, can be drawn from the study of living forms—the more complex nonhuman primates and the most primitive humans. In doing so, we must be cautious because: (a) the living nonhuman primates are not our direct ancestors—rather, the contemporary old-world primates and *Homo sapiens* has come from some common ancestor; (b) all the living humans are *Homo sapiens,* they have had some contact with European culture, and many of them have been driven into marginal subsistence areas by more technologically developed peoples. Nevertheless, they have something to teach us.

Sahlins (1959) has recently published a provocative analysis of the most rudimentary of documented human social systems, based on an extensive survey of available data. I have selected a few excerpts from his paper that are relevant to my main theme.

> We include in our comparison the following primitive societies: Australian Aborigines, Tasmanians, Semang, Andamanese, Philippine and Congo pygmies, Bushmen, Eskimo, Great Basin Shoshoni, Naskapi, Ona and Yahgan. It is assumed that these societies parallel early cultural society in general features. This is simply an assumption of order and regularity. The technologies and low productivity of modern hunters and gatherers resemble the archaeologically revealed productive systems of early cultures. Granting that a cultural social system is functionally related to its productive system, it follows that early human society resembles rudimentary, modern human society. This reasoning is supported by the large degree of social similarity among the present hunters and gatherers themselves, despite the fact that some of them are as historically distant from each other, as separated in contact and connection, as the paleolithic is separated from modern times. Further, simply because many food gatherers have been driven into marginal areas, they are not thereby disqualified from consideration. There still remain strong social resemblances between marginal peoples, such as Bushmen, Ona, and Eskimo, and those found in isolated, but otherwise not ecologically marginal areas, such as many Australian groups and the Andaman Islanders. . . .
>
> Hunters and gatherers live in relatively open groups between which relations are usually friendly. . . . It is the kin-

> ship ethic of mutual aid that permits populations of hunters and gatherers to shift about according to the distribution of resources. Kinship is thus selectively advantageous in a zoological sense; it permits primitives to adjust to more variable habitats than subhuman primates. . . .
>
> Given the division of labor by sex and the formation of domestic units through marriage, it follows that sharing food and other items, rather than being non-existent, as among monkeys and apes, is a *sine qua non* of the human condition. Food sharing is an outstanding functional criterion of man. In the domestic economy of the family there is constant reciprocity and pooling of resources. And, at the same time that kinship is extended throughout the band of families, so are the principles of the domestic economy. Among all hunters and gatherers there is a constant give and take of vital goods through hospitality and gift exchange. Everywhere, generosity is a great social virtue. Also general is the custom of pooling large game among the entire band, either as a matter of course, or in times of scarcity. Where kinship is extended beyond the local group by interband marriage, so are reciprocity and mutual aid. Goods may pass over great distances by a series of kinship transactions. Trade is thus established. Hunters and gatherers are able to take mutual advantage of the exploitation of distant environments, a phenomenon without parallel in the primate order.

Goldschmidt (1959) has quite recently published a stimulating work of synthesis on the evolution of human societies, drawing from diverse sources chiefly in the field of cultural anthropology. I wish to quote a few passages pertinent to the present discussion.

> There is no reason to suppose that the earliest man had anything but a nomadic hunting and food-gathering system. In every major land area a few of these still exist. . . . The common and recurrent elements in their social system offer us the closest approximation to the earliest form of human social life that can be reconstructed on the basis of ethnographic data. . . .
>
> The general characteristics of nomadic hunting and food-gathering societies are these: they are formed into bands of from twenty to fifty persons who camp together, share a ter-

ritory which they protect from enemy invasion, and interact with other coequal bands inhabiting contiguous but separate territories. . . . The band is subdivided into families or hearth groups, a marital couple . . . and their immature and unmarried children. The individual family (or sometimes groups of closely related families) may split off into separate units under dire economic circumstances, but the band usually remains together throughout the year . . . most characteristically the band is the core of social unity and action. . . .

Values remain personal and direct. Where a population is close to subsistence, as is usually the case, the knowledge necessary for finding food, skill in hunting, and the requisite energy and industry to do so are likely to loom large.

[On the basis of his exhaustive review of the ethnographic evidence, Goldschmidt draws this important conclusion:] . . . man is by nature committed to social existence, and is therefore inevitably involved in the dilemma between serving his own interests and recognizing those of the group to which he belongs. Insofar as this dilemma can be resolved, it is resolved by the fact that man's self-interest can best be served through his commitment to his fellows. . . . *Need for positive affect* means that each person craves response from his human environment. It may be viewed as a hunger, not unlike that for food, but more generalized. Under varying conditions it may be expressed as a *desire for contact,* for *recognition* and *acceptance,* for *approval,* for *esteem,* or for *mastery.* . . . As we examine human behavior, we find that persons not only universally live in social systems, which is to say they are drawn together, but also *universally act in such ways as to attain the approval of their fellow men* [my italics].

Margaret Mead (1958) has recently contributed an important paper on cultural determinants of behavior. She says:

. . . each cultural system which survives has to meet the same set of minimum requirements for maintenance and for survival. Each human language—highly diversified though languages appear to be—must be one which every normal member of the group can learn to speak; each culturally patterned dietary must provide for human growth; each family and community system must provide for the care of human

> children during their long dependency and for their education, must regulate the patterns of mating and of competition, and must pattern the behavior of members of the social group. As each variant of culture must meet the same basic requirements, cultural systems have a regularity which makes it possible for human beings, of whatever level of culture, to recognize and borrow from the cultural behavior of members of other cultural systems.
>
> . . . only those cultural behaviors which are shared by every group of human beings are irreversible gains . . . these irreversible patterns would include language; the family (including a sexual and an age-graded division of labor); tool using; selective exploitation of the environment to provide food, shelter, and protection; the idea of a group organization which unites a group of families and determines their relationship to other like groups; some idea of the elaboration of ornamentation . . . and some system of relating man to the perceived universe.

Thus, the past few years have seen substantial progress in the integration of a great variety of observations on technologically primitive human populations. The available evidence strongly indicates that, throughout the long course of his evolution, man has been a group-living form—probably characterized by intense and persistent attachments between individuals within an organized, cohesive small society. Moreover, it is very likely that the human group, throughout the history of the species, has been a powerful problem-solving tool, coping with all sorts of harsh and taxing environmental contingencies. It has been an adaptive mechanism *par excellence.*

Another field of research that has a significant bearing on human evolution is the observation of behavior of the more complex nonhuman primates under natural conditions. The past few years have seen a burst of activity in this direction, with six species being carefully, systematically, and extensively observed under free-ranging conditions. These species are: baboon, gorilla, howler monkey, Indian langur, Japanese macaque, and rhesus macaque (the usual laboratory monkey). Most of the studies have not yet been reported in detail, but some important features are emerging.

The one fact that I wish to emphasize here is that all of these species are pre-eminently group-living forms. They do not come together in some minimal fashion that simply permits reproduction. They are not loosely associated herds. Rather they are intensely and persistently bound up with each other, living usually in cohesive troops, organized in a fairly complex way. Bourliere (1962) has recently made an extensive review of available field observations on social organization of primates including the most primitive ones. While field observations are very limited for many species, the evidence to date suggests that practically all living primate species are intensely and persistently group-living forms. Only a few of the most primitive Prosimians species may turn out to be exceptions. So far as the more highly developed primates are concerned, it seems clear enough that strong interanimal bonds are highly characteristic of them.

Washburn, from his extensive baboon observations, points out that the troop is a survival mechanism. The competence of the troop as a whole far exceeds that of any individual. For example, Washburn and DeVore (1962) put considerable emphasis on protection of the entire group by the powerful adult male baboon. DeVore (1962) says:

> Once a monkey group begins living on the ground, the much greater danger from predators would alone be sufficient to account for a more strictly organized social system, one which, e.g., placed a premium upon male specialization in group defense.... While observing free-ranging baboons, Washburn found that the adult males were continually solicitous of the welfare of the young baboons, especially, e.g., when a troop was moving (a situation of more than usual danger) . . . the females with infants, not necessarily those in estrus, stayed nearest the protective, dominant males.

Altmann's observations of rhesus macaque and Carpenter's of howler monkeys also indicate the role of the adult males in policing the group internally as well as protecting it from outside danger.

All of this recent work—both the field observations of nonhuman primates and the synthesis of observations on preagricultural human groups—suggests that group living has conferred a powerful selective advantage upon more highly developed primates. This includes: (1) protection against predation; (2) obtaining food and water supply; (3) dealing with climatic problems; (4) coping with injury and illness; (5) facilitating reproduction, especially in care and training of the young. Indeed, it is likely that a wide range of adaptive functions have been facilitated by the evolution of primate social organization. The selective advantage of such organization must lie not only in the impressive extension of sensorimotor equipment which the group provides over that available to any individual, but also in the greatly increased possibilities for generating, storing, and mobilizing alternative coping strategies for dealing with a wide variety of environmental contingencies. The latter point seems to be particularly important in the case of early man.

Schultz (1950) has pointed out a high incidence of injury and illness among living primates in the wild. In this connection, one of Washburn and DeVore's baboon observations is especially pertinent:

> When the troop moves out on the daily round, *all* members must move with it, or be deserted. We have seen sick and wounded animals making great efforts to keep up with the troop, and finally falling behind. At least three of these were killed, and the only protection for a baboon is to stay with the troop, no matter how injured or sick. In wild primates injuries are common . . . and animals which are so sick that they can be spotted by a relatively distant human observer are frequent. For a wild primate, a fatal sickness is one which separates it from the troop.

This observation suggests one of the many ways in which selection pressure may have operated in favor of those individuals having strong motivation for group membership.

In a situation such as the one described, those individuals having powerful attachment to others in the troop would be more likely to stay with the troop, in spite of the difficulty, and so be more likely to survive and pass their genes along to the next generation.

The adaptive function of primate groups should alert us to look for processes in the individual that facilitate the development of interindividual bonds. In seeking such processes, we may find useful guidance in the principle that *individuals seek and find gratifying those situations that have been highly advantageous in survival of the species.* That is, tasks that must be done (for species survival) tend to be quite pleasurable; they are easy to learn and hard to extinguish. Their blockage or deprivation leads to tension, anger, substitutive activity, and (if prolonged) depression. Such blockage is often accompanied by emergency-type physiological responses that support actions necessary to correct the situation. In the postinfancy human, a remarkable variety of coping behavior may be mobilized by such blockage or deprivation, determined in substantial part by cultural patterning.

In view of the extreme dependence on learning in the human species, such bonds would most likely be greatly strengthened through learning. Selection may operate on *differential readiness for learning responsiveness and attachment to others of the same species.*

Harlow's work (1958) gives us one important lead as to how the development of such motivational systems may be analyzed experimentally. He found that infant monkeys form attachment for an object that provides contact comfort. This attachment is very persistent—exceptionally difficult to extinguish. More recently, Harlow has shown that in the infant rhesus macaque, the clinging response even takes precedence over the postural righting reflex. When this fact is related to observations of macaques and baboons in the wild, its significance is clarified. When the troop moves, the mother moves, and the infant can only stay with the mother by clinging securely to her. There is no alternative: cling or perish. The mother's hands are not free to hold the baby; she must use them for locomotion. Those infants born with weak clinging responses do not get a chance to pass their genes along to the next generation.

This situation provides a nice illustration of the evolutionary concept of emotion I am trying to delineate. The monkey infant must cling to survive; apparently the infant likes to cling and forms attachment to an object that provides the opportunity for clinging; he wants to do what in fact he has had to do over the course of many generations.

But the human mother is practically hairless, and in any event the motor equipment of the human infant does not permit effective clinging. Yet the human infant is even less capable of fending for itself than monkey infants. How is this adaptive problem resolved? Simple—the mother must hold the baby: sometimes for long periods, under very difficult circumstances. In that event, the mother must *want* to hold the baby, must find pleasure in it, must seek out the opportunity, must experience some unpleasant feeling if she is deprived of the opportunity. This, in fact, turns out not to be so simple. It is a remarkable evolutionary achievement which, like so many other important phenomena, only seems simple when we take it for granted.

Since the mother's motivation for holding the child probably has so much adaptive significance, it is worth examining the factors that affect such motivation. There are several mother-infant transactions which probably serve to strengthen the motivational-emotional bond between the two. Among these transactions are: (1) close bodily contact; (2) nursing; (3) smiling; (4) stroking, patting; (5) rhythmic movement. All of these are situations in which most mothers in most human cultures find considerable pleasure. The likelihood is that some or all of these situations strengthen the mother's motivation to care for her infant. Indeed, it is reasonable to surmise that selection has favored infants whose behavior most effectively elicited caretaking motivational patterns in the mother. Those babies who evoke pleasure in the mother are more likely to survive under harsh conditions. Thus, future developmental research may find it profitable to analyze such transactions, seeking the characteristics in each of the participants that tend to strengthen the attachment of the other. This is one way in which an evolutionary view may suggest fresh observation and experiment in unanticipated directions.

Another side of the evolutionary coin may be stated in the principle that *individuals avoid and find distressing those situations that have been highly disadvantageous in species survival.* Applied to the specific issue of interindividual bonds, it seems reasonably clear that disruption of such bonds in primates is perceived as seriously threatening. It is usually felt as unpleasant and is often associated with emergency-type physiological responses. Such disruptive events usually mobilize coping behavior that tends toward restoration of strong bonds.

There is a great mass of human experience and clinical observation that bears on these questions, but I will limit myself here to mentioning briefly a few recent studies, carried out in a relatively systematic and critical way, that go a little beyond our previous impressions.

The classic investigations in this field are those having to do with the developmental consequences of mother-child separation in early childhood. Newer research has generally supported the earlier work indicating that prolonged mother-infant separation tends to produce damaging long-term aftereffects in intellectual, emotional, and social development (see G.A.P. Committee on Research, 1959). However, it has become clear that such effects are not a necessary result of separation; many factors have a bearing on the long-range outcome, one of the most important being the adequacy of substitute mothering during the period of separation. Further work is needed to clarify what constitutes adequacy of mothering under these circumstances.

For some years, psychoanalytic and psychosomatic observations have suggested that threat of separation and loss in deeply meaningful personal relationships is one important factor in precipitating depressive reactions; and that the problem of loss and grief may be one significant class of precipitating factors in psychosomatic disorders.

Significant work in this area has been going on during the past decade under the leadership of George Engel. A recent report from this group by Schmale (1958) has been especially intriguing. He carried out a systematic survey of the medical (not psychiatric or surgical) services in a university hospital and found a remarkably high incidence of major interpersonal separation and loss accompanied by feelings of helplessness and hopelessness—occurring shortly before onset of the symptoms leading to hospitalization. A variety of medical disorders were involved, not just the ones usually regarded as psychosomatic disorders. If this survey finding holds up when put to rigorous tests, it would have important implications for a wide gamut of medical problems.

Another line of recent research, in which I have been actively engaged for some years, has begun to work out the endocrine responses to disruption of personally crucial relationships. In the behavior-hormone investigations, one approach has involved the study of patients hospitalized because of profound depression, often following the disruption of a very important interpersonal bond. In such patients, there is now abundant evidence of substantial increase in adrenocortical activity over extended time periods—manifested by persistent elevation in plasma level and urinary excretion of 17-hydroxycorticosteroids. The extent of these elevations roughly parallels the severity of the clinical syndrome (Board, et al., 1956, 1957; Bunney, et al., 1962). Another approach has examined the effect of experimental probing interviews, chiefly concerned with jeopardy to respect and affection in close personal relationships, on emotional and adrenocortical responses (Persky, et al., 1958). These interviews evoke transient, mild-to-moderate affective responses—principally anxiety, anger, and depression. In these experiments, a linear relation between intensity of emotional distress and tendency to hydrocortisone elevation has been demonstrated.

Three other adrenal hormones—all of great biological significance—have been similarly implicated in emotional responses to jeopardy in acceptance by significant other people. These are epinephrine, norepinephrine, and aldosterone. While the evidence is not as decisive as in the case of hydrocortisone, it is certainly suggestive that a similar linkage exists (Hamburg, 1962).

Thus, disruption of interindividual bonds may have profound consequences in carbohydrate, protein, fat, electrolyte, and water metabolism, and on crucial functions of the circulation. Such disruption is felt as deeply unpleasant, and an extraordinary variety of coping behavior patterns may be mobilized to restore acceptance, affection, and mutual respect. Perhaps serious threat to a key relationship may be as much emergency in psychophysiological terms as threat of attack by a predator.

Society is not composed of neutral actors but of emotional beings—whether we speak of baboons, chimpanzees, or man, emotion lies at the core of the social process. We fear for ourselves, a few loved ones, and the infants of the species. We are positively bound deeply by a few relations. Threat to these relations is equivalent to an attack on life itself. From the standpoint of the species, these are the critical relations for survival. The physiology of emotion insures the fundamental acts of survival: the desire for sex, the extraordinary interest in the infant, the day-to-day reinforcement of interindividual bonds.

From the standpoint of the individual, the greatest satisfaction and fulfillment come from relations with the biologically essential few. Even if we colonize a planet, the development of an infant there will depend on the presence of another person—a mother, to hold, to love, to give security, to train for the problems ahead. Conquest of the outer world does not free the species from the inner world which made its evolution possible. Social life is rooted in emotion and is basic to survival. A comprehensive human biology must surely take account of one of man's fundamental properties —his social nature.

CHAPTER 17

Some General Considerations

MARGARET MEAD, PH.D.

Dr. Hamburg's paper makes it possible for me to bring together in this closing session the contributions made by the whole Symposium. I hope the initiator of this Symposium, Dr. Knapp, realizes how revolutionary this whole topic is and how unlikely the occurrence of the Symposium is, even now. As an illustration: in 1954 I was asked to write an introduction to a new edition of Darwin's *Expression of the Emotions in Man and Animals,* originally published in 1872. I telephoned George Simpson, who had been engaged in a definitive re-examination of Darwin's writing, to ask him what he had done with this book in his systematizing of Darwin's thinking. He replied that it was right off the main line and that he had not considered it at all. A year later, in 1955, a conference was held on Behavior and Evolution, organized by the American Psychological Association and the Society for the Study of Evolution; the results of the second conference were published as *Behavior and Evolution,* edited by Anne Roe and George Simpson (1958). Now, several years later, we have a five-session symposium on Expression of the Emotions in Man, in which the closing and summary paper is entitled, "Emotions in the Perspective of Evolutionary Theory."

Interest in this field has been moving very fast. However, the actual developments have not been so smooth as they have been rapid. This Symposium started off with evolution and it ends with evolution. But in between, often, the relationship to evolution has been very inexplicit. Some of the participants reported special investigations on methods of identifying, exploring, and analyzing particular problems without reference to an evolutionary context. But this apparent discrepancy between some of the presentations and the over-all evolutionary emphasis is not so great as it looks. These other presentations have stressed instrumentation, and it is only with our modern types of instrumentation—film and tape and methods of dealing very precisely with time—that it has become possible to tackle these problems.

We have the kind of material on characteristics of population on which Dr. Hamburg has drawn. We have the combination of experiments in simulation and in the use of models, a combination which has been used in modern ethology. It is now possible for us to step outside the closed, unobservable, two-person system of the classical psychiatric interview and to find out through filmed records, for example, what the cues are that make an infant smile, as Spitz and Wolf (1946) did. So the emphasis in this Symposium on methods of recording and analysis and on computer design is quite appropriate.

I should like to comment first on what might appear to be two contrasting, if not opposed, directions in the use of primate materials for the elucidation of the evolution of human emotions: controlled laboratory experimentation and observation in the wild. The Symposium started with the squirrel monkey observed in captivity; it ended with primate behavior and with quotations from modern studies of free-living forms. Primate material is of great value provided that the distinction between free-living conditions and captive-laboratory conditions is more carefully recognized than it sometimes has been in this Symposium. In the brief interval between the time that Dr. Hamburg wrote his paper and the time that I received it, new work has been reported by Phyllis Jay on Indian langurs (1960). This work has already upset some of the current generalizations about the structure of interpersonal bonds in primate groups. Jay reports that adult males show no interest in infants or juveniles. Langur society is organized along the lines of sex solidarity and sex dichotomization; groups of females care for infants, and there are elaborate relationships between adult and juvenile females and between adult and juvenile males. Information on free-living primates is coming in very fast, and the new materials are so diverse that it is necessary to exercise the greatest caution in treating current generalizations as if they were already properly underwritten by adequate samples of different kinds of primate behavior. My comment does not, I should add, call into question Dr. Hamburg's basic point that primates are group-living creatures dependent on the formation of interpersonal bonds.

But if we are to get full benefit of modern studies of behavior in evolutionary context, it is also very important to use materials on other living creatures besides primates. There is, for example, a great deal of material on bird behavior which can provide insights into some of the processes underlying relatedness among individuals of the same species, even though birds do not stand in the same degree of evolutionary closeness to man as do the primates. The behavior of mated pairs and the relationship of members of a pair to present and future residences provide many valuable analogues to human behavior (Sladen, 1956). Studies of the behavior of hoofed animals are an equally important source. Especially important is the research being done by Margaret Altmann (1956) on free-ranging elk and bison in which she compares, in different species, the contrasting roles of old males and old females in protective relationships to the young. One of our problems at present is the enlargement of our imagination in respect to the diversity of patterns which may have characterized different species of hominids, and these studies of creatures in other evolutionary lines can make important contributions to the broadening of our expectations and the direction of our research.

In contrast to the work which has emphasized the importance of establishing viable interpersonal bonds, for which we can draw on research on human infants (Bowlby, 1952), experimental work like that done by Helen Blauvelt (1956, 1957), and studies of free-living forms, other work is bringing us to a recognition of the importance of methods of weaning—of breaking established bonds in order to establish new ones. Dr. Harlow, in his discussion, did not really describe his experimental monkeys reared by cloth "mothers." He has put great efforts into producing normal mating behavior in these young monkeys, so far without success (Harlow, 1962). One possible factor here may be the "overpermissiveness" of the mechanical, "soft" mother in comparison with the vivid interaction of a real mother and her infant. These findings are in keeping with other findings, some of which were quoted by Dr. Hamburg, on mother-child separation and the damaging effect it may have on the child's capacity later to form interpersonal bonds.

In recent years both the clinical and the experimental literature have tremendously emphasized the importance for development of this aspect of the mother-child relationship (Bowlby, 1952). This has been accompanied by considerable reformist activity in an attempt to persuade all mothers to breast feed their infants (Newton, 1960; Mead, 1954). This approach has stressed the importance of the biological mother in human nurture and the significance of her performance of sheerly biological functions But these discussions have neglected another aspect which is exceedingly relevant to problems of evolution and to our consideration here of some of the clinical implications of evolution.

When an infant fails to thrive on its mother's breast milk, the mother who becomes progressively less able to feed the infant is behaving with biological adequacy at the level of a nomadic hunting people. In the case of the infant for whom there is no other form of nourishment, this failure to thrive sets in motion a circular process through which the mother's milk fails and the infant weakens and eventually dies. The mother is then freed to produce another infant whom she may be able to feed effectively. Between the mother and the new child there may be—as there was not between herself and the child who sickened and died—what has been called (in another part of this Symposium) a "communicative fit." Where the group's survival depends on the population at least replacing itself, the mother's response is not pathological but biologically adequate (Mead, 1957).

Today the great variety of interventions which it is possible to make during gestation and the neonatal period have confused the picture of biologically adequate maternal behavior. Today the mother is asked to will a sick child to live, and with the help of artificial feeding and drugs this can be done. But if she is also asked to breast feed the child, whether or not she and the child are compatible, then her behavior, which is adequate at the evolutionary biological level, conflicts with behavior which is appropriate at the level of modern, technological civilization and to our expectation of saving every infant which is born. As the number of mother and infant pairs who do not "communicatively fit" seems to be increasing, it is apparent that there is a contradiction between our insistence on maternal behavior which carries with it a provision for the elimination of the child who does not thrive and our desire for behavior which is adequate to carry out the demands of our present ethic and expectations (Mead, 1963). The tendency to brand all mothers who cannot breast feed as "rejecting mothers" and to regard their behavior as "pathological" obscures this issue and does considerable harm.

In discussions of the mother-child tie our emphasis is on the formation of early trust and the development of early object relationships. If we now turn to the problem of weaning, the necessity for the young to separate themselves from their parents and to form new ties, we can focus on the universality of incest barriers within the biological family as a condition of the formation of larger groups. This then provides us with another link between our evolutionary history and the clinical findings of psychoanalysis on the oedipal situation.

Here I would like to propose some considerations (Mead, 1960) which are at least as conjectural as any proposals made by Dr. Lacey earlier in this Symposium, even though I may not make my point with the same degree of adventurous gusto. Coming to the revelations of which Dr. Hamburg spoke, I predict that explorations of the behavior of the precursors of *Homo sapiens* will give us a new understanding of oedipal behavior by revealing the existence of a connection between the human life span and the parent-child relationship which is dependent on the relative size and age of the parent and the child. In ontogenetic terms, we usually interpret the oedipal conflict as a conflict between a tall, grown man and a small boy in whom we find behavior which seems extraordinarily inappropriate to his stature and state of maturation. However, this behavior on the part of a six- or seven-year-old boy would be perfectly appropriate if he was reaching physical maturity and was already as tall as his father and if his father was already declining in strength. In this situation the conflict between father and son would have a quite different biological efficiency than it has in the present with our long life span and the long period of growth following on the oedipal period, before the child is ready for parenthood. In any comparison of human behavior and primate behavior, it is necessary to take into account both the prolonged learning period in adolescence and the prolonged period of freedom from the hazards of reproduction at the end of the female's life. These are biological innovations which have facilitated the development of human culture. Dr. Lacey discussed the characteristic heart acceleration in a person doing intellectual work. At the same time we have to take into account the implications of the continuance in man of types of behavior appropriate to maturation at the age of seven or eight years and a much earlier death. Other comparable biological changes, such as puberty and the menopause, and the social inventions which have followed on them will provide us with additional materials on those aspects of human nature which differentiate human beings from other primates. Thus as we emphasize the extent to which *Homo sapiens* is behaviorally related to other living creatures, we also accumulate information on his biologically based and culturally implemented distinctive humanity. This will provide further links between clinical materials and evolutionary theory. With these, we may examine culturally styled resolutions of the oedipal conflict and culturally patterned and socially enforced incest regulations for their full significance at our present stage of evolution.

We may then hope to construct a framework for asking questions, in the construction of which we shall draw simultaneously on clinical and experimental materials, neurological findings, comparative studies of primates and other ethological studies, our knowledge of early forms of man, and our knowledge of the behavior of living human groups of varying degrees of primitiveness. Within a framework of this kind we can ask, and hope to answer, such questions as: Which of man's potentialities are possibly obsolete, no longer appropriate for the present-day world? Which of man's potentialities are we drawing on appropriately or could we draw on more appropriately (for example, the child's capacity for self-selection of diet)? Which of man's potentialities do we need to supplement by conscious invention and intervention?

Our society has learned to make spectacles for those with poor eyesight and hearing aids for those who cannot hear. So also one of our contemporary evolutionary tasks, a task to which psychoanalytic theory and practice should make important contributions, is to identify aberrations in individual endowment and the particular cultural forms in which their experience is cast so that we will be able to invent the necessary supplements and protect those individuals who are now the casualties of diversities of fit and failure to fit.

Finally, I should like to take up something that Dr. Kennard hinted at very briefly when he discussed the fact that all human beings do use words and that even the words they use consciously do tell the investigator something. In his maturational style and reproductive style man has diverged very strikingly from any of the creatures to whom he is closely or distantly related, and he is special and peculiar in his use of the brain, his ability to mate all the year round, and his prolonged learning period. So also, it is possible that there is instinctive behavior which is as specific to *Homo sapiens* as certain types of behavior have been shown to be specific to other species. In working on this problem we must look not only at the types of behavior which we can compare fruitfully with the behavior of primates or other living creatures but also at types of behavior with evolutionary rewards which differentiate man from other species. It is true, for example, that there are unmated adult males and females in other species. Among the penguins a kind of low-grade bachelor has been identified. Before the sex of these birds was known, they were regarded as "nurses"; now they are seen to be a loitering and irresponsible group of unmated males, near whom the chicks cluster and from whom they obtain inadvertant protection against predators while their parents are away foraging for food (Sladen, 1956). In group or herd situations, a case may be made for the unmated creature or the aging creature, and it is possible that the timid creature, which has difficulty in mating, may perform some other function for the group. But only among human beings may the contribution of the individual, as an individual, far exceed in evolutionary importance the contribution of the same individual as a producer of viable offspring. Once conditions have been established in which the population can be maintained, the *individual* who can think, who can borrow and innovate, who is curious and related to the universe can make a tremendous evolutionary contribution. It is he who makes possible the increase in man's control of his own survival, and ultimately makes possible man's control of his cultural forms and his evolutionary future. This is an aspect of human evolution which is inadequately dealt with by those geneticists who discuss evolution sheerly in terms of reproductive fitness (Dobzhansky, 1958).

Recently Hutchinson (1959) published a very interesting paper in which he suggested that various forms of sexual deviance may be the result of mutations such that the individual fails in the appropriately timed establishment of those necessary relationships with parental figures of both sexes that underlie later successful mating. We do not yet know what the evolutionary devices are that result in the sterile individual, the individual who is prevented from mating or from reproduction by a variety of preferences and deviances. Quite possibly the ability to produce, by means of biological or social processes, enough individuals who neither mate nor reproduce but who, surviving in the group, turn their full energies to work in philosophy, the arts, and the sciences may prove to be one of our principal evolutionary devices.

Indeed, it is quite possible that there is an order of human instinctive behavior, a need to relate to the universe or to the natural order, which is expressed in philosophy and art and, today, scientific inquiry. This particular need may be distinctively human and as biologically demanding of satisfaction as are the drives which have been discussed earlier in this Symposium. The affects accompanying this need—or drive—have been variously described; I suppose the most useful word for the kind of affect involved is "ecstasy." And the striking thing about the human experiences that come under this heading—experiences of scientific discovery, artistic creativity, or religious vision—is that they are not interpersonal. Rather they are experiences primarily of the relationship between an individual and the universe as he perceives it. He seems to have, in fact, something which has been called a "cosmic sense" (Cobb, 1959).

It is therefore desirable, as we explore those parts of our

behavior which stem directly from our prehuman past, that we do not forget the possibility that there may be instinctually based behavior which is distinctively human, as specific and as biologically based as the specific behavior of any other species. Thus we can explore the possibility that the failure to satisfy the child's craving for a perceptually meaningful relationship to the universe around him may produce as serious disturbances in human development as does the failure to allow for the formation of bonds of trust and affection to other human beings and for the supercession of the bonds of early childhood by later ties which permit successful mating and reproduction.

CHAPTER 18

In Conclusion: Emotional Expression—A Glance at the Future

PETER H. KNAPP, M.D.

The papers in this Symposium have formed a tapestry. Its threads may appear diverse. The sociogram, the couch of the analyst, the analysis of motion pictures, observations from polygraph, animal and biological laboratories are woven into a pattern that at first seems obscure. The reader may have found cross-fertilization and even stimulation, but disappointment if he sought for a unified viewpoint. No single "theory" of emotion is found in these pages.

Several authors have recently commented on the lack of such a theory. For example, Plutchik (1955) has specified some of the problems facing such a theory and has recently (1962) attempted a broad solution of them. The Introduction to this Symposium indicated still further problems, particularly those encountered in the human, such as the relationship of emotions on the one hand to postulated drive processes and on the other hand to cognitive, fantasy, and ego processes; also the need to understand the progressive differentiation of emotions in the human, including processes of restraint and control. Engel also discusses the complex issues facing a theory of emotion, referring as well to Novey's similar discussion (1959). Engel's synthesis is the most comprehensive in these pages, yet it can only do partial justice to the task in the available space.

As remarked at the outset, even this volume, focused upon expression of the emotions, had to omit more than passing mention of a number of relevant areas, for example: organic and particularly psychopharmacologic effects upon emotional expression; experimental arousal of emotions; psychological testing in relation to emotion; aesthetic productions, both as they arouse and as they express emotions; a systematic consideration of how processes of "discharge" relate to learning and to the special kind of learning we know as psychotherapy; systematic consideration of the developmental vicissitudes of emotion beyond the first year of life. To embrace all these and the other areas of study included under the heading of emotion a theory must be broad, indeed. The fact is that it may not be too soon for a general theory, but too late. Emotions may be so interwoven with other behavioral processes that they cannot easily be split off into a separate compartment. Future advances may be in the form of generalizations that cut across traditional boundaries to integrate some of the multiple vistas opened in these pages.

Given such multiplicity, the question might be asked whether these papers form truly a tapestry or a patchwork quilt. Actually they contain a number of common strands, some having to do with method and some with content.

Those concerning method are perhaps more obvious. In ways this is the age of methods, especially in the study of behavior. Tools must be forged before they can be used. After a romantic era, particularly in depth psychology, marked by proliferation of hypotheses, workers are settling down to the unromantic anvil, hammering out operational ways for testing them.

Several themes, relating to methods, have appeared here. First, the naturalistic approach, relying on painstaking, detailed observation, is by no means exhausted: witness the wealth of new information which emerges from the study of one brief interview sequence. Second, we now have an impressive number of devices to aid our precision: electronic transcription, photography, physiologic measurements, computers for handling of data, and the vast array of recording and observational techniques available for work with animals. Third, the flexibility of tactics, advocated particularly by Harlow, permits the introduction of a variety of experimental techniques at different levels, depending upon the specific problems encountered, in order to supplement the naturalistic approach. Finally, awareness of the state of the organism, particularly as it may be affected by the meaning of the observational situation itself, is a crucial consideration, one which cannot be ignored in human experiments, and one which, if recognized, as Lacey's work suggests, can itself be put to good experimental use.

Some will ask what such sophistication of techniques contributes to the assessment of emotional expression in the human. This issue led to one of the few sparks of controversy kindled in these pages. Colby decried the undue emphasis on methods, to the neglect of what he as a clinician needed to study, namely, the emotional meanings discernible in his patients. A careful reading discloses that Colby does not condemn methods per se, only "problemless" methods. His own studies (1960, 1961) indicate his high regard for precision and quantification. The issue is perhaps: what is a real problem; what constitutes a relevant question? One can agree that little will be disclosed about emotion to the observer guided only by obsessional need for precision, or hoping to rescue himself from ignorance by the vain reductionist fantasy that hard questions will automatically be answered by hard science. In so far as he is guided by curiosity, however, that can only be satisfied by progressively better methods. True, physiology is not a magical key to the understanding of all emotions; but that does not mean we must exclude inquiry into the relationships between psychological and physiological observations. The interdisciplinary approach has assets and liabilities. It offers the advantages of validation across disciplinary boundaries; it poses formidable difficulties of translation. But no one can deny that it asks fascinating questions.

Pribram defends the view that no single group has an inherent monopoly on truth, either by divine right or reductionist fiat. He also argues, and this is my point here, that translation, however difficult, is fruitful. One of the remarkable features of present-day science, reflected in this Symposium, as Morton Reiser remarked during its course, is a feature which promises to accelerate progressively: that is the breakdown of disciplinary isolation, and the dissemination of information in widely understood terms.

The beginning of such a common language can be differentiated in these papers as a series of conceptual threads. The first and most basic theme, set by the title, is that of evolution. Underlined in the paper by MacLean, and continuing through the closing contributions of Hamburg and Mead, was the importance of seeing emotions in phylogenetic and historical perspective. A similar view is stressed by Plutchik (1962) who lists a group of "prototypic adaptive patterns" taken largely from Scott (1958) from which emotions develop.

Evolution implies a state to which something evolves. We must indicate not only the origins but also the distinguishing characteristics of human emotion. These are not simple. Emotions cannot be explained as simple "discharge" or simple "conflict," and certainly not, as Engel points out, as simply conscious "feeling," though all of these are important concepts. Perhaps we can say that the eventual human emotion differs from the aboriginal impulse because of the interposition of adaptive delaying, switching, controlling processes, that is, by virtue of man's unique psychic apparatus. The epigenesis of emotion, starting from relatively undifferentiated states is thus a second important theme stated in this volume, principally by Spitz. Early development of the two kinds of pleasure, positive excitation and relief of distress, elaborated by Escalona, deserves much further exploration. A parallel question for the future is whether or not pain, which is often referred to as though monolithic and indivisible, does not also include crucial subtypes, with their own developmental histories.

The differential character of adult emotional response patterns is a third theme, echoed from different viewpoints by Lacey, Birdwhistell, and Bateson. The concept of varying specificities seems particularly fruitful: individual differences stem from different levels—prevailing cultural stereotypes, early fixed learned patterns, and inherited differences. To this Lacey adds the intriguing possibility that there may be basic biological differences in type of response, depending upon the nature of the stimulus, particularly its inclination to foster environmental intake or environmental exclusion. The inherent configuration which he postulates as existing between stimulus and a category of response is the needed sort of "building block" mentioned in the Introductory Comments prefacing Part III of this volume.

The communicative aspect of emotional expression is a fourth theme, perhaps the one most emphasized and for that reason requiring least comment here. From the start of life emotions signalize needs, attitudes, anticipations, and impulses toward action. They are socially adaptive. Within limits, they are regulated by interpersonal processes.

It is important to recognize the limits. The social, communicative aspect of emotional expression should not conflict with a fifth aspect, stressed particularly by Scott, though by Pribram and Engel as well. This is the view that emotions are processes within the organism, of communication but also of release and homeostatic self-regulation. They are relatively slow-moving mechanisms, in comparison with the extraordinary rapidity of certain cognitive processes. To an extent emotions are isolated from outside stimuli. They sustain crucial instinctual patterns and are necessary for the ongoing function of the organism, regardless of social context.

Communication utilizes and modifies emotional processes; but their origin and their regulatory function lie beyond communication, built into man's neurophysiological being, part of his basic adaptive machinery.

Nor should we forget a sixth element, stressed by Novey and implicit in the clinical discussion of Deutsch's case, that emotions may also be maladaptive. Unpleasure and the variety of psychosomatic processes associated with it may impair the functioning of an individual and serve as a motive, reparative or disintegrating in its further consequences.

Finally, as stated earlier, and more fully elsewhere (Knapp and Bahnson, 1963), many of the contributions to this volume are consistent with what may be called a field theory of emotions. This implies that overt emotional expressions exist in a complicated balance with other elements, particularly unconscious drive and ego processes. As indicated in the Introduction, and as amplified by Pribram, Spitz, Engel, and others, it may be that we are on the threshold of linking up the major elements within such a field to the organization of man's own nervous system and his adaptive place in the animal kingdom, seeing phylogenetically and ontogenetically more archaic elements in transaction with more recent ones within the individual, and seeing both in transaction with the outer world.

I am not sure that we are at this point ready to abandon the purely mental model and to rejoin Freud in his original efforts to give birth to a schematization which integrated psychological and neurological concepts. Yet the labor may have started.

Bibliography

ADEY, W. R. (1962), Studies of Slow Wave Activity in the Hippocampal System in Approach Learning and Use of Correlation Analysis of the Wave Process. In preparation for *Cybernetics and Brain Mechanisms,* ed. E. N. Sokolov. Moscow: in press.

ALEXANDER, F. (1938). Remarks about the Relation of Inferiority Feeling to Guilt Feelings. *Int. J. Psychoanal., 19*:41.

ALLPORT, G. W. & VERNON, P. E. (1933), *Studies in Expressive Movement.* New York: Macmillan.

ALTMANN, M. (1956), Patterns of Social Behavior in Big Game. *Transactions of the Twenty-first North American Wildlife Conference, March 5-7, 1956,* ed. J. B. Trefethen. Washington, D.C.: Wildlife Management Institute.

ARISTOTLE, *The Works of Aristotle.* Vol. 1. In *Great Books of the Western World,* ed. R. M. Hutchins. Chicago: Encyclopedia Britannica Press, 1952.

AULD, F. & MURRAY, E. J. (1955), Content-analysis Studies of Psychotherapy. *Psychol. Bull., 52*:377.

AX, A. F. (1953), The Physiological Differentiation Between Fear and Anger in Humans. *Psychosom. Med., 15*:433.

—— (1960), Computers and Psychophysiology in Medical Diagnosis. *IRE Trans. on Med. Electronics,* Vol. ME-7.

BALINT, M. (1939), Early Developmental States of the Ego: Primary Object Love. *Int. J. Psychoanal., 20*:265.

BALKEN, E. R. & MASSERMAN, J. (1940). The Language of Phantasy. *J. Psychol., 10*:75.

BATESON, G., BIRDWHISTELL, R. L., BROSIN, H., HOCKETT, C. H., & MCQUOWN, N. (1962), *The Natural History of an Interview* (in preparation).

BENEDEK, T. (1949), The Psychosomatic Implications of the Primary Unit: Mother-Child. *Amer. J. Orthopsychiat., 19*:642.

—— (1956), Toward the Biology of the Depressive Constellation. *J. Amer. Psychoanal. Assn., 4*:389.

BENJAMIN, J. D. (1959), Predictions and Psychopathologic Theory. In *Dynamics of Psychopathology in Childhood,* ed. L. Jessner & E. Pavenstedt. New York: Grune & Stratton.

—— (1961), Some Developmental Observations Relating to the Theory of Anxiety. *J. Amer. Psychoanal. Assn., 9*:4.

BIBRING, E. (1953), The Mechanism of Depression. In *Affective Disorders,* ed. P. Greenacre. New York: International Universities Press, 1953.

BIRDWHISTELL, R. L. (1959a), Contribution of Linguistic-Kinesic Studies to the Understanding of Schizophrenia. In *Schizophrenia: An Integrated Approach,* ed. A. Auerback. New York: Ronald Press, p. 99.

—— (1959b), The Frames in the Communication Process. Paper read at The American Society of Clinical Hypnosis, Annual Scientific Assembly, Chicago.

—— (1961), Paralanguage: 25 Years After Sapir. In *Lectures in Experimental Psychiatry,* ed. H. W. Brosin. Pittsburgh: University of Pittsburgh Press, p. 43.

BLAUVELT, H. (1956), Neonate-Mother Relationship in Goat and Man. *Group Processes: Transactions of the Second Conference, October 9-12, 1955,* ed. B. Schaffner. New York: Josiah Macy, Jr., Foundation.

—— (1957), Further Studies on Maternal-Neonate Interrelationships. *Group Processes: Transactions of the Third Conference, October 7-10, 1956,* ed. B. Schaffner. New York: Josiah Macy, Jr., Foundation.

BLOCH, B. & TRAGER, G. L. (1942), *Outline of Linguistic Analysis.* Baltimore: Linguistic Society of America.

BOARD, F., PERSKY, H., & HAMBURG, D. (1956), Psychological Stress and Endocrine Functions: Blood Levels of Adrenocortical and Thyroid Hormones in Acutely Disturbed Patients. *Psychosom. Med., 18:*324.

——, WADESON, R., & PERSKY, H. (1957), Depressive Affect and Endocrine Functions, Blood Levels of Adrenocortical and Thyroid Hormones in Patients Suffering from Depressive Reactions. *A.M.A. Arch. Neurol. & Psychiat., 78:*612.

BODER, D. P. (1939-40), The Adjective-Verb Quotient: A Contribution to the Psychology of Language. *Psychol. Record., 3:*310.

BOOMER, D. C. & GOODRICH, D. W. (1961), Speech Disturbances and Judged Anxiety. *J. Consult. Psychol., 25:*160.

BORING, E. (1929), *A History of Experimental Psychology.* New York: Appleton Century Crofts, 2nd ed., 1950.

BOURLIERE, F. (1962), The Various Types of Social Structure Among Primates, Based on Field Studies. In *Social Life of Early Man,* ed. S. L. Washburn. Viking Fund Publication No. 31. Chicago: Aldine Publishing Co.

BOWLBY, J. (1952), *Maternal Care and Mental Health.* Geneva: World Health Organization.

—— (1960), Separation Anxiety. *Int. J. Psychoanal., 41*:89.

BRAATOY, T. (1954), *Fundamentals of Psychoanalytic Technique.* New York: Wiley.

BRADY, J. V. & HUNT, H. F. (1955), An Experimental Approach to the Analysis of Emotional Behavior. *J. Psychol., 40*:313-324.

BROSIN, H. (1960), Evolution and Understanding Diseases of the Mind. In *Evolution After Darwin,* ed. S. Tax. Chicago: University of Chicago Press.

BROWN, J. S. (1948), Gradients of Approach and Avoidance Responses and Their Relation to Level of Motivation. *J. Comp. Physiol. Psychol., 41*:450-465.

BROWN, N. (1959), *Life Against Death.* Middletown, Conn.: Wesleyan University Press.

BRUNER, J. S. (1957), On Perceptual Readiness. *Psychol. Rev., 64*:123.

BUHLER, C. (1931), *Kindheit und Jugend.* Leipzig: Hirzl.

BUNNEY, W., SACHAR, E., MASON, J., & HAMBURG, D. (1962), Excretion of Hydrocortisone, Epinephrine, Norepinephrine, and Aldosterone in Severely Depressed Patients. Unpublished.

BURTON, I. & DERBYSHIRE, A. J. (1958), "Sleeping Fit" Caused by Excruciating Pain in an Infant. *A.M.A. J. Dis. Children, 95*:258.

BYKOV, K. M. (1959), *The Cerebral Cortex and The Internal Organs,* tr. H. Gantt. New York: Chemical Publishing Co.

CHAPPLE, E. D. (1940), Measuring Human Relations: An Introduction to the Study of Interaction of Individuals. *Genet. Psychol. Monogr., 22*:3.

—— (1953), The Standard Experimental (Stress) Interview as Used in Interaction Chronograph Investigations. *Human Organization, 12*:23.

COBB, E. (1959), The Ecology of Imagination in Childhood. *Daedalus, 88*:537.

COLBY, K. M. (1955), *Energy and Structure in Psychoanalysis.* New York: Ronald Press.

—— (1960), Experiment on the Effects of an Observer's Presence on the Imago System During Psychoanalytic Free Association. *Behav. Sci., 5*:216.

—— (1961), On the Greater Amplyfying Power of Causal–Correlative Inputs on Free Association in an Experimental Psychoanalytic Situation. *J. Nerv. Ment. Dis., 133*:233.

COLEMAN, R., GREENBLATT, M., & SOLOMON, H. C. (1956), Physiological Evidence of Rapport During Psychotherapeutic Interviews. *Dis. Nerv. Syst., 17*:2.

DARROW, C. W., JOST, H., SOLOMON, A. P., & MERGENER, J. C. (1942), Autonomic Indications of Excitatory and Homeostatic Effects on the Electroencephalogram. *J. Psychol., 14*:115.

DARWIN, C. (1872), *The Expression of Emotions in Man and Animal.* New York: Philosophical Library, 1955.

DAVIS, R. C. (1957), Response Patterns. *Trans. N. Y. Acad. Sci., 19*:731.

—— & BUCHWALD, A. M. (1957), An Exploration of Somatic Response Patterns: Stimulus and Sex Differences. *J. Comp. Physiol. & Psychol., 50*:44.

——, ——, & FRANKMANN, R. W. (1955), Autonomic and Muscular Responses, and Their Relation to Simple Stimuli. *Psychol. Monogr., 69*:1 (Whole No. 405).

——, LUNDERVOLD, A., & MILLER, J .D. (1957), The Pattern of Somatic Response During a Repetitive Motor Task and Its Modification by Visual Stimuli. *J. Comp. Physiol. & Psychol., 50*:53.

DEUTSCH, F. (1942), Autonomic Skin Test with Electrophoresis. *J. Investig. Dermatol., 5*:2.

—— (1946), Psychosomatic Aspects of Dermatology with Special Consideration of Allergic Phenomena. *Nerv. Child, 5*:4.

—— (1952), Analytic Posturology. *Psychoanal. Quart., 21*:196.

—— (1959), Correlative of Verbal and Non-Verbal Communication in Interviews Elicited by Associative Anamnesis. *Psychosom. Med., 21*:123.

—— (1962), Body, Mind, and the Sensory Gateways. *Advances in Psychosomatic Medicine,* Vol. 2. New York: S. Karger.

—— & MURPHY, W. F. (1955), *The Clinical Interview,* 2 Vols. New York: International Universities Press.

DEVORE, I. (1962), Primate Behavior and Social Evolution. Unpublished.

DIBNER, A. S. (1956), Cue-Counting: A Measure of Anxiety in Interviews. *J. Consult. Psychol., 20*:475.

DIMASCIO, A. (1959), Some Physiological Correlates of the Psycholinguistic Patterns of Two Psychiatric Interviews. Presented at the New York Divisional Meeting, American Psychiatric Association. In *Comparative Psycholinguistic Analysis of Two Psychotherapeutic Interviews,* ed. L. A. Gottschalk. New York: International Universities Press, 1961.

——, BOYD, R. W., & GREENBLATT, M. (1957), Physiological Correlates of Tension and Antagonism During Psychotherapy: A Study of "Interpersonal Physiology." *Psychosom. Med., 19*:99.

——, ——, ——, & Solomon, H. C. (1955), The Psychiatric Interviews: A Sociophysiologic Study. *Dis. Nerv. Syst., 16*:2.

—— & Brooks, G. W. (1961), A Case Report on the Effects of Free Association to a Fantasied Psychotherapist. *Arch. Gen. Psychiat., 4*:513.

Dittman, A. T. & Wynne, L. C. (1961), Linguistic Techniques and the Analysis of Emotionality in Interviews. *J. Abn. Soc. Psychol., 63*:201.

Dobzhansky, T. (1956), *The Biological Basis of Human Freedom.* New York: Columbia University Press.

—— (1958), Evolution at Work. *Science, 127*:1091.

Dollard, J. & Auld, F. (1959). *Scoring Human Motives.* New Haven: Yale University Press.

—— & Mowrer, O. H. (1947), A Method of Measuring Tension in Written Documents. *J. Abn. Soc. Psychol., 42*:3.

DuBos, R. (1959), *Mirage of Health.* New York: Harper.

Dykman, R. A., Reese, W. G., Galbrecht, C. R., & Thomasson, J. (1959), Psychophysiological Reactions to Novel Stimuli: Measurement, Adaptation, and Relationship to Psychological and Physiological Variables in the Normal Human. *Ann. N. Y. Acad. Sci., 79*:43.

Eldred, S. H. & Price, D. B. (1958), A Linguistic Evaluation of Feeling States in Psychotherapy. *Psychiatry, 21*:115.

Engel, B. T. (1960), Stimulus-Response and Individual-Response Specificity. *Arch. Gen. Psychiat., 2*:305.

Engel, G. L. (1960), A Unified Concept of Health and Disease. *Perspectives in Biology and Medicine, 3*:459.

—— (1962), Anxiety and Depression-Withdrawal: The Primal Affects of Unpleasure. *Int. J. Psychoanal. 43*:89-97.

—— & Reichsman, F. (1956), Spontaneous and Experimentally Induced Depression in an Infant with a Gastric Fistula: A Contribution to the Problem of Depression. *J. Amer. Psychoanal. Assn., 4*:428.

Erikson, E. H. (1950a), *Childhood and Society.* New York: W. W. Norton.

—— (1959), Growth Crises of the Healthy Personality. *Identity and the Life Cycle. Psychological Issues, 1*:50. New York: International Universities Press.

Escalona, S. & Heider, G. M. (1959), *Prediction and Outcome, A Study in Child Development.* New York: Basic Books.

Farber, I. E. & West, L. J. (1960), Conceptual Problems of Research on Emotions. *Psychiat. Research Reports, 12*:1.

Fenichel, O. (1941), The Ego and the Affects. In *Collected Papers, 2:*215-227. New York: Norton, 1954.

Fisher, A. E. (1955), The Effects of Differential Early Treatment on the Social and Exploratory Behavior of Puppies. Ph.D. Thesis, Pennsylvania State University.

Frankl, L. & Rubinow, O. (1934), Die erste Dingauffassung beim Säugling. *Z. Psychol.,* No. 133.

Freeman, W. J. (1960), Correlation of Electrical Activity of Prepyriform Cortex and Behavior in Cat. *J. Neurophysiol., 23:* 111.

Freud, S. (1895), Project for a Scientific Psychology. In *The Origins of Psychoanalysis: Sigmund Freud's Letters, Drafts and Notes to Wilhelm Fliess (1887-1902).* New York: Basic Books, 1954.

—— (1901), The Psychopathology of Everyday Life. *Standard Edition, 6.* London: Hogarth Press, 1960.

—— (1905), Three Essays on the Theory of Sexuality. *Standard Edition, 7:*125. London: Hogarth Press, 1953.

—— (1915a), Instincts and Their Vicissitudes. *Standard Edition, 14:*109. London: Hogarth Press, 1957.

—— (1915b), The Unconscious. *Standard Edition, 14:*159. London: Hogarth Press, 1957.

—— (1926), Inhibitions, Symptoms and Anxiety. *Standard Edition, 20:*87. London: Hogarth Press, 1959.

—— (1937), Analysis Terminable and Interminable. *Collected Papers, 5:*317. London: Hogarth Press, 1950.

Fries, M. (1944), Psychosomatic Relationships Between Mother and Infant. *Psychosom. Med., 6:*159.

Fuller, J. L. (1961), Programmed Life Histories and the Socialization of the Dog. Unpublished.

Funkenstein, D. H., King, S. H., & Drolette, M. E. (1957), *Mastery of Stress.* Cambridge: Harvard University Press.

Galambos, R. (1956), Suppression of Auditory Nerve Activity by Stimulation of Efferent Fibers to Cochlea. *J. Neurophysiol., 19:*424.

Goldman-Eisler, F. (1958), Speech Analysis and Mental Processes. *Language & Speech, 1:*59.

Goldschmidt, W. (1959), *Man's Way.* Cleveland: World Publishing Company.

Goldstein, K. (1928), Beobachtungen über die Veränderung des Gesamtverhaltens bei Gehirnschädigung. *Mschr. Psychiat. & Neurol.,* No. 68.

Gottschalk, L. A., Ed. (1961), *Comparative Psycholinguistic*

Analysis of Two Psychotherapeutic Interviews. New York: International Universities Press.

——, ET AL. (1956), Explorations in Testing Drugs Affecting Physical and Mental Activity. *J. Amer. Med. Assn., 161:*1054.

——, GLESER, G. C., DANIELS, R. S., & BLOCK, S. (1958), The Speech Patterns of Schizophrenic Patients: A Method of Assessing Relative Degree of Personal Disorganization and Social Alienation. *J. Nerv. & Ment. Dis., 127:*153.

——, ——, & HAMBRIDGE, G., JR. (1957), Verbal Behavior Analysis. *A.M.A. Arch. Neurol. & Psychiat., 77:*300.

—— & HAMBRIDGE, G., JR. (1955), Verbal Behavior Analysis: A Systematic Approach to the Problem of Quantifying Psychologic Processes. *J. Proj. Tech., 19:*387.

—— & KAPLAN, S. (1958), A Quantitative Method of Estimating Variations in Intensity of a Psychologic Conflict or State. *A.M.A. Arch. Neurol. & Psychiat., 79:*688.

GRANIT, R. (1955a), Centrifugal and Antidromic Effects on Ganglion Cells of Retina. *J. Neurophysiol., 18:*388.

—— (1955b), *Receptors and Sensory Perception.* New Haven: Yale University Press.

GRAY, P. H. (1960), Evidence that Retinal Flicker Is Not a Necessary Condition of Imprinting. *Science, 132:*1834.

GREENBLATT, M. (1959), Discussion in *Research in Psychotherapy,* eds. E. A. Rubinstein & M. B. Parloff. Washington, D.C.: American Psychological Association. National Publishing Co., p. 209.

GREENSON, R. (1954), About the Sound "Mm...". *Psychoanal. Quart., 23:*234.

GROUP FOR THE ADVANCEMENT OF PSYCHIATRY, COMMITTEE ON RESEARCH (1959), *Some Observations on Controls in Psychiatric Research.* Report No. 42. New York: Group for the Advancement of Psychiatry.

HAMBURG, D. (1959), Some Issues in Research on Human Behavior and Adrenocortical Function. *Psychosom. Med., 21:*386.

—— (1962), Plasma and Urinary Corticosteroid Levels in Naturally Occurring Psychological Stresses. In *Ultra Structure and Metabolism of the Nervous System,* ed. S. Korey. Baltimore: Williams & Wilkins.

——, SABSHIN, M. A., BOARD, F. A., & GRINKER, R. R. (1958), Classification and Rating of Emotional Experiences. *A.M.A. Arch. Neurol. & Psychiat., 79:*415.

HARLOW, H. F. (1958), The Nature of Love. *Amer. Psychologist, 13:*673.

—— (1962), The Heterosexual Affectional System in Monkeys. *Amer. Psychologist, 17*:1.

HARTMANN, H., KRIS, E., & LOEWENSTEIN, R. M. (1946), Comments on the Formation of Psychic Structure. *The Psychoanalytic Study of the Child, 2*:11. New York: International Universities Press.

HESS, W. R. (1957), *The Functional Organization of the Diencephalon*. New York: Grune & Stratton.

HILGARD, E. R. (1960), *Psychology after Darwin in Evolution after Darwin*. Chicago: University of Chicago Press.

HOCKETT, C. D. (1960). The Origin of Speech. *Sci. American, 203*: 89.

HOLLENDER, M. (1958), The Seeking of Sympathy or Pity. *J. Nerv. Ment. Dis., 126*:579.

HOLLINGSHEAD, A. B. & REDLICH, F. C. (1958), *Social Class and Mental Illness: A Community Study*. New York: John Wiley.

HUTCHINSON, G. E. (1959), A Speculative Consideration of Certain Possible Forms of Sexual Selection in Man. *Amer. Naturalist, 93*:81.

HUXLEY, J. (1943), *Evolution, the Modern Synthesis*. New York: Harper.

JACOBSON, E. (1953), The Affects and Their Pleasure-Unpleasure Qualities in Relation to Psychic Discharge Processes. In *Drives, Affects, and Behavior*, ed. R. M. Loewenstein, New York: International Universities Press.

—— (1954), The Self and the Object World. *The Psychoanalytic Study of the Child, 9*:75. New York: International Universities Press.

JAFFE, J. (1957), An Objective Study of Communication in Psychiatric Interviews. *J. Hillside Hosp., 6*:207.

—— (1959), Dyadic Analysis of Two Psychotherapeutic Interviews. Presented at the New York Divisional Meeting, American Psychiatric Association. In *Comparative Psycholinguistic Analysis of Two Psychotherapeutic Interviews*, ed. L. A. Gottschalk. New York: International Universities Press, 1961.

JAY, P. (1960), Indian Langur. Paper presented at the Symposium on Primate Behavior, American Anthropological Association, Minneapolis, Minnesota, November 20, 1960.

JENSEN, K. (1932), Differential Reaction to Taste and Temperature in Newborn Infants. *Genet. Psychol. Monogr., 12*:361.

JOHNSON, W. (1944), Studies in Language Behavior: I. A Program of Research. *Psychol. Monogr., 56* (2) :1.

Joos, M. (1950), Description of Language Design. *J. Acoustical Society of America, 22:*701.

Kagan, J. & Moss, H. A. (1962), *Birth to Maturity: A Study in Psychological Development.* New York: John Wiley.

Kasl, W. V. & Mahl, G. F. (1958), Experimentally Induced Anxiety and Speech Disturbances. *Amer. Psychologist, 13:*349.

Kelly, E. L. (1955), Consistency of the Adult Personality. *Amer. Psychol., 10:*659-681.

Kepecs, J. G., Robin, M., & Munro, C. (1958), Responses to Sensory Stimulation in Certain Sensory Diseases. *Psychosom. Med., 20:*351.

Klüver, H. & Bucy, P. D. (1939), Preliminary Analysis of Functions of the Temporal Lobe in Monkeys. *A.M.A. Arch. Neurol. & Psychiat., 42:*979.

Knapp, P. H. (1958), Conscious and Unconscious Affects. *Psychiat. Research Reports, 8:*55.

—— (1960), Acute Bronchial Asthma: II. Psychoanalytic Observations on Fantasy, Emotional Arousal and Partial Discharge. *Psychosom. Med., 22:*88.

—— & Bahnson, C. (1963), The Emotional Field: A Sequential Study of Two Asthmatic Patients. In preparation.

Kris, E. (1939), Laughter as an Expressive Process: Contributions to the Psychoanalysis of Expressive Behavior. In: *Psychoanalytic Explorations in Art.* New York: International Universities Press, 1952, pp. 217-239.

Krout, M. H. (1935), Autistic Gestures: An Experimental Study in Symbolic Movement. *Psychol. Monogr., 46.* (Whole No. 208.)

Kuffler, S. W. & Gerard, R. W. (1947), The Small-Nerve Motor System to Skeletal Muscle. *J. Neurol. Physiol., 10:*383.

—— & Hunt, C. C. (1952), The Mammalian Small-Nerve Fibers: A System for Efficient Nervous Regulation of Muscle Spindle Discharge. *Res. Publ. Assn. Nerv. Ment. Dis., 30:*24.

Lacey, J. I. (1956), The Evaluation of Autonomic Responses: Toward a General Solution. *Ann. N. Y. Acad. Sci., 67:*123.

—— (1959), Psychophysiological Approaches to the Evaluation of Psychotherapeutic Process and Outcome. In *Research in Psychotherapy,* eds. E. A. Rubinstein & M. B. Parloff. Washington, D. C.: American Psychological Association. National Publishing Co.

—— & Lacey, B. C. (1958), Vertification and Extension of the Principle of Autonomic Response Stereotypy. *Amer. J. Psychol., 71:*50.

Lasswell, H. D. (1935), Verbal References and Physiological

Changes During the Psychoanalytic Interview: A Preliminary Communication. *Psychoanal. Rev., 22*:10.
—— (1936), Certain Prognostic Changes during Trial (Psychoanalytic) Interviews. *Psychoanal. Rev., 23*:241.
LIVINGSTON, R. B. (1958), Central Control of Afferent Activity. In *Reticular Formation of the Brain.* Boston: Little, Brown.
LORENZ, M. (1952), Language Concepts as Related to Psychiatry. *Quart. Rev. Psychiat. & Neurol., 7*:123.
—— (1955), Expressive Behavior and Language Patterns. *Psychiatry, 18*:353.
—— (1953a), Language Behavior in Manic Patients: A Qualitative Study. *A.M.A. Arch. Neurol. & Psychiat., 69*:14.
—— (1953b), Language as Expressive Behavior. *A.M.A. Arch. Neurol. & Psychiat., 70*:277.
—— & COBB, S. (1952), Language Behavior in Manic Patients. *A.M.A. Arch. Neurol. & Psychiat., 69*:763.
——, —— (1953), Language Behavior in Psychoneurotic Patients. *A.M.A. Arch. Neurol. & Psychiat., 69*:684.
MACLEAN, P. D. (1952), Some Psychiatric Implications of the Physiological Studies on Frontotemporal Portion of Limbic System (Visceral Brain). *EEG Clin. Neurophysiol., 4*:407.
—— (1954), In *Recent Developments in Psychosomatic Medicine,* ed. E. Wittkower & R. Cleghorn. London: Pitman.
—— (1955), The Limbic System ("Visceral Brain") in Relation to Central Gray and Reticulum of the Brain Stem. Evidence of Interdependence in Emotional Processes. *Psychosom. Med., 17*:355.
—— (1957), Chemical and Electrical Stimulation of Hippocampus in Unrestrained Animals. Part II. Behavioral Findings. *A.M.A. Arch. Neurol. & Psychiat., 78*:128.
—— (1958a), Contrasting Functions of Limbic and Neocortical Systems of the Brain and Their Relevance to Psychophysiological Aspects of Medicine. *Amer. J. Med., 25*:611.
—— (1958b), The Limbic System with Respect to Self-Preservation and the Preservation of the Species. *J. Nerv. Ment. Dis., 127*:1.
—— (1959), The Limbic System with Respect to Two Basic Life Principles. In *The Central Nervous System and Behavior.* New York: Josiah Macy, Jr., Foundation, p. 31.
—— & DELGADO, J. M. R. (1953), Electrical and Chemical Stimulation of Frontotemporal Portion of Limbic System in the Waking Animal. *EEG Clin. Neurophysiol., 5*:91.

——— & Ploog, D. W. (1961), Cerebral Representation of Penile Erection. *J. Neurophysiol., 25*:29.

Magoun, H. W. (1958), Non-Specific Brain Mechanisms. In *Biological and Biochemical Bases of Behavior,* ed. H. F. Harlow & C. N. Woolsey. Madison, Wisc.: University of Wisconsin Press.

Mahl, G. F. (1955), Disturbances and Silences in the Patient's Speech in Psychotherapy. Progress report.

——— (1956a), "Normal" Disturbances in Spontaneous Speech: General Quantitative Aspects. *Amer. Psychologist, 11*:390.

——— (1956b), Disturbances and Silences in the Patient's Speech in Psychotherapy. *J. Abn. Soc. Psychol., 53*:1.

——— (1956c), Disturbances in the Patient's Speech as a Function of Anxiety. Paper read at Annual Meeting, Eastern Psychol. Assn.

——— (1957), Speech Disturbances and Emotional Verbal Content in Initial Interviews. Paper read at Annual Meeting, Eastern Psychol. Assn.

——— (1959a), Measuring the Patient's Anxiety During Interviews from "Expressive" Aspects of his Speech. *Trans. N. Y. Acad. Sci., 21*:249.

——— (1959b), Exploring Emotional States by Content Analysis. In *Trends in Content Analysis,* ed. I. Pool. Urbana: University of Illinois Press, pp. 83-130.

——— (1959c), Measures of Two Expressive Aspects of a Patient's Speech in Two Psychotherapeutic Interviews. Presented at the New York Divisional Meeting, American Psychiatric Association. In *Comparative Psycholinguistic Analysis of Two Psychotherapeutic Interviews,* ed. L. A. Gottschalk. New York: International Universities Press, 1961.

Mandler, G., Mandler, J., Kremen, I., & Sholiton, R. D. (1961), The Response to Threat: Relations Among Verbal and Physiological Indices. *Psychol. Monogr., 75*:1. (Whole No. 513.)

Margolin, S. (1951), The Behavior of the Stomach During Psychoanalysis. *Psychoanal. Quart., 20*:349.

Mason, W. A. Differential responses of monkeys. Personal communication.

Massachusetts Mental Health Center (1956), Psychophysiological Studies of the Psychotherapeutic Process. USPHS Project M-354 (C3), Progress Report, February 1, 1956.

Matarazzo, J. D., Saslow, G., & Matarazzo, R. G. (1956), The Interaction Chronograph as an Instrument for Objective

Measurement of Interaction Patterns During Interviews. *J. Psychol., 41*:347.

McLeary, R. A. (1960), Type of Responses as a Factor in Interocular Transfer in the Fish. *J. Comp. Physiol. Psychol., 53*: 311-321.

McQuown, N. A. (1957), Linguistic Transcription and Specification of Psychiatric Interview Materials. *Psychiatry, 20*:79.

Mead, G. H. (1934), *Mind, Self and Society*. Chicago: University of Chicago Press.

—— (1938), *The Philosophy of the Act*. Chicago: University of Chicago Press.

Mead, M. (1954), Some Theoretical Considerations on the Problem of Mother-Child Separation. *Amer. J. Orthopsychiat., 24*: 471.

—— (1957), Changing Patterns of Parent-Child Relations in an Urban Culture. *Int. J. Psychoanal., 38*:369.

—— (1958), Cultural Determination of Behavior. In *Behavior and Evolution,* ed. A. Roe & G. G. Simpson. New Haven: Yale University Press.

—— (1960), Totem and Taboo Reconsidered with Respect. Paper presented at the Topeka Psychoanalytic Society, Topeka, Kansas, September 22, 1960.

—— (1963), A Cultural Anthropologist's Approach to Maternal Deprivation. In press.

Mendelson, M. (1960), *Psychoanalytic Concepts of Depression*. Springfield, Ill.: Charles C Thomas.

Miller, G. A., Galanter, E., & Pribram, K. H. (1958), *Plans and the Structure of Behavior*. New York: Holt, Rinehart & Winston.

Miller, N. E. (1948), Studies of Fear as an Acquirable Drive: I. Fear as a Motivation and Fear Reduction as Reinforcement in the Learning of New Responses. *J. Exp. Psychol., 38*:89-101.

Mirsky, I. A., et al. (1952), Blood Plasma Pepsinogen II. *J. Lab. Clin. Med., 40*:188.

Murray, E. J. (1956), A Content-Analysis Method for Studying Psychotherapy. *Psychol. Monogr., 70,* No. 13. (Whole No. 420.)

Nauta, W. J. H. (1960), Anatomical Relationships Between the Amygdaloid Complex, the Dorsomedial Thalamic Nucleus and the Orbitofrontal Cortex in Monkey. *Anat. Rec., 136*:251.

Newton, N. (1960), New Help for Nursing Mothers. *Child Family Digest, 19*:45.

NOVEY, S. (1958), The Meaning of the Concept of Mental Representation of Objects. *Psychoanal. Quart., 27*:57.

—— (1959), A Clinical View of the Affect Theory in Psychoanalysis. *Int. J. Psychoanal., 40*:94.

—— (1961), Further Considerations on Affect Theory in Psychoanalysis. *Int. J. Psychoanal., 42*:21.

OBRIST, P. A. (1962), Cardiovascular Differentiation of Sensory Stimuli. *Abstr. Meetings Amer. Psychosom. Soc.*

OLDS, J. (1956), A Preliminary Mapping of Electrical Reinforcing Effects in the Rat Brain. *J. Comp. Physiol. Psychol., 49*:281.

—— (1958), Self-Stimulation of the Brain. *Science, 127*:315.

—— & MILNER, P. (1954), Positive Reinforcement Produced by Electrical Stimulation of Septal Areas and Other Regions of the Rat Brain. *J. Comp. Physiol. Psychol., 47*:419.

PANEK, D. M. & MARTIN, B. (1959), The Relationship Between GSR and Speech Disturbances in Psychotherapy. *J. Abn. Soc. Psychol., 58*:402.

PAPEZ, J. W. (1937), A Proposed Mechanism of Emotion. *A.M.A. Arch. Neurol. & Psychiat., 38*:725.

PERSKY, H., HAMBURG, D., BASOWITZ, H., GRINKER, R., SABSIN, M., KORCHIN, S., HERZ, M., BOARD, F., & HEATH, H. (1958), Relation of Emotional Responses and Changes in Plasma Hydrocortisone Level After Stressful Interview. *A.M.A. Arch. Neurol. & Psychiat., 79*:434.

PIAGET, J. (1937), *The Construction of Reality in the Child.* New York: Basic Books, 1954.

PIERS, G. & SINGER, M. (1953), *Shame and Guilt.* Springfield, Ill.: Charles C Thomas.

PIKE, K. L. (1946), *The Intonation of American English.* Ann Arbor: University of Michigan Press.

PITTENGER, R. E. (1958), Linguistic Analysis of Tone of Voice in Communication of Affect. *Psychiat. Research Reports, 8*:41.

——, HOCKETT, C. F., & DANEHY, J. J. (1960), *The First Five Minutes.* Ithaca, N. Y.: Paul Martineau.

—— & SMITH, H. L., JR. (1957), A Basis for Some Contributions of Linguistics to Psychiatry. *Psychiatry, 20*:61.

PLATO, *Selections,* ed. R. Demos. New York: Scribners, 1927, pp. 290, 295.

PLOOG, D. W. & MACLEAN, P. D. (1963), Display of Penile Erection in Squirrel Monkey (Saimiri Sciureus). *Animal Behavior, 11*: 32-39.

PLUTCHIK, R. (1955), Some Problems for a Theory of Emotion. *Psychosom. Med., 17*:306-310.

—— (1962), *The Emotions: Facts, Theory and a New Model.* New York, Random House.

Pool, I., Ed. (1959), *Trends in Content Analysis.* Urbana: University of Illinois Press.

Prechtl, H. F. R. (1958), The Directed Head-Turning Response and Allied Movements of the Human Baby. *Behavior, 13*:213.

Pribram, K. H. (1962a), The Neuropsychology of Sigmund Freud. In *Experimental Foundations of Clinical Psychology,* ed. A. J. Backrach. New York: Basic Books.

—— (1962b), Interrelations of Psychology and the Neurological Disciplines. In *Psychology: A Study of a Science,* ed. S. Koch. New York: McGraw-Hill.

Rangell, L. (1954), The Psychology of Poise—with a Special Elaboration on the Psychic Significance of the Snout or Perioral Region. *Int. J. Psychoanal., 35*:313.

Rapaport, D. (1953), On the Psychoanalytic Theory of Affects. *Int. J. Psychoanal., 34*:177.

—— (1960), *The Structure of Psychoanalytic Theory: A Systematizing Attempt* [*Psychological Issues,* Monogr. No. 6]. New York: International Universities Press.

Reich, W. (1933). *Character Analysis.* New York: Farrar, Straus & Cudahy, 1961.

Reid, J. R. (1950), Introduction to *Emotions and Clinical Medicine,* by S. Cobb. New York: W. W. Norton.

Reis, D. J., Carmichael, M., & MacLean, P. D. (1963), Cerebral Representation of Genital Function. IV. Frontotemporal Region. Unpublished.

Reiser, M. F., Reeves, R. B., & Armington, J. (1955), Effects of Variations in Laboratory Procedure and Experimenter Upon the Ballistocardiogram, Blood Pressure and Heart Rate in Healthy Young Men. *Psychosom. Med., 17*:185.

Roe, A. & Simpson, G. G., Eds. (1958), *Behavior and Evolution.* New Haven: Yale University Press.

Ruesch, J. (1957), *Disturbed Communication.* New York: W. W. Norton.

Sahlins, M. (1959), The Social Life of Monkeys, Apes, and Primitive Man. In *The Evolution of Man's Capacity for Culture,* ed. J. Spuhler. Detroit: Wayne State University Press.

Sanford, F. H. (1941-42), Speech and Personality: A Comparative Case Study. *Character and Personality, 10*:169.

—— (1942), Speech and Personality. *Psychol. Bull., 39*:811.

Sapir, E. (1951), Speech as a Personality Trait. In *Language, Culture and Personality, Selected Writings of Edward Sapir,* ed.

D. Mandelbaum. Berkeley and Los Angeles: University of California Press, p. 533.

SASLOW, G. & MATARAZZO, J. D. (1959), A Technique for Studying Changes in Interview Behavior. In *Research in Psychotherapy*, ed. E. A. Rubinstein & M. B. Parloff. Washington, D. C.: American Psychol. Assn., p. 125.

——, ——, PHILLIPS, J. S., & MATARAZZO, R. G. (1957), Test-Retest Stability of Interaction Patterns During Interviews Conducted One Week Apart. *J. Abn. Soc. Psychol., 54*:295.

SCHACHTER, J. (1957), Pain, Fear and Anger in Hypertensives and Normotensives: A Psychophysiologic Study. *Psychosom. Med., 19*:17.

SCHACHTER, S. & SINGER, J. E. (1962), Cognitive, Social and Physiological Determinants of Emotional State. *Psychol. Rev. 65* (in press).

SCHAFER, R. (1959), Generative Empathy in the Treatment Situation. *Psychoanal. Quart., 28*:342.

SCHAFFER, H. R. (1958), Objective Observations of Personality Development in Early Infancy. *Brit. J. Med. Psychol., 31*:175.

SCHMALE, A. H., JR. (1958), Relationship of Separation and Depression to Disease. I. A Report on a Hospitalized Medical Population. *Psychosom. Med., 20*:259.

—— (1962), The Affects of Helplessness and Hopelessness in Health and Disease. Unpublished.

SCHNORE, M. M. (1959), Individual Patterns of Physiological Activity as a Function of Task Differences and Degree of Arousal. *J. Exp. Psychol., 58*:117.

SCHULTZ, A. (1950), The Specializations of Man and His Place Among the Catarrhine Primates. *Cold Spring Harbor Symposia on Quantitative Biology, 15*:37.

SCHULZE, G., MAHL, G. F., & MURRAY, E. J. (1960), Speech Disturbances and Content Analysis Categories as Indices of Underlying Emotional States of Patients in Psychotherapy. *Amer. Psychologist, 15*:405.

SCHUR, M. (1953), The Ego in Anxiety. In *Drives, Affects and Behavior,* ed. R. M. Loewenstein. New York: International Universities Press.

—— (1960), Discussion of John Bowlby's Paper, "Grief and Mourning in Infancy and Early Childhood." *The Psychoanalytic Study of the Child, 15*:63. New York: International Universities Press.

SCOTT, J. P. (1958), *Animal Behavior*. Chicago: University of Chicago Press.

SEARL, M. N. (1933), The Psychology of Screaming. *Int. J. Psychoanal., 24*:193.

SHAKOW, D. (1960), The Recorded Psychoanalytic Interview as an Objective Approach to Research in Psychoanalysis. *Psychoanal. Quart., 29*:82.

SHERRINGTON, C. (1906), *The Integrative Action of the Nervous System*. New Haven: Yale University Press, 1947.

—— (1940), *Man on His Nature*. New York: Doubleday Anchor Books, 2nd ed., 1953.

SIMPSON, G. G. (1958), The Study of Evolution: Methods and Present Status of Theory. In *Behavior and Evolution,* ed. A. Roe & G. G. Simpson. New Haven: Yale University Press.

——, PITTENDRIGH, C., & TIFFANY, L. (1957), *Life, Introduction to Biology*. New York: Harcourt, Brace.

SLADEN, W. J. L. (1956), Social Structure among Penguins. In *Group Processes,* ed. B. Schaffner. New York: Josiah Macy, Jr., Foundation.

SNYDER, W. U. (1947), The Present Status of Psychotherapeutic Counseling. *Psychol. Bull., 44*:297.

SPIELREIN, S. (1922), Die Entstehung der kindlichen Worte Papa und Mama. *Imago, 8*:345-367.

SPEISMAN, J. C., OSBORNE, J., & LAZARUS, R. S. (1961), Cluster Analyses of Skin Resistance and Heart Rate at Rest and Under Stress. *Psychosom. Med., 23*:323.

SPINOZA, *The Chief Works of Spinoza,* tr. R. H. M. Elwes. New York: Dover Press, 1951.

SPITZ, R. A. (1945), Hospitalism. An Inquiry into the Psychiatric Conditions in Early Childhood. *The Psychoanalytic Study of the Child, 1*:53. New York: International Universities Press.

—— (1946), Anaclitic Depression: An Inquiry into the Genesis of Psychiatric Conditions in Early Childhood, II. *The Psychoanalytic Study of the Child, 2*:313. New York: International Universities Press.

—— (1950), Anxiety in Infancy: A Study of Its Manifestations in the First Year of Life. *Int. J. Psychoanal., 31*:138.

—— (1955), The Primal Cavity. A Contribution to the Genesis of Perception and its Role for Psychoanalytic Theory. *The Psychoanalytic Study of the Child, 10*:215. New York: International Universities Press.

—— (1957), *No and Yes*. New York: International Universities Press.

—— (1959), *A Genetic Field Theory of Ego Formation*. New York: International Universities Press.

—— & Wolf, K. M. (1946), The Smiling Response: A Contribution to the Ontogenesis of Social Relations. *Genet. Psychol. Monogr., 34*:57.

Strupp, H. (1959), An Analysis of Therapist Activity in Two Psychotherapeutic Interviews. Presented at New York Divisional Meeting, American Psychiatric Association. In *Comparative Psycholinguistic Analysis of Two Psychotherapeutic Interviews,* ed. L. A. Gottschalk. New York: International Universities Press, 1961.

—— Symposium on Primate Social Behavior (1959), American Anthropological Association, Minneapolis, November, 1959.

Terman, L. M. (1947), *The Gifted Child Grows Up.* Stanford: Stanford University Press.

Trager, G. L., (1958), Paralanguage: A First Approximation. *Studies in Linguistics,* No. 13 (1-2).

—— & Smith, H. L., Jr. (1957), An Outline of English Structure. *Studies in Linguistics, Occasional Papers,* No. 3.

Travers, P. L. (1934), *Mary Poppins.* New York: Harcourt Brace, (pp. 121-122).

Tyron, R. C. (1929), *The Genetics of Learning Ability in Rats.* Stanford: University of California Press, *4*:71-89.

Volkelt, H. (1928), Neuuntersuchungen über die kindliche Auffassung und Wiedergabe von Formen. *Bericht über den 4. Kongress für Heilpädagogik,* Berlin, 1929.

von Foerster, C., Ed. (1951), *Cybernetics: Circular Causal and Feedback Mechanisms in Biological and Social Systems.* New York: Josiah Macy, Jr. Foundation.

von Frisch, K. (1950), *Bees. Their Vision, Chemical Senses, and Language.* New York: Cornell University Press.

Washburn, S. L. (1960), Tools and Human Evolution. *Sci. American, 203*:63.

—— & DeVore, I. (1962), Social Life of Baboons. In *Social Life of Early Man,* ed. S. L. Washburn. Chicago: Aldine Publishing Co.

Watson, P. D., DiMascio, A., Kanter, S. S., Suter, E., & Greenblatt, M. (1957), A Note on the Influence of Climatic Factors on Psychophysiological Investigations. *Psychosom. Med., 19*:419.

Wells, R. S. (1945), The Pitch Phonemes of English. *Language, 21*:27.

Wenger, M. A., Clemens, T. L., Coleman, D. R., Cullen, T. B., & Engel, B. T. (1961), Autonomic Response Specificity. *Psychosom. Med., 23*:185.

Whitehead, A. N. (1929), *Process and Reality*. New York: Macmillan.

Whitehorn, J. C. & Zipf, G. K. (1943), Schizophrenic Language. *A.M.A. Arch. Neurol. & Psychiat., 49*:831.

Wilcoxon, F. (1949), *Some Rapid Approximate Statistical Procedures*. Stamford, Conn.: American Cyanamid Co.

Wisdom, J. O. (1953), A General Hypothesis of Psychosomatic Disorder. *Brit. J. Med. Psychol., 26*:15.

Wittkower, E. D. (1957), Psychoanalysis as Science: A Psychophysiologic Approach. *Canad. Psychiat. Assn. J., 2*:125.

Zacharopoulos, G. & Ax, A. F. (1961), Psychophysiological Data Processing. Presented at the Fourth International Conference on Medical Electronics, New York City.

Zipf, G. K. (1949), *Human Behavior and the Principle of Least Effort*. Cambridge: Addison-Wesley Press.